This book is in the
**ADDISON-WESLEY SERIES
IN BEHAVIORAL SCIENCES: QUANTITATIVE METHODS**

Consulting Editor

FREDERICK MOSTELLER

SETS, FUNCTIONS, AND PROBABILITY

SETS, FUNCTIONS, AND PROBABILITY

JOHN B. JOHNSTON
General Electric
Research and Development Center

G. BALEY PRICE
The University of Kansas

FRED S. VAN VLECK
The University of Kansas

ADDISON-WESLEY PUBLISHING COMPANY
Reading, Massachusetts · Menlo Park, California
London · Don Mills, Ontario

populations (see the Lanchester equations of combat and the lions-and-antelopes problem in Section 5 of Chapter 3), (c) the estimation of biological populations (see Section 4 of Chapter 6), (d) an application of Bayes' Theorem in medical diagnosis (see Section 3 of Chapter 7), (e) an application of Bayes' Theorem in the Mosteller-Wallace method of examining cases of disputed authorship (see Section 3 of Chapter 7), and (f) a number of important optimization problems (see Section 8 of Chapter 8). The book also contains other illustrations and applications such as acceptance sampling (see Section 3 of Chapter 6) and elementary applications of probability theory to genetics (see Section 6 of Chapter 7).

A minimum course on probability theory can be taught from this book in about thirty class sessions by using the material in Chapter 1, Sections 1 through 5 of Chapter 2, Sections 1 through 4 of Chapter 4, all of Chapter 5, Sections 1, 2, 4, and 5 of Chapter 7, and Sections 1, 2, 4, 5, and 6 of Chapter 8. The sections omitted in this outline for a minimum course contain applications and additional topics. This minimum course can be expanded to a longer course by adding Section 6 of Chapter 2, Section 3 of Chapter 7, and Sections 3 and 7 of Chapter 8, and by adding illustrations and applications of the basic material according to interest. The book contains sufficient material for a course which meets five times per week for a semester.

We are grateful to those who have encouraged and assisted us. Friends and colleagues encouraged us to develop a course which would include the topics found in this book. The National Science Foundation provided support for the development of the course and for the writing of an experimental textbook entitled *An Introduction to Mathematics* which was published in 1963. The first part of this experimental textbook was rewritten, and it was published in 1966 with the title *Linear Equations and Matrices* by the Addison-Wesley Publishing Company. The present book is the rewritten form of the second part of *An Introduction to Mathematics*. We are grateful to Professor Frederick Mosteller for his encouragement, his helpful suggestions, and his criticisms. We acknowledge with thanks the assistance of Mrs. Patricia Swope Croat and of the staff of the Addison-Wesley Publishing Company. Mrs. Croat assisted us in many ways, but especially by typing several versions of the manuscript, and the staff of Addison-Wesley has edited and produced our book with patience and skill.

J.B.J.
G.B.P.
F.S.V.V.

October, 1967

Preface

This book contains an introductory treatment of finite probability theory and some of its applications. The treatment is elementary in the sense that it does not employ the calculus and that it should be understandable to a student who has had three years of college preparatory mathematics in high school. The book is self-contained in the sense that the first four chapters include everything the reader needs to know about sets, functions, and counting methods to understand the probability theory and its applications as presented in the last four chapters. Matrix multiplication, however, is occasionally employed in certain applications; it is not treated in this book, but can be found in the authors' *Linear Equations and Matrices*. The present book is oriented toward the business and management sciences, the biological sciences, and the social sciences inasmuch as the illustrations, the applications, and the exercises are chosen largely from these fields. Finally, the treatment of probability theory given here is abstract to the extent that the proofs of the fundamental properties of a probability space are valid without change in case the sample space is not finite.

The first four chapters provide a more detailed and complete treatment of sets, functions, and counting methods than is customary in books of this type. Chapter 1 treats elementary set theory, Chapter 2 treats relations and functions, and Chapter 4 treats counting methods. Chapter 3, entitled "Difference Equations and Growth Functions," presents a number of applications of functions to problems in the biological, management, and social sciences. Difference equations supply a unifying method in the treatment of these applications.

This book contains many illustrations, applications, and exercises which have not appeared previously in any elementary textbook. Examples of these illustrations and applications are: (a) pictures treated as functions (see Section 8 of Chapter 2), (b) difference equation treatments of the growth of two interacting

v

Contents

CHAPTER 1

Elementary Set Theory

1.1 INTRODUCTION

The theory of sets has proved to be of the highest significance not only in pure mathematics, but also in every area of application. Furthermore, the use of sets will continue to increase. Thus it seems reasonable to present in this chapter a brief introduction to the basic facts concerning sets. More important, we shall need most of the theory developed here in connection with our discussion of probability in Chapters 5, 6, 7, and 8; the use of sets has clarified and unified the mathematical foundations of probability theory.

Most of us have an intuitive idea of what a *set* is: a collection of objects which is treated as a single entity. Similar terms in common usage are class, collection, and aggregate. In fact, there are many words in the English language which convey essentially the same idea; we speak of a *herd* of sheep, a *mob* of people, a *pride* of lions, a *colony* of ants, and a *fleet* of ships.

An informal definition of a set is just that it is a single entity consisting of a collection of objects. The objects comprising a set may themselves be sets. For example, we speak of the set of classes meeting on Tuesday in a certain school; each class is itself a set of students. The National League, apart from some administrative structure, consists of ten baseball teams each of which is a set of players. A hierarchy of sets of even greater depth occurs in taxonomy. The major groups of life forms are the phyla; each phylum consists of several orders; each order contains many families; each member of a family is called a genus; the elements of a genus are called species; and this is not yet the most detailed refinement. So the members of a set may very well themselves be sets. Indeed, in probability theory and other areas of mathematics this situation is nearly always the case.

A set consists of a collection of objects. These objects are said to be *members* of the set, to be *elements* of the set, to be *contained* in the set, or to *belong* to the

1

set. The set is said to *contain* the objects. A set is completely described by its membership; there is no property other than membership which can be used to distinguish between sets. Two sets can be distinct only if one of them contains an element which the other does not contain. The notion of membership is thus of prime importance in the study of sets.

Since the notion of set membership is so important in mathematics, a notation has evolved which is in almost universal use. The notation employs the symbol $\in$, derived from the Greek letter epsilon. Specifically, the notation is described as follows:

Let S be a set and let a be an object (perhaps also a set). The statement

$$a \text{ is an element of } S \tag{1}$$

is equivalent to the formal abbreviation

$$a \in S. \tag{2}$$

Statement (2) may be read in any one of the following ways: a is a member of S; a is an element of S; a is contained in S; a belongs to S; S contains a; or simply a epsilon S. Also, the statement

$$a \text{ is not an element of } S \tag{3}$$

may be abbreviated in a standard manner to

$$a \notin S. \tag{4}$$

EXAMPLE 1. Let J be the set of all integers, J^+ be the set of positive integers, and J^-, the set of negative integers. Then

$$
\begin{array}{llll}
0 \in J, & 1 \in J, & -1 \in J, & \tfrac{1}{2} \notin J, \\
0 \notin J^+, & 1 \in J^+, & -1 \notin J^+, & \tfrac{1}{2} \notin J^+, \\
0 \notin J^-, & 1 \notin J^-, & -1 \in J^-, & \tfrac{1}{2} \notin J^-.
\end{array}
$$

EXAMPLE 2. Let S denote the set of all presidents of the United States. Then Truman $\in S$, Dewey $\notin S$, Eisenhower $\in S$, and Stevenson $\notin S$.

We have been considering the concept of "belongs to" which relates elements of sets to the sets themselves. The next basic concept is that of *equality* of sets; this concept relates sets to other sets. The symbol $=$ between two symbols denoting sets is symbolic shorthand to assert that the two symbols are names for the same set. For example, $\{7\}$ and $\{\tfrac{2268}{324}\}$ are just two names for the set whose only element is the integer 7.

Intuitively, as we said earlier, a set should be completely described by its membership. Hence, two sets should be the same if they have the same elements.

Thus we adopt, as an axiom,* the following criteria for deciding when two sets are the same.

Axiom of extensionality. Two sets A and B are equal if and only if they have exactly the same set of elements. Expressed in terms of the symbols $=$ and $\in$, $A = B$ if and only if the following two statements are true:

(a) if $x \in A$, then $x \in B$; and
(b) if $x \in B$, then $x \in A$.

In accordance with the above axiom, to show that two sets are equal, we must show that they have exactly the same elements.

EXAMPLE 3. Let A be the set of ancestors of a particular man, and let B be the set of ancestors of his sister. Then, although the definitions of the sets A and B are not identical, $A = B$, because if $x \in A$, then $x \in B$, and if $x \in B$, then $x \in A$.

So far we do not have any way of naming sets except to describe the sets in sentences, a procedure which is very inconvenient at times. However, we have described a set whose only element was the number 7 by the symbol $\{7\}$; the next section will be devoted to a brief discussion of this method of naming a set and to one other very useful method.

1.2 NAMES OF SETS

To make a statement about an object, it is usually necessary to designate the object by a name. For example, when we speak of a particular person, we usually use his name; however, at other times, a pronoun like "he" may be sufficient to name the person. It is the same in mathematics; when we make a statement about a collection of objects, we need a *name* for the set, especially if we intend to refer to the set very often. Therefore we shall consider in this section two common types of names that are used to designate sets. A set may have several different names; in fact, this situation is a common occurrence. If we suspect that two sets are the same, then we use the Axiom of Extensionality to test whether or not the two sets are equal.

Conjoining the names

$$\text{Roosevelt, Churchill, and Stalin,} \tag{1}$$

conveys the notion of the Big Three Allies of the Second World War quite effectively. In a similar manner we could use the following name for the set which contains just the numbers 0, 1, and 2:

$$\text{0, 1, and 2.} \tag{2}$$

_____

* An axiom is a basic assumption which is made to develop a theory.

However, the name (2) is somewhat unsatisfactory because it contains the word "and," which is included out of grammatical, rather than mathematical, necessity, and the name (2) does not involve grouping symbols on its left or right ends to indicate that it names a single entity. A more satisfactory alternative to (2) is

$$\{0, 1, 2\}. \tag{3}$$

The name (3) contains grouping symbols, the curly brackets { and }, and no extraneous grammatical separators; clearly, the commas are essential.

The notation in the name (3) is frequently used for naming sets which have only a small number of elements. For example, if a, b, and c are objects, then $\{a, b, c\}$ is a name of the set whose members are precisely a, b, and c. Note that the name

$$\{a, b, c\} \tag{4}$$

is formed by writing names of the elements of the set, separating them by commas, and enclosing them in curly brackets. Note that $a \in \{a, b, c\}$, $b \in \{a, b, c\}$, and $c \in \{a, b, c\}$; furthermore, if $d \in \{a, b, c\}$, then either $d = a$, or $d = b$, or $d = c$.

As a further example, let us consider the set $\{0, 1, 2\}$ and the set $\{1, 0, 2\}$. These are two different names for the same set since both have exactly the same elements. Thus $\{0, 1, 2\} = \{1, 0, 2\}$. Similarly, $\{0, 0, 1, 2\} = \{0, 1, 2\}$ because these have the same elements.

Let us return to the naming procedure discussed above. Let a be an object and let A be the set whose sole member is a. Another name for A is $\{a\}$; that is, $A = \{a\}$. The set $\{a\}$ is usually called *singleton a*. Observe that $a \in \{a\}$ and that, if $c \in \{a\}$, then $a = c$. Next, suppose that a and b are objects, and that B is the set whose sole members are a and b. Another name for the set B is $\{a, b\}$; that is, $B = \{a, b\}$. The set $\{a, b\}$ is usually called *doubleton a, b*. As a more general example, suppose that n is a particular positive integer and that $a_1, a_2,$, $\ldots, a_n$ are objects, not necessarily all distinct. A name for the set whose members are precisely the objects $a_1, a_2, \ldots, a_n$ is

$$\{a_1, a_2, \ldots, a_n\}. \tag{5}$$

The set $\{a_1, a_2, \ldots, a_n\}$ can contain at most n distinct elements, but may contain as few as just one element. For example,

$$\{7, 7, 7, 7\} = \{7, 7, 7\} = \{7, 7\} = \{7\}; \tag{6}$$

we note that repetitions of object names may be eliminated from a set name such as (5).

EXAMPLE 1. The set of even integers n such that $0 \le n \le 10$ has the following as one of its names:

$$\{0, 2, 4, 6, 8, 10\}.$$

EXAMPLE 2.   The set of squares of integers n for which $-3 \leq n \leq 3$ has, as one of its names,

$$\{9, 4, 1, 0, 1, 4, 9\}.$$

A shorter name for the same set is

$$\{0, 1, 4, 9\},$$

that is, $\{9, 4, 1, 0, 1, 4, 9\} = \{0, 1, 4, 9\}$.

EXAMPLE 3.   The solution set of the equation $x^2 - 1 = 0$ is the set $\{-1, 1\}$.

EXAMPLE 4.   Suppose that A and B are the following matrices:

$$A = \begin{Vmatrix} 1 & -2 & 1 \\ 1 & -1 & 2 \\ -2 & 4 & -1 \end{Vmatrix}, \qquad B = \begin{Vmatrix} 8 & -4 \\ 5 & -1 \\ -16 & 9 \end{Vmatrix}.$$

The solution set of the matrix equation $A * X = B$ has as one of its names

$$\left\{ \begin{Vmatrix} 2 & -1 \\ -3 & 2 \\ 0 & 1 \end{Vmatrix} \right\}.$$

EXAMPLE 5.   Let A and B be the matrices of Example 4. The matrix equation

$$B * X = A \tag{7}$$

has no solution. The solution of Eq. (7) is empty. Using a method analogous to the naming method (5) for sets having a positive finite number of elements, we might name the empty solution set of Eq. (7)

$$\{ \ \}. \tag{8}$$

However, the name (8) is not very satisfactory, since it could easily be interpreted as a typographical error rather than a name. We shall introduce a standard name for the empty set in the next paragraph.

A set is an *empty set* if and only if it contains no members. Such sets occur in mathematics, as the above example points out. If A and B are empty sets, then according to the Axiom of Extensionality, $A = B$ (they have exactly the same elements, namely, none). Therefore we should speak of *the* empty set. Since there is a unique empty set, it is legitimate and useful to set aside a special symbol to serve as its permanent name. The symbol commonly reserved in mathematics for this purpose is $\emptyset$. Thus, from now on in this text, $\emptyset$ designates the empty set. Observe that for every object a, $a \notin \emptyset$.

If we wish to speak about the set of men who were presidents of the United States prior to the year 1968, we can construct a name for this set by enclosing a list of the appropriate names in curly brackets. However, such a name is rather unwieldy to use. Moreover, without careful checking, we could not be sure that such a long name really is a name of exactly the intended set. It is quite evident that the name "the set of men who were presidents of the United States before 1968" is not only easier to use, but also less confusing. Similarly, the name "the set of all n such that n is an integer and $1 \leq n \leq 100$" is more useful than a bracketed list containing names of 100 integers.

In both the examples in the previous paragraph, the set in which we are interested is the set of all objects having a certain property. In the first example we were interested in the set of all x having the following property:

$$x \text{ was a president of the United States before 1968.} \qquad (9)$$

In the second example we were interested in the set of all n having the following property:

$$n \text{ is an integer and } 1 \leq n \leq 100. \qquad (10)$$

Both (9) and (10) are phrases containing variables which may take on certain specified values. We may call such phrases *designational phrases*. Designational phrases can be used to form names of sets in a very satisfactory manner. For example, the set of all n satisfying condition (10) can be given the name

$$\{n \mid n \text{ is an integer, } 1 \leq n \leq 100\}. \qquad (11)$$

The various portions of the name (11) should be read as indicated below:

$\{$	The set of all
n	n
$\mid$	such that
n is an integer	n is an integer
,	and
$1 \leq n \leq 100$	$1 \leq n \leq 100$
$\}$	

More generally, let $P(x)$ be an arbitrary designational phrase and assume that we wish to name the set of exactly those objects x for which $P(x)$ is true. The standard name in mathematics for this set is

$$\{x \mid P(x)\}. \qquad (12)$$

Again, the name (12) is read "the set of all x such that $P(x)$." Thus $a \in \{x \mid P(x)\}$ if and only if $P(a)$ is a true statement. The notation in (12) is called the *set builder notation*.

EXAMPLE 6. The set of all even integers n such that $0 \le n \le 10$ (see Example 1) has as another of its names:

$$\{n \mid n \text{ is an even integer and } 0 \le n \le 10\}.$$

This name happens to be longer and more cumbersome than the list in Example 1.

EXAMPLE 7. The set of integers has as one of its names the following:

$$\{n \mid n \text{ is an integer}\}.$$

We shall usually denote this set by J. Similarly,

$$
\begin{aligned}
J^+ &= \{n \mid n \text{ is a positive integer}\} \\
&= \{n \mid n \in J, \ n > 0\}.
\end{aligned}
\tag{13}
$$

The comma in (13) is an abbreviation of the connective "and"; this abbreviation is common usage.

EXAMPLE 8. $\{x \mid x^2 - 1 = 0\} = \{-1, 1\}$.

EXAMPLE 9. Let a and b be objects. Then,

$$\{x \mid x = a\} = \{a\},$$

and

$$\{x \mid x = a \text{ or } x = b\} = \{a, b\}.$$

EXAMPLE 10. Let $P(x)$ be the sentence "x is a real number and $x^2 + 1 = 0$." Then

$$\{x \mid P(x)\} = \emptyset.$$

EXAMPLE 11. $\{x \mid x \ne x\} = \emptyset$.

There is a useful generalization of the set builder notation which we shall sometimes employ. We do not presently have the tools needed to make an accurate description of this generalization but we can give some examples of its use. From these examples the reader should understand how to employ it.

EXAMPLE 12. The set of even integers n such that $0 \le n \le 10$ (see Example 6) has the name

$$\{2n \mid n \in J, \ 0 \le n \le 5\},$$

where J denotes the set of positive integers.

EXAMPLE 13. The set $\{0, 1, 4, 9\}$ (see Example 2) has as one of its names:

$$\{n^2 \mid n \in J, \ 0 \le n \le 3\}.$$

EXAMPLE 14. The set of all even integers greater than 5 which are the sum of two odd prime numbers has the name

$$\{p + q \mid p, q \text{ odd primes}\}.$$

The famous, but as yet unproven, Goldbach Conjecture states that

$$\{p + q \mid p, q \text{ odd primes}\} = \{2n \mid n \in J, \quad n \geq 3\}.$$

EXERCISES

1. Write two distinct names for the set which contains the number zero and nothing else.

2. Determine another name for the following set of real numbers which is more clearly indicative of the content of the set (R^1 is the set of real numbers):

$$\{x \mid x \in R^1, \quad 3x + 2 = 4\}.$$

3. Repeat Exercise 2 for the following sets.
   (a) $\{x \mid x \in R^1, x^2 + 2 = 3\}$ (b) $\{x \mid x \in R^1, x^2 + 2x = -1\}$
   (c) $\{x \mid x \in R^1, |x - 2| \leq 3\}$ (d) $\{x \mid x \in J, |x - 2| \leq 3\}$

4. (a) Find another name for $\{x \mid x \text{ is a congressman from Kansas}\}$.
   (b) Find another name for $\{x \mid x \text{ is a United States senator from Kansas}\}$.

5. Show that

$$\{x \mid x \in R^1, 1 \leq |x - 3| \leq 2\} = \{x \mid x \in R^1, 1 \leq x \leq 2 \text{ or } 4 \leq x \leq 5\}.$$

6. Find another name for the set

$$\{x \mid x \text{ is the number of dots on a face of a die}\}.$$

7. If A is a set, what is $\{x \mid x \in A\}$?

8. Show that $\{a, b\} = \{b, a\}$.

9. Show that $\{t \mid P(t)\} = \{x \mid P(x)\}$; that is, show that the choice of variables in the set builder notation is immaterial.

10. Explain why $\emptyset \notin \emptyset$.

11. Explain why $\emptyset \neq \{\emptyset\}$.

1.3 THE SUBSET RELATION

From a given set we may form new sets which we call subsets of the given set. For example, if A is the set of all presidents of the United States before 1968, then the set of all Republican presidents of the United States before 1968 is a subset of A. The subset relation is a relation between two sets. Clearly, the essential feature of the subset relation is that every element of one set is an element of the other. As another example, $\{n \mid n \text{ is an even integer}, 0 \leq n \leq 10\}$ is a subset of $\{n \mid n \text{ is an integer}, 0 \leq n \leq 10\}$. In general, we have the following definition.

Definition 1.1. Let A and B be sets. We say that A is a *subset* of B, and write

$$A \subset B,$$

if and only if every element of A is also an element of B. If $A \subset B$, we say that B *contains* A or that A *is contained in B*. The negation "A is not a subset of B" is written $A \not\subset B$.

To show that $A \subset B$ we must show that for all x, if $x \in A$, then $x \in B$.

EXAMPLE 1. Let $A = \{4, 8\}$, $B = \{2, 4, 6, 8\}$, and $C = \{4, 6, 8, 10\}$. Then

$$A \subset B, \quad A \subset C, \quad B \not\subset C, \quad C \not\subset B.$$

EXAMPLE 2. Let n be a positive integer, and let R_n and S_n be, respectively, the set of all square n-by-n matrices and the set of all nonsingular square n-by-n matrices. Then $S_n \subset R_n$ but $R_n \not\subset S_n$ (since, for example, $0_{n \times n} \in R_n$, but $0_{n \times n} \notin S_n$).

EXAMPLE 3. If A is any set, then $\emptyset \subset A$. Furthermore, if A is a set such that $A \subset \emptyset$, then $A = \emptyset$.

The first statement says that the empty set is a subset of every set; the second states that any subset of the empty set is itself empty and hence is the empty set. To establish that $\emptyset \subset A$, we can argue as follows. We must show that every element in $\emptyset$ is an element of A; since there are no elements in $\emptyset$, the condition is automatically satisfied. The reader may find this argument unsatisfying. Another argument which also establishes the result is the following argument by contradiction. Suppose that it is false that $\emptyset \subset A$. Then $\emptyset \not\subset A$ and hence $\emptyset$ contains an element that does not belong to A. Since $\emptyset$ has no elements, this is impossible. Therefore we cannot have $\emptyset \not\subset A$, and hence we must have $\emptyset \subset A$.

The statement $A \subset B$ does not rule out the possibility that $B \subset A$. In fact, $A \subset A$ is always true. More generally, we may have $A \subset B$ and $B \subset A$, but this happens only if A and B have the same elements. Thus we have the following theorem.

Theorem 1.1. Let A and B be sets. Then $A = B$ if and only if $A \subset B$ and $B \subset A$.

This theorem may be used instead of the Axiom of Extensionality to check the equality of two sets. Two sets are proved to be equal by first showing that $A \subset B$ and then showing that $B \subset A$, or conversely.

EXAMPLE 4. Let A be the set of positive even integers, and let B be the set of positive integers expressible as a sum of two odd integers. Then, although these sets are defined differently, they are the same, that is, $A = B$.

To show that $A = B$ we will show that $A \subset B$ and that $B \subset A$. We begin by showing the former. Let x be any element of A. Then $x = 2m$ for some integer m. But $2m = (2m - 1) + 1$, and $2m - 1$ and 1 are both positive odd integers. Hence $x \in B$ and $A \subset B$.

Next, we shall show that $B \subset A$. To do so, we must show that any element in B is also an element in A. Let x be any element in B. Then $x = (2p - 1) + (2q - 1)$, where p and q are positive integers, since x is the sum of two odd positive integers. Thus

$$x = (2p - 1) + (2q - 1) = 2p + 2q - 2 = 2(p + q - 1).$$

Since $p + q - 1$ is a positive integer, x is an even positive integer. Thus $x \in A$, and we have shown that $B \subset A$.

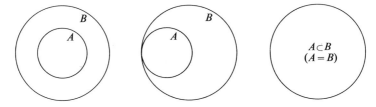

Fig. 1.1. Venn diagrams representing $A \subset B$.

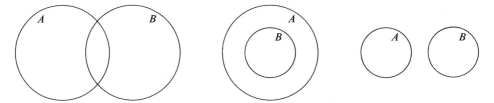

Fig. 1.2. Venn diagrams representing $A \not\subset B$.

A convenient device for picturing sets and relationships among sets is to use *Venn diagrams*. The idea is to represent sets by simple plane areas. Thus if $A \subset B$, we can represent this situation graphically as shown in Fig. 1.1. If $A \not\subset B$, then we have pictures such as those shown in Fig. 1.2. By examining these figures, the reader will see that we have represented A and B as the points enclosed in the circles labeled A and B. We shall use these visual aids to help us understand other relationships between sets; Venn diagrams, as we shall see, are useful for testing the validity of theorems in set theory or for suggesting methods to prove them. Of course, the proofs themselves must rely only on definitions and already established theorems and not on the diagrams.

We have seen that $A \subset B$ does not rule out the possibility that $A = B$. If we wish to indicate that A is a subset of B which is not equal to B, we will write $A \subsetneq B$ and say that A is a proper subset of B.

Definition 1.2. Let A and B be sets. We say that A is a *proper subset* of B and write $A \underset{\neq}{\subset} B$ if and only if

$$A \subset B \quad \text{and} \quad A \neq B.$$

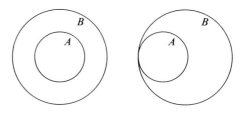

Fig. 1.3. Venn diagrams representing $A \underset{\neq}{\subset} B$.

Observe that we cannot have both $A \underset{\neq}{\subset} B$ and $B \underset{\neq}{\subset} A$. Venn diagrams which represent $A \underset{\neq}{\subset} B$ are given in Fig. 1.3.

Note that Fig. 1.3 is the same as Fig. 1.1 except that the last diagram in Fig. 1.1 has been deleted; the last diagram must be omitted because if $A = B$, then we cannot have $A \underset{\neq}{\subset} B$.

To show that A is a proper subset of B, we must show that for any x, if $x \in A$, then $x \in B$, and also that there is an $x \in B$ such that $x \notin A$. Usually we shall be interested in showing only that one set is a subset of another, but occasionally it is important to show that one set is a proper subset of another.

EXERCISES

1. Let A be the set of all presidents of the United States, B be the set of all living presidents, and C the set of all presidents who were over 50 years of age when elected.
   (a) Show that $B \subset A$, $C \subset A$.
   (b) Is $C \subset B$? Is $B \underset{\neq}{\subset} A$? Is $C \underset{\neq}{\subset} A$?

2. Let A be the set of positive integers, and let B be the set of positive rational numbers. Show that $A \subset B$. Is $A = B$?

3. Prove that $A \subset A$ for every set A.

4. Let A, B, and C be sets. Prove the following.
   (a) If $A \subset B$ and $B \subset C$, then $A \subset C$. (b) If $A \underset{\neq}{\subset} B$ and $B \subset C$, then $A \underset{\neq}{\subset} C$.
   (c) If $A \subset B$ and $A \not\subset C$, then $B \not\subset C$.

5. Prove Theorem 1.1.

1.4 SOME PROPERTIES OF $=$, $\subset$, $\underset{\neq}{\subset}$, AND $\in$

In this brief section we shall indicate the basic properties of the set relations we have already defined. Most of these properties are obvious, but a collection of them may prove useful. In addition, these properties are indicative of the properties that may be useful (if they exist) when other relations are studied.

The relation of equality has three important properties with which the reader has undoubtedly been familiar for many years, although these properties may not yet have been brought to his attention explicitly. First, regardless of what object A is, it is the case that $A = A$ (a rose is a rose); the relation of equality is said to be *reflexive*. Second, if A and B are any objects and if it is the case that

$A = B$, then it is also the case that $B = A$; the relation of equality is said to be *symmetric*. Third, if A, B, and C are objects such that $A = B$ and $B = C$, then it is also the case that $A = C$; the relation of equality is said to be *transitive*. Any relation which is reflexive, symmetric, and transitive is said to be an *equivalence relation;* thus equality is an equivalence relation. These three properties— reflexivity, symmetry, and transitivity—are quite important in mathematics; we shall wish to determine for each of the relations we investigate whether or not it has these properties. We summarize the properties of $=$ below.

Properties of $=$. Let A, B, and C be sets. Then
(a) $A = A$ (reflexivity).
(b) If $A = B$, then $B = A$ (symmetry).
(c) If $A = B$ and $B = C$, then $A = C$ (transitivity).

Next, we investigate the relation $\subset$. The subset relation is reflexive, since, if A is any set, $A \subset A$. The subset relation is also transitive: if A, B, and C are sets and if $A \subset B$ and $B \subset C$, then $A \subset C$. To show this we argue as follows: for any $x \in A$, we have $x \in B$ since $A \subset B$. Thus $x \in B$ and hence, since $B \subset C$, $x \in C$. Thus for any x, if $x \in A$, then $x \in C$; this is just the definition of $A \subset C$. So far so good; but the symmetric law does not hold for the subset relation. We can have $A \subset B$ without having $B \subset A$. For example, $\emptyset \subset \{\emptyset\}$, but $\{\emptyset\} \not\subset \emptyset$ since $\{\emptyset\}$ has one element, namely $\emptyset$. On the other hand, there are sets for which $A \subset B$ and $B \subset A$; for example, these two statements are true for any two equal sets. We say that the subset relation is *nonsymmetric*.

Properties of $\subset$. Let A, B, and C be sets. Then
(a) $A \subset A$ (reflexivity).
(b) $\subset$ is nonsymmetric.
(c) If $A \subset B$ and $B \subset C$, then $A \subset C$ (transitivity).

Having looked at the properties of the subset relation, we proceed to study the properties of the proper subset relation. First, since there is no set A for which $A \subsetneq A$, we say that the relation $\subsetneq$ is *antireflexive*. Next, it is never the case that $A \subsetneq B$ and $B \subsetneq A$ and we say that the relation $\subsetneq$ is *antisymmetric*. The reader should note the difference between a nonsymmetric relation and an antisymmetric relation: the former is a relation which is not in general symmetric (although there may be some particular instance in which it is symmetric), and the latter is a relation which is never symmetric. Finally, the relation $\subsetneq$ is transitive: if $A \subsetneq B$ and $B \subsetneq C$, then $A \subsetneq C$. To show this, use the transitivity of $\subset$ to show that $A \subset C$. Next choose any $x \in C$ such that $x \notin B$; such an x exists because B is a proper subset of C. Then $x \in C$ and $x \notin A$; thus $A \subset C$ and $A \neq C$ and hence $A \subsetneq C$.

Properties of $\subseteq$. Let A, B, and C be sets. Then
(a) $\subsetneq$ is antireflexive: $A \subsetneq A$ is never true.
(b) $\subsetneq$ is antisymmetric: $A \subsetneq B$ and $B \subsetneq A$ is never true.
(c) If $A \subsetneq B$ and $B \subsetneq C$, then $A \subsetneq C$ (transitivity).

Finally, we come to the first relation we introduced in this chapter, that of belonging to. Since it is *not* the case that $\emptyset \in \emptyset$, the relation $\in$ is not reflexive; we say $\in$ is *nonreflexive*. Also, since it is the case that both $\emptyset \in \{\emptyset\}$ and $\{\emptyset\} \notin \emptyset$, the relation $\in$ is *nonsymmetric*. Furthermore, the relation $\in$ is not transitive. For example, it is the case that both $\emptyset \in \{\emptyset\}$ and $\{\emptyset\} \in \{\{\emptyset\}\}$, but it is not the case that $\emptyset \in \{\{\emptyset\}\}$ ($\{\emptyset\}$ is the only element of $\{\{\emptyset\}\}$ and $\emptyset \neq \{\emptyset\}$). However, there do exist sets A, B, and C such that $A \in B$, $B \in C$, *and* $A \in C$. For example, $\emptyset \in \{\emptyset\}$, $\{\emptyset\} \in \{\emptyset, \{\emptyset\}\}$, and $\emptyset \in \{\emptyset, \{\emptyset\}\}$; thus we say that $\in$ is *nontransitive*.

Properties of $\in$:
(a) $\in$ is nonreflexive,
(b) $\in$ is nonsymmetric,
(c) $\in$ is nontransitive.

We should observe that in our discussion we did not settle the questions:
(i) Is $\in$ antireflexive?
(ii) Is $\in$ antisymmetric?
We did show, however, that $\in$ is *not* antitransitive. In regard to questions (i) and (ii), no one has been able, on the basis of what we have already established, to decide whether or not the $\in$ relation is antireflexive; further, it is not known whether or not the $\in$ relation is antisymmetric. If $\in$ is antireflexive, then it is never true that $A \in A$; if $\in$ is antisymmetric, then there are no sets A and B such that both $A \in B$ and $B \in A$. Often it is postulated, in further axioms of set theory, that $\in$ is antireflexive and antisymmetric. Since we shall have no need for this refinement, we shall not postulate these axioms.

The reader should observe that we have frequently used the empty set $\emptyset$ (sometimes called the *null set*) in giving examples. We have done so because the empty set is easy to work with, and because it has no elements to cause difficulties.

Finally, for more careful definitions of the properties (reflexivity, symmetry, transitivity) of relations, the interested reader should consult Exercises 8, 9, 10, and 11 of Section 2.3.

EXERCISES

1. Consider the relation "father of." This is a relation between people. Which of the following nine possible properties of a relation does it possess: (1) reflexive, (2) non-reflexive, (3) antireflexive, (4) symmetric, (5) nonsymmetric, (6) antisymmetric, (7) transitive, (8) nontransitive, (9) antitransitive?

2. Repeat Exercise 1 for the relation "brother of."

3. Which of the nine properties of a relation listed in Exercise 1 does the relation "speaks to" possess if it is assumed that a person can never speak to himself?

4. A relation among people is called a *dominance relation* if (i) a person can never dominate himself, (ii) given two distinct persons P and Q, either P dominates Q or Q dominates P but not both. Repeat Exercise 1 for a dominance relation.

5. In a certain intrabusiness communication model, a *communication relation* is defined between people as follows: (i) A person cannot communicate with himself. (ii) If a person P communicates with a person Q, then Q communicates with P. Which of the nine properties listed in Exercise 1 does this relation possess?

1.5 INTERSECTION AND UNION

Let A and B be the following sets: $A = \{0, 1, 2, 3, 4, 5\}$ and $B = \{1, 3, 5, 7, 9\}$. These two sets have the numbers 1, 3, and 5 in common, although neither $A \subset B$ nor $B \subset A$. The set of common elements, $\{1, 3, 5\}$, is called the intersection of A and B and is denoted by $A \cap B$ (read, A intersect B). In general, the intersection of two sets is the set of elements common to both sets. The concept of set intersection can be formulated as follows.

Definition 1.3. Let A and B be sets. The *intersection* of A and B, denoted by $A \cap B$, is the set consisting of those elements which belong to both A and B; to be precise

$$A \cap B = \{c \mid c \in A \text{ and } c \in B\}.$$

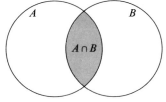

Fig. 1.4. Venn diagram representation of $A \cap B$.

We may represent set intersection graphically by means of Venn diagrams, which were introduced earlier. Figure 1.4 shows a Venn diagram for $A \cap B$.

EXAMPLE 1. If $A = \{1, 2\}$ and $B = \{2, 3, 5\}$, then $A \cap B = \{2\}$.

EXAMPLE 2. If $A = \{1, 2\}$ and $B = \{3, 4\}$, then $A \cap B = \emptyset$. More generally, the intersection of two sets having no elements in common is the empty set.

EXAMPLE 3. If $A = \{1, 2, 3, 4, 5\}$ and $B = \{2, 4\}$, then $A \cap B = B$. More generally, if $B \subset A$, then $A \cap B = B$. This statement, of course, requires a proof. We furnish a proof by showing that $A \cap B \subset B$ and $B \subset A \cap B$; remember that we are given $B \subset A$. Let c be any element of $A \cap B$. Then c is common to A and B. Hence $c \in A$ and $c \in B$; then, in particular, $c \in B$. Thus $A \cap B \subset B$. Next, suppose c is any element of B. Then $c \in B$, and, since $B \subset A$, $c \in A$. Thus $c \in A$ and $c \in B$, and by definition, $c \in A \cap B$; hence, $B \subset A \cap B$. Then, by Theorem 1.1, $A \cap B = B$ if $B \subset A$.

EXAMPLE 4. Let J^+ be the set of positive integers, and let F be the set of positive integers n for which there exist positive integers x, y, and z such that $x^n + y^n = z^n$; that is,

$$F = \{n \mid n \in J^+, \text{ there exist } x, y, z \in J^+ \text{ such that } x^n + y^n = z^n\}.$$

Since $1^1 + 1^1 = 2^1$ and $3^2 + 4^2 = 5^2$, it is evident that $\{1, 2\} \subset F$.

The famous Fermat's Last Theorem (FLT) states that $F = \{1, 2\}$. Actually FLT is not yet a theorem in mathematics; it is only an unproved conjecture. However, the tremendous efforts of some of the greatest mathematicians of the last three centuries on FLT have produced a substantial amount of beautiful mathematical theory.

As a result of work done on the large computer SWAC by Vandiver and others in 1955, there is now a published proof that

$$\{n \mid 3 \le n \le 4{,}002\} \cap F = \emptyset.$$

Here is an example of one of the instances in which the computer has been used to aid the mathematician in establishing a theorem.

Two of the most basic properties of set intersection are contained in the following theorem.

Theorem 1.2. Let A, B, and C be sets. Then

(a) $A \cap B = B \cap A$ (commutative law of set intersection);
(b) $A \cap (B \cap C) = (A \cap B) \cap C$ (associative law of set intersection).

Proof of (a). The proof of this part of the theorem has been left as an exercise for the reader.

Proof of (b). We shall establish the result by showing that both $A \cap (B \cap C) \subset (A \cap B) \cap C$ and $(A \cap B) \cap C \subset A \cap (B \cap C)$ and applying Theorem 1.1. To establish the first inclusion, suppose that x is any element of $A \cap (B \cap C)$. Then $x \in A$ and $x \in B \cap C$. But, since $x \in B \cap C$, it follows that $x \in B$ and $x \in C$. Thus $x \in A$, $x \in B$, and $x \in C$. Since $x \in A$ and $x \in B$, $x \in A \cap B$. Hence, $x \in A \cap B$ and $x \in C$. Therefore $x \in (A \cap B) \cap C$, and we have shown that

$$A \cap (B \cap C) \subset (A \cap B) \cap C.$$

The second inclusion can be established in a similar manner. Let x be any element of $(A \cap B) \cap C$. Then $x \in A \cap B$ and $x \in C$. But, since $x \in A \cap B$, it follows that $x \in A$ and $x \in B$. Thus $x \in A$, $x \in B$, and $x \in C$. Since $x \in B$ and $x \in C$, $x \in B \cap C$. Then $x \in A$ and $x \in B \cap C$. Therefore $x \in A \cap (B \cap C)$, and we have shown that

$$(A \cap B) \cap C \subset A \cap (B \cap C).$$

Since we have shown that both $A \cap (B \cap C) \subset (A \cap B) \cap C$ and $(A \cap B) \cap C \subset A \cap (B \cap C)$, we have, by Theorem 1.1,

$$A \cap (B \cap C) = (A \cap B) \cap C. \blacktriangle *$$

This proof of part (b) of Theorem 1.2 is unduly long, but it does use the basic idea of Theorem 1.1. In Exercise 3(b), the reader is asked to furnish a simpler proof.

The results of Theorem 1.2 are very important. Part (a) states that the order of the sets in an intersection is immaterial, and part (b) asserts that the parentheses are unnecessary. In fact, in view of part (b), $A \cap B \cap C$ could unambiguously be defined as either $(A \cap B) \cap C$ or $A \cap (B \cap C)$; each of these is in fact the set of elements common to the sets A, B, and C. This suggests that we define the intersection of more than two sets to be the set consisting of those elements common to *all* of the sets.

Definition 1.4. Let S be a nonempty set of sets. The *intersection of all the sets* in S, denoted by

$$\bigcap_{A \in S} A,$$

is the set of those elements which belong to every one of the sets in S; more precisely,

$$\bigcap_{A \in S} A = \{x \mid x \in A \text{ for all } A \in S\}.$$

If S is a finite collection of sets (the case we shall always be concerned with in this text), say $S = \{A_1, A_2, \ldots, A_n\}$, we write

$$\bigcap_{A \in S} A = \bigcap_{k=1}^{n} A_k = A_1 \cap A_2 \cap \cdots \cap A_n.$$

It can easily be shown that, in view of the definition, there is no ambiguity involved in writing $A_1 \cap A_2 \cap \cdots \cap A_n$.

EXAMPLE 5. If A is the set of human males living in the United States, B is the set of blue-eyed people, and C is the set of left-handed people, then $A \cap B \cap C$ is the set of blue-eyed, left-handed males living in the United States.

EXAMPLE 6. For each positive integer n, define A_n as

$$A_n = \{x \mid x \in R^1, -1/n < x < 1 + 1/n\}.$$

---

* Note the use of the symbol ▲ to mark conclusion of proof.

Let $S_k = \{A_1, A_2, \ldots, A_k\}$ for $k = 1, 2, \ldots$. Then S_k is a nonempty set of sets, and

$$\bigcap_{A \in S_k} A = \bigcap_{i=1}^{k} A_i = A_k, \tag{1}$$

since $A_1 \supset A_2 \supset \cdots \supset A_k$. (The reader is urged at this point to draw a picture of the sets $A_1, A_2, \ldots, A_k$ and to show that the assertion in Eq. (1) is true using Theorem 1.1.)

Next, let $S = \{A_n \mid n \text{ is a positive integer}\}$. What is

$$\bigcap_{A \in S} A? \tag{2}$$

This intersection is commonly denoted by

$$\bigcap_{n \geq 1} A_n \qquad \text{or} \qquad \bigcap_{n=1}^{\infty} A_n.$$

Let B denote the set in (2); we shall show that

$$B = C, \tag{3}$$

where C denotes the set $C = \{x \mid x \in R^1, 0 \leq x \leq 1\}$.

First, if $x \in C$, then $0 \leq x \leq 1$ and hence $x \in A_n$ for every $A_n \in S$. Thus $x \in B$ and $C \subset B$. Next we show that there are no elements $x \in B$ such that $x \notin C$ and hence show that $B = C$. (This argument works only because we know already that $C \subset B$.) Suppose then that $x \notin C$; then either $x > 1$ or $x < 0$. If $x > 1$, then $x - 1 > 0$ and there is a positive integer n_1 such that $1/n_1 < x - 1$. Thus $x > 1 + 1/n_1$ and hence $x \notin A_{n_1}$. Since $x \notin A_{n_1}$, $x \notin \bigcap_{n=1}^{\infty} A_n = B$. If $x < 0$, then $-x > 0$ and there is a positive integer n_2 such that $1/n_2 < -x$. Thus $-1/n_2 > x$ and hence $x \notin A_{n_2}$. Since $x \notin A_{n_2}$, $x \notin \bigcap_{n=1}^{\infty} A_n = B$. From these considerations we may conclude that C is a subset of B which is not a proper subset of B, and hence $C = B$.

Closely allied to the operation of set intersection is the operation of set union. Again, let A and B be the following sets: $A = \{0, 1, 2, 3, 4, 5\}$ and $B = \{1, 3, 5, 7, 9\}$. The numbers 0, 1, 2, 3, 4, 5, 7, 9 are precisely the objects which belong to at least one of the sets A and B. The set consisting of these numbers is called the union of the sets A and B and is denoted by $A \cup B$ (read A union B), that is,

$$A \cup B = \{1, 2, 3, 4, 5, 7, 9\}.$$

In general, the union of any two sets is the set of all objects belonging to at least one (and perhaps both) of the two sets. The concept of set union can be formulated as follows.

Definition 1.5. Let A and B be sets. The *union* of A and B, denoted by $A \cup B$, is the set of all elements which belong either to A or to B (or to both); to be precise,

$$A \cup B = \{c \mid c \in A \text{ or } c \in B\}.$$

Set unions also can be represented by means of Venn diagrams (see Fig. 1.4 for a Venn diagram representation of set intersection). Let A and B be sets whose union is to be considered. We may consider A and B to be represented by the areas whose boundaries are labeled A and B in the Venn diagram of Fig. 1.5. If we do so, then clearly we shall consider the set union, $A \cup B$, to be represented by the shaded area in the Venn diagrams.

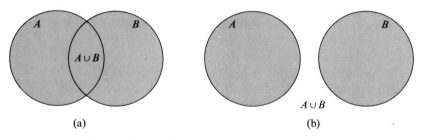

(a)   (b)

Fig. 1.5. Venn diagram representation of $A \cup B$.

EXAMPLE 7. If $A = \{1, 2\}$ and $B = \{2, 3, 5\}$, then $A \cup B = \{1, 2, 3, 5\}$.

EXAMPLE 8. If $A = \{1, 2\}$ and $B = \{3, 5\}$, then $A \cup B = \{1, 2, 3, 5\}$.

EXAMPLE 9. If $A = \{1, 2, 3, 4, 5\}$ and $B = \{2, 4\}$, then $A \cup B = A$.
More generally, if $B \subset A$, then $A \cup B = A$. The reader is asked to prove this fact in Exercise 5.

EXAMPLE 10. If A is the set of all human males in the United States and B is the set of all human females in the United States, then $A \cup B$ is the set of all human beings in the United States.

Two basic properties of set union are given in the following theorem. Note that this theorem is an analog of Theorem 1.2.

Theorem 1.3. Let A, B, and C be sets. Then

(a) $A \cup B = B \cup A$ (commutative law of set union);
(b) $A \cup (B \cup C) = (A \cup B) \cup C$ (associative law of set union).

Proof of (a). We shall give a short proof of (a). Another proof can be given using Theorem 1.1. We suggest that the reader construct such a proof.

By Definition 1.5, $A \cup B = \{c \mid c \in A \text{ or } c \in B\}$ and $B \cup A = \{c \mid c \in B \text{ or } c \in A\}$. But $c \in A$ or $c \in B$ if and only if $c \in B$ or $c \in A$; hence,

$$\{c \mid c \in A \text{ or } c \in B\} = \{c \mid c \in B \text{ or } c \in A\}.$$

Therefore $A \cup B = B \cup A$.

Proof of (b). This proof has been left as an exercise for the reader (see Exercise 6).▲

The results of Theorem 1.3 assert that the order of the sets in a union is immaterial and that the parentheses are not really necessary; $A \cup B \cup C$ could be defined unambiguously to be either $A \cup (B \cup C)$ or $(A \cup B) \cup C$, for each of these is in fact the set of elements which belong to at least one of the sets A, B, or C. This suggests that we define the union of more than two sets to be the set consisting of exactly those elements which belong to at least one of the sets.

Definition 1.6. Let S be a nonempty set of sets. The *union of all the sets in S*, denoted by

$$\bigcup_{A \in S} A,$$

is the set of those elements which belong to at least one set in S. More precisely,

$$\bigcup_{A \in S} A = \{x \mid x \in A \text{ for some } A \in S\}.$$

If S is a finite collection of sets (the case we shall always be concerned with in this book), say $S = \{A_1, A_2, \ldots, A_n\}$, we write

$$\bigcup_{A \in S} A = \bigcup_{k=1}^{n} A_k = A_1 \cup A_2 \cup \cdots \cup A_n.$$

In view of the definition, it can easily be shown that there is no ambiguity involved in writing $A_1 \cup A_2 \cup \cdots \cup A_n$.

EXAMPLE 11. If $A_n = \{n\}$ for $n = 1, 2, \ldots, k$, then

$$\bigcup_{n=1}^{k} A_n = \{1\} \cup \{2\} \cup \cdots \cup \{k\} = \{1, 2, \ldots, k\}.$$

EXAMPLE 12. If $S = \{\{1\}, \{2\}, \{3\}, \ldots\}$, then $\bigcup_{A \in S} A = J^+$, the set of positive integers. Usually such a union is written $\bigcup_{n \geq 1} A_n$, where $A_n = \{n\}$.

EXAMPLE 13. Let F be the set of all family units in the United States and let A_1 be those whose income in 1967 was less than \$1000, A_2, those whose income for 1967 was at least \$1000 but less than \$5000, A_3, those whose income was at least \$5000 but less than \$10,000, A_4, those whose income was at least \$10,000 but less than \$20,000, and A_5, those whose income was at least \$20,000. If we let $S = \{A_1, A_2, A_3, A_4, A_5\}$, then $\bigcup_{A \in S} A = A_1 \cup A_2 \cup A_3 \cup A_4 \cup A_5 = F$. Observe that $A_i \cap A_j = \emptyset$ for $i \neq j$. Such a set S is called a *partition* of F; it divides the population (in this case family units) into various parts so that no family unit belongs to more than one set A_i.

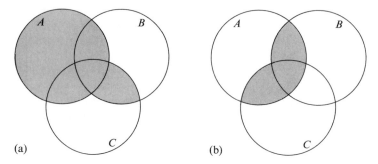

Fig. 1.6. Venn diagrams for $A \cup (B \cap C)$ and $A \cap (B \cup C)$.

So far we have considered only sets such as $A \cup B$, $A \cup B \cup C$, $A \cap B$, and $A \cap B \cap C$. Of course, there is no reason why we could not consider sets such as $A \cup (B \cap C)$ and $A \cap (B \cup C)$. Figure 1.6 gives Venn diagrams of these two sets. The shaded area in the first diagram shows $A \cup (B \cap C)$ and the shaded area in the second shows $A \cap (B \cup C)$. If the reader examines these diagrams carefully, he will become convinced that the following theorem is true.

Theorem 1.4. Let A, B, and C be sets. Then

(a) $A \cup (B \cap C) = (A \cup B) \cap (A \cup C)$ (set union is distributive over set intersection);

(b) $A \cap (B \cup C) = (A \cap B) \cup (A \cap C)$ (set intersection is distributive over set union).

Proof of (a). We shall prove (a) by showing that $A \cup (B \cap C) \subset (A \cup B) \cap (A \cup C)$ and that $(A \cup B) \cap (B \cup C) \subset A \cup (B \cap C)$. To show the first inclusion, let x be any element of $A \cup (B \cap C)$. Then $x \in A$ or $x \in B \cap C$ (or both). If the former, then $x \in A \cup B$ and $x \in A \cup C$. So in the first case $x \in (A \cup B) \cap (A \cup C)$. Suppose then that $x \in B \cap C$. Then $x \in B$ and $x \in C$. Since $x \in B$, $x \in A \cup B$; and since $x \in C$, $x \in A \cup C$. Therefore $x \in (A \cup B) \cap (A \cup C)$ in this case. Thus, in either case, $x \in (A \cup B) \cap (A \cup C)$, and hence we have shown that

$$A \cup (B \cap C) \subset (A \cup B) \cap (A \cup C).$$

Next we shall show that $(A \cup B) \cap (A \cup C) \subset A \cup (B \cap C)$. If x is any element of $(A \cup B) \cap (A \cup C)$, then $x \in A \cup B$ and $x \in A \cup C$. Therefore $x \in A$ or $x \in B$, and $x \in A$ or $x \in C$. If $x \in A$, then $x \in A \cup (B \cap C)$. If $x \notin A$, then $x \in B$ and $x \in C$. Thus, in this case $x \in B \cap C$, and hence $x \in A \cup (B \cap C)$.

Thus, in either case, we have shown that $x \in A \cup (B \cap C)$, and hence

$$(A \cup B) \cap (A \cup C) \subset A \cup (B \cap C).$$

By Theorem 1.1, we have shown that the two sets are equal.

The proof for (b) is similar to the proof given for (a); it will be left as practice for the reader.▲

There are certain generalizations of Theorems 1.2, 1.3, and 1.4 to the case in which we are dealing with unions and intersections of many sets. The most useful of these generalizations are summarized in the following theorem.

Theorem 1.5. Let S be a nonempty set of sets, and let B be a set. Then

$$\text{(a)} \quad B \cap \left(\bigcap_{A \in S} A \right) = \bigcap_{A \in S} (B \cap A);$$

$$\text{(b)} \quad B \cup \left(\bigcup_{A \in S} A \right) = \bigcup_{A \in S} (B \cup A);$$

$$\text{(c)} \quad B \cup \left(\bigcap_{A \in S} A \right) = \bigcap_{A \in S} (B \cup A);$$

$$\text{(d)} \quad B \cap \left(\bigcup_{A \in S} A \right) = \bigcup_{A \in S} (B \cap A).$$

It will be useful to state these identities for the case in which

$$S = \{A_1, A_2, \ldots, A_n\},$$

that is, for the case in which S is a finite set of sets. Then we have

$$\text{(a')} \quad B \cap \left(\bigcap_{A \in S} A \right) = B \cap \left(\bigcap_{k=1}^{n} A_k \right) = \bigcap_{k=1}^{n} (B \cap A_k)$$
$$= (B \cap A_1) \cap (B \cap A_2) \cap \cdots \cap (B \cap A_n);$$

$$\text{(b')} \quad B \cup \left(\bigcup_{A \in S} A \right) = B \cup \left(\bigcup_{k=1}^{n} A_k \right) = \bigcup_{k=1}^{n} (B \cup A_k)$$
$$= (B \cup A_1) \cup (B \cup A_2) \cup \cdots \cup (B \cup A_n);$$

$$\text{(c')} \quad B \cup \left(\bigcap_{A \in S} A \right) = B \cup \left(\bigcap_{k=1}^{n} A_k \right) = \bigcap_{k=1}^{n} (B \cup A_k)$$
$$= (B \cup A_1) \cap (B \cup A_2) \cap \cdots \cap (B \cup A_n);$$

$$\text{(d')} \quad B \cap \left(\bigcup_{A \in S} A \right) = B \cap \left(\bigcup_{k=1}^{n} A_k \right) = \bigcup_{k=1}^{n} (B \cap A_k)$$
$$= (B \cap A_1) \cup (B \cap A_2) \cup \cdots \cup (B \cap A_n).$$

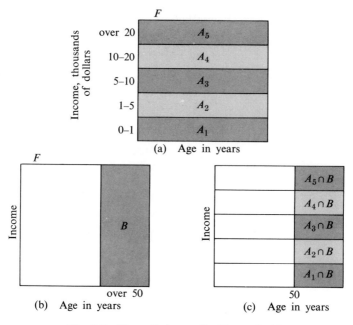

Fig. 1.7. Venn diagrams for Example 14.

EXAMPLE 14. Let F, A_1, A_2, . . . , A_5 be defined as in Example 13. Let B be the set of families (in the United States) where the main wage earner is over 50 years of age. Then

$$B \cap F = B,$$

and hence, by (a'),

$$B = B \cap F = B \cap \left(\bigcup_{k=1}^{5} A_k \right) = \bigcup_{k=1}^{5} (B \cap A_k).$$

For each k, $1 \leq k \leq 5$, $B \cap A_k$ is the set of family units whose main wage earner is over 50 and whose income in 1967 was in the range specified by A_k. Observe that

$$(B \cap A_k) \cap (B \cap A_j) = \emptyset \qquad \text{for} \quad j \neq k,$$

since, by (a'),

$$(B \cap A_k) \cap (B \cap A_j) = B \cap (A_k \cap A_j) = B \cap \emptyset = \emptyset.$$

Thus the sets $B \cap A_k$, $1 \leq k \leq 5$, form a partition of the family units whose principal wage earner is over 50. The various sets are shown schematically in the Venn diagram in Fig. 1.7. Note that instead of using circles, we are using rectangles since they afford a more realistic picture of this situation.

More generally, we could let B_1 be the set of those families in F whose principal wage earner is under 20; B_2 the set of those in which the age of the principal wage earner is from 20 to 29; B_3, from 30 to 39; B_4, from 40 to 49; B_5, from

50 to 64; B_6, 65 and over. (We consider, for example, a person to be 29 from his 29th birthday until his next birthday.) Then we have

$$F = \bigcup_{i=1}^{6} B_i,$$

and

$$B_i \cap B_j = \emptyset \qquad \text{for} \quad i \neq j.$$

Thus the sets B_1, B_2, . . . , B_6 also form a partition of F. We can form a *cross partition* by considering the sets

$$B_i \cap A_k, \qquad 1 \leq i \leq 6, \quad 1 \leq k \leq 5.$$

For example, a family belongs to the set $B_2 \cap A_3$ if and only if the principal wage earner is from 20 to 29 years of age *and* the 1967 family income was between $1000 and $5000. Observe that

$$F = F \cap F = \left(\bigcup_{i=1}^{6} B_i \right) \cap \left(\bigcup_{k=1}^{5} A_k \right) = \bigcup_{k=1}^{5} \left[\left(\bigcup_{i=1}^{6} B_i \right) \cap A_k \right]$$

$$= \bigcup_{k=1}^{5} \left[\bigcup_{i=1}^{6} (B_i \cap A_k) \right] = \bigcup_{k=1}^{5} \bigcup_{i=1}^{6} (B_i \cap A_k).$$

Thus these sets $B_i \cap A_k$ form a partition of F. Figure 1.8 shows the partition of F determined by the age brackets, and Fig. 1.9 shows the cross partition determined by age and income brackets (see also Fig. 1.7).

The idea of a cross partition is used in many places, notably in the biological sciences and in surveying procedures.

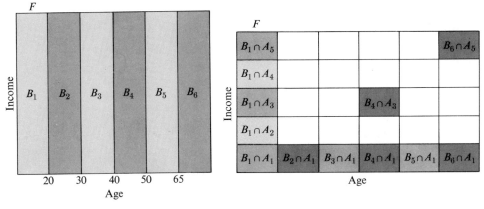

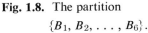

Fig. 1.8. The partition
$\{B_1, B_2, \ldots, B_6\}$.

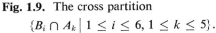

Fig. 1.9. The cross partition
$\{B_i \cap A_k \mid 1 \leq i \leq 6, 1 \leq k \leq 5\}$.

EXERCISES

1. Compute the intersection, $A \cap B$, for each of the following pairs of sets.
   (a) $A = \{-1, 2, 5, 8, 11, 14\}$, $B = \{0, 2, 4, 8, 12, 16\}$
   (b) $A = \{n \mid n \in J, -7 < n < 17\}$, $B = \{n^2 \mid n \in A\}$ (J is the set of all integers—positive, negative, and zero.)
   (c) $A = \{x \mid x \in R^1, -1 \leq x \leq 5\}$, $B = \{x \mid x \in R^1, -5 < x < 1\}$ (R^1 is the set of real numbers.)
   (d) $A = \{x \mid x \in R^1, |x - 2| \leq 3\}$, $B = \{x \mid x \in R^1, -5 < x < 1\}$
   (e) $A = \{(x, y) \mid x, y \in R^1, 2x + y = 3\}$, $B = \{(x, y) \mid x, y \in R^1, x + y = 1\}$
   (f) $A = \{x \mid x \in R^1, x^2 - 4x + 5 = 0\}$, $B = \{x \mid x \in R^1, x^2 + 4x + 5 \geq 1\}$

2. Complete the following statements so that the results are theorems; then prove the theorems.
   (a) If A is a set, then $\emptyset \cap A = $ _____.
   (b) If A is a set, then $A \cap A = $ _____.
   (c) If A and B are sets such that $A \subset B$, then $A \cap B = $ _____.
   (d) If A and B are sets such that $A \cap B = A$, then _____.

3. (a) Prove part (a) of Theorem 1.2.
   (b) Give a simpler proof of part (b) of Theorem 1.2 (see the proof of part (a) of Theorem 1.3).

4. Compute the union, $A \cup B$, for each of the following pairs of sets.
   (a) $A = \{-1, 2, 5, 8, 11, 14\}$, $B = \{0, 2, 4, 8, 12, 16\}$
   (b) $A = \{x \mid x \in R^1, -1 \leq x \leq 5\}$, $B = \{x \mid x \in R^1, -5 < x < 1\}$
   (c) $A = \{x \mid x \in R^1, |x - 2| \leq 3\}$, $B = \{x \mid x \in R^1, -5 < x < 1\}$
   (d) $A = \{(x, y) \mid x, y \in R^1, 2x + y = 3, x + y = 1\}$,
       $B = \{(x, y) \mid x, y \in R^1, x + y = 1\}$

5. Given that A and B are sets such that $B \subset A$, show that $A \cup B = A$.

6. Complete the following statements so that the results are theorems; then prove the theorems. Venn diagrams may be helpful.
   (a) If A is a set, then $\emptyset \cup A = $ _____.
   (b) If A is a set, then $A \cup A = $ _____.
   (c) If A and B are sets such that $A \subset B$, then $A \cup B = $ _____.
   (d) If A and B are sets such that $A \cup B = B$, then _____.

7. Prove part (b) of Theorem 1.3.

8. Prove part (b) of Theorem 1.4.

9. Prove that there is a set which acts as an identity for the operation of set union and determine what that set is. (An identity for the operation $\cup$ would, of course, be a set E having the property that for every set A, $E \cup A = A \cup E = A$.)

10. Let S and T be nonempty sets of sets such that $S \subset T$. Show that

$$\bigcap_{B \in T} B \subset \bigcap_{A \in S} A.$$

11. Let S and T be nonempty sets of sets having the following property: for each set $A \in S$, there is a set $B \in T$ such that $B \subset A$. Show that

$$\bigcap_{B \in T} B \subset \bigcap_{A \in S} A.$$

12. Given that B is a set, that S is a nonempty set of sets, and that for each $A \in S$, $B \subset A$, show that

$$B \subset \bigcap_{A \in S} A.$$

13. Let S and T be nonempty sets of sets such that $S \subset T$. Show that

$$\bigcup_{A \in S} A \subset \bigcup_{B \in T} B.$$

14. Let S and T be nonempty sets of sets having the following property: for each set $A \in S$ there is a set $B \in T$ such that $A \subset B$. Show that

$$\bigcup_{A \in S} A \subset \bigcup_{B \in T} B.$$

15. Given that B is a set and S is a nonempty set of sets, and that for each $A \in S, A \subset B$, show that

$$\bigcup_{A \in S} A \subset B.$$

16. Prove Theorem 1.5.

17. In Example 14, describe the following sets:
   (a) $(B_6 \cap A_5) \cup (B_6 \cap A_4)$,
   (b) $(B_6 \cap A_5) \cup (B_5 \cap A_5)$,
   (c) $(A_2 \cap B) \cup (A_1 \cap B)$.

18. In Example 14, show that the sets $(B_i \cap A_k) \cap (B_j \cap A_n) = \emptyset$ if $i \neq j$, or $k \neq n$, or both.

1.6 RELATIVE COMPLEMENT AND POWER SET

In the previous section we considered two operations on sets, namely union and intersection. Another useful operation is that of *set difference*, or *relative complement*. As before, let A and B be the following sets: $A = \{0, 1, 2, 3, 4, 5\}$ and $B = \{1, 3, 5, 7, 9\}$. There are certain numbers which belong to the set A but do not belong to the set B, namely 0, 2, and 4. The set containing just these numbers is called the *complement of B relative to A*, or the *relative complement of B in A*, or A *minus* B; it is denoted by $A - B$ (read A minus B). Thus $A - B = \{0, 2, 4\}$. In general, the difference of two sets, $A - B$, consists of those elements of A which are not in B. To put it another way, we remove from A those elements of A which are also elements of B. Note that B may very well contain elements not belonging to A; the presence or absence of such elements is irrelevant. We formulate the concept of relative complement precisely as follows.

Definition 1.7. Let A and B be sets. The *complement of B relative to A*, denoted by $A - B$, is the set

$$A - B = \{c \mid c \in A \text{ and } c \notin B\}.$$

Relative complements can be represented effectively by Venn diagrams. Let us suppose that A and B are sets and that we wish to consider the relative complement, $A - B$. In each of the Venn diagrams in Fig. 1.10 the area representing the relative complement $A - B$ is shaded.

EXAMPLE 1. Suppose that $A = \{1, 2\}$ and $B = \{2, 3, 5\}$. Then $A - B = \{1\}$, while $B - A = \{3, 5\}$.

EXAMPLE 2. Suppose that $A = \{1\}$ and $B = \{3, 5\}$. Then $A - B = \{1\}$, while $B - A = \{3, 5\}$. More generally, if $A \cap B = \emptyset$ [see Fig. 1.10(b)], then $A - B = A$.

EXAMPLE 3. Suppose that $A = \{2, 3\}$ and $B = \{2, 3, 5\}$. Then $A - B = \emptyset$. More generally, if $A \subset B$ [see Fig. 1.10(c)], then $A - B = \emptyset$.

EXAMPLE 4. Suppose that E is the set of positive even integers and that G is the set of even integers which can be written as the sum of two (not necessarily distinct) odd primes. Since 3 is the smallest odd prime and $6 = 3 + 3$, the number 6 is evidently the smallest number in G; furthermore, $6 \in E \cap G$. It is evident that $G \subset E$ and that $\{2, 4\} \subset E - G$. A famous conjecture by Goldbach, as yet unproven, states that $E - G = \{2, 4\}$, that is, Goldbach's conjecture states that every even integer greater than 5 is the sum of two odd primes.

There are some basic relationships between unions, intersections, and differences. Four of the more important ones are stated in the next theorem.

Theorem 1.6. Let S be a nonempty set of sets and let B be a set. Then

(a) $\left(\bigcap_{A \in S} A \right) - B = \bigcap_{A \in S} (A - B);$

(b) $\left(\bigcup_{A \in S} A \right) - B = \bigcup_{A \in S} (A - B);$

(c) $B - \left(\bigcap_{A \in S} A \right) = \bigcup_{A \in S} (B - A);$

(d) $B - \left(\bigcup_{A \in S} A \right) = \bigcap_{A \in S} (B - A).$

The last two equations, (c) and (d), are known as De Morgan's laws. The reader should draw Venn diagrams to illustrate each of these equations when S is a finite set, say for $S = \{A_1, A_2\}$. We shall give a proof of part (c) only; the proofs of the other parts are similar.

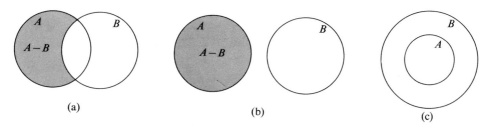

(a)   (b)   (c)

Fig. 1.10. Venn diagrams representing $A - B$.

Proof of (c). Let $C = \bigcap_{A \in S} A$ and let $D = \bigcup_{A \in S} (B - A)$; this notation is introduced for convenience only. Then we wish to show that $B - C = D$. As usual, we establish this equality by showing that $B - C \subset D$ and $D \subset B - C$ and using Theorem 1.1. We begin by showing that $B - C \subset D$. Let x be any element of $B - C$; then $x \in B$ and $x \notin C$. Since $x \notin C$, $x \notin \bigcap_{A \in S} A$, and hence $x \notin A$ for some $A \in S$. Denote this set by $\hat{A}$. Thus $x \in B$ and $x \notin \hat{A}$; $\hat{A} \in S$. Then $x \in B - \hat{A}$ and hence $x \in \bigcup_{A \in S} (B - A) = D$ because $B - \hat{A}$ is a term in this union. Thus $B - C \subset D$.

Next we establish $D \subset B - C$. Let x be any element of D. Then $x \in \bigcup_{A \in S} (B - A)$ and hence $x \in B - A$ for some $\tilde{A} \in S$. Thus $x \in B$ and $x \notin \tilde{A}$. Since $x \notin \tilde{A}$ and $\tilde{A} \in S$, $x \notin \bigcap_{A \in S} A$. So $x \in B$ and $x \notin C$, and hence $x \in B - C$. This result establishes the fact that $D \subset B - C$, and by Theorem 1.1 the proof of (c) is complete. ▲

A comment on notation is in order. Often we are working within a given set S and wish to consider only subsets of S. When this happens, S is called the *universe* or a *universal set*, and the difference $S - A$, $A \subset S$, is denoted by A^c (read A *complement*, or *the complement of* A), that is,

$$A^c = S - A.$$

This notation is meaningful only when we have in mind a particular universal set S. In this case we draw our Venn diagram a little differently. We represent S by a rectangle and the subsets of S by circles. Figure 1.11 shows A^c as the shaded area.

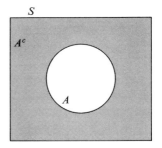

Fig. 1.11. Venn diagram for A^c.

In probability theory we shall be interested in the collection of all subsets of a particular set S. Such a collection of sets is itself a set; it is a set whose elements are sets. Suppose that S is the set containing just the numbers 0 and 1, $S = \{0, 1\}$. What are the subsets of S? We have discovered already that $\emptyset$ and S are subsets of S, and there are evidently exactly two more subsets: $\{0\}$ and $\{1\}$. Thus S has a total of exactly four distinct subsets:

$$\emptyset, \quad \{0\}, \quad \{1\}, \quad S.$$

Let T be that set whose elements are precisely these sets:

$$T = \{\emptyset, \{0\}, \{1\}, S\}.$$

The set T is just the set of all subsets of S. This set of subsets of S is commonly called the power set of S and is denoted by $\Pi(S)$. Thus

$$\Pi(S) = \{\emptyset, \{0\}, \{1\}, S\}.$$

Intuitively, it is evident that such a construction can be made for any set S.

Definition 1.8. Let S be a set. The set of all subsets of S is called the *power set* of S and is denoted by $\Pi(S)$:

$$\Pi(S) = \{A \mid A \subset S\}.$$

EXAMPLE 5. Let $S = \emptyset$, the empty set. Then $\Pi(S) = \{\emptyset\}$ has exactly one element.

EXAMPLE 6. Let S be a set which contains just one member a; $S = \{a\}$. Then the power set, $\Pi(S)$, of S is

$$\Pi(S) = \Pi(\{a\}) = \{\emptyset, \{a\}\}.$$

EXAMPLE 7. Let S be a set which contains exactly two distinct members, a and b; $S = \{a, b\}$. Then

$$\Pi(S) = \Pi(\{a, b\}) = \{\emptyset, \{a\}, \{b\}, \{a, b\}\}.$$

EXAMPLE 8. For the sets S in Examples 6 and 7 above, a more informative listing of the elements of the power set can be given in which some of the subset relations between subsets of S are indicated by connecting lines. For each set S the resulting diagram is, loosely speaking, the *lattice* of subsets of S. The lattices of subsets of the two sets $\{a\}$ and $\{a, b\}$ are shown below.

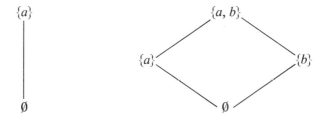

EXAMPLE 9. Suppose that a, b, and c are three distinct objects. The lattice of subsets of the tripleton $\{a, b, c\}$ is shown below.

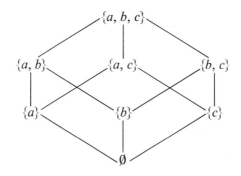

The power set $\Pi(\{a, b, c\})$ of $\{a, b, c\}$ is just the set of eight elements of the lattice:

$$\Pi(\{a, b, c\}) = \{\emptyset, \{a\}, \{b\}, \{c\}, \{a, b\}, \{a, c\}, \{b, c\}, \{a, b, c\}\}.$$

EXERCISES

1. Determine the relative complement, $A - B$, for each of the following pairs of sets.
   (a) $A = \{3, 6, 9, 12\}$, $B = \{n \mid n$ is an integer and $n/3$ is an integer$\}$
   (b) $A = \{3, 6, 9, 12\}$, $B = \{1, 2, 3, 10, 11, 12\}$
   (c) $A = \{n \mid n \in J^+\}$, $B = \{2n \mid n \in J^+\}$ (Here J^+ is the set of positive integers.)
   (d) $A = \{x \mid x \in R^1, -1 \leq x \leq 1\}$, $B = \{x \mid x \in R^1, x \leq 0\}$ (Here R^1 is the set of real numbers.)
   (e) A is the set of people who bought a television set in 1967 and B is the set of people who bought a color television set in 1967.

2. Prove the following two propositions.
   (a) The operation of relative complement is not commutative; that is, show that $A - B$ may be different from $B - A$.
   (b) The operation of relative complement is not associative; that is, show that $A - (B - C)$ may be different from $(A - B) - C$. [*Hint:* A Venn diagram may be helpful.]

3. Complete the following statements so that the results are theorems; then prove the theorems.
   (a) If A is a set, then $\emptyset - A = $ _____.
   (b) If A is a set, then $A - \emptyset = $ _____.
   (c) If A is a set, then $A - A = $ _____.
   (d) If A and B are sets and if $A \subset B$, then $A - B = $ _____.
   (e) If A and B are disjoint sets, then $A - B = $ _____.
   (f) If A and B are sets, then $(A - B) \cup B = $ _____.
   (g) If A and B are sets, then $(A - B) \cup (A \cap B) = $ _____.
   (h) If A and B are sets, then $(A - B) \cap B = $ _____.
   (i) If A, B, and C are sets, then $A - (B \cap C) = $ _____.
   (j) If A, B, and C are sets, then $A - (B \cup C) = $ _____.

4. In each of the following statements, fill in the relation which makes the result a theorem. Then prove the theorem. Venn diagrams may be helpful.

   (a) If A and B are sets, then $A - B \underline{\quad} A$.
   (b) If A and B are sets, then $(A - B) \cup B \underline{\quad} A$.
   (c) If A, B, and C are sets, and if $B \subset C$, then $B - A \underline{\quad} C - A$.
   (d) If A, B, and C are sets, and if $B \subset C$, then $A - B \underline{\quad} A - C$.

5. Draw the lattice of all subsets of a set containing four distinct elements a, b, c, and d. How many subsets are there?

6. From Exercise 5 and Examples 5, 6, 7, and 9, formulate a conjecture as to how many subsets a set containing n distinct elements has. Can you prove your conjecture?

7. Write a list of all the elements of the set $\Pi(\Pi(\{0, 1\}))$.

In Exercises 8 through 12, complements denoted by A^c, B^c, etc. are understood to be relative to a common universal set S.

8. Draw a Venn diagram illustrating the fact that $(A^c)^c = A$ and give a proof.

9. Prove that $A \subset B$ if and only if $B^c \subset A^c$. [*Hint:* Draw a Venn diagram so that you can see what is going on.]

10. Prove the simple De Morgan's laws:

   (a) $(A \cup B)^c = A^c \cap B^c$,   (b) $(A \cap B)^c = A^c \cup B^c$.

   [*Hint:* These are special cases of Theorem 1.6.]

11. Prove that $A \cup A^c = S$ and $A \cap A^c = \emptyset$.

12. Prove that $S^c = \emptyset$ and $\emptyset^c = S$.

13. Prove that $A = (A - B) \cup (A \cap B)$ for any two sets A and B.

14. Prove parts (a), (b), and (d) of Theorem 1.6.

15. Prove the following theorem. If A and B are sets, then $A \subset B$ if and only if

$$\Pi(A) \subset \Pi(B).$$

16. There exist sets which have the peculiar property that every element of A is also a subset of A. Construct such a set.

17. Standard blood classification is accomplished by three tests—the A-test, the B-test, and the Rh-test—to each of which a specimen *reacts* or does *not react*. The four standard blood groups are A, B, AB, and O. The blood group to which an individual belongs is determined from the results of the first two tests by the following chart.

Blood group	A-Test	B-Test
A	Reacts	No reaction
B	No reaction	Reacts
AB	Reacts	Reacts
O	No reaction	No reaction

Let A be the set of humans who react to the A-test, let B be the set of humans who react to the B-test, and let A^c and B^c, respectively, be the complements of A and B.
(a) Show that a person is in blood group A if and only if he is in the set $A \cap B^c$. What set contains those and only those persons who are in blood group B? In blood group AB? In blood group O?
(b) Show that the sets A and A^c form a partition of the set of all people. Do the same for B and B^c. What is the cross partition of these two partitions? Illustrate with a Venn diagram.

18. (Continuation of Exercise 17) A person is said to be Rh-positive if he reacts to the Rh-test; otherwise he is said to be Rh-negative. Let Rh be the set of Rh-positive people.
(a) Show that Rh^c is the set of Rh-negative people and show that Rh and Rh^c form a partition of the set of all people.
(b) Form the cross partition of the partition in (a) with the cross partition in part (b) of Exercise 17. List all the different sets in this cross partition and explain their significance.

19. (Continuation of Exercises 17 and 18) Let U be the set of tests—A-test, B-test, and Rh-test. Let D be the set of all tests to which a prospective donor's blood reacts, and let R be the set of all tests to which a prospective recipient's blood reacts. A blood transfusion is safe if and only if D is a subset of R.
(a) Who can safely donate blood to a person belonging to the set $A \cap B^c \cap Rh$? To the set $A^c \cap B^c \cap Rh^c$? To the set $A \cap B \cap Rh^c$?
(b) To whom can a person in the set $A \cap B^c \cap Rh$ donate blood?
(c) What set consists of "universal donors"?
(d) What set consists of "universal recipients"?

20. According to *The World Almanac* 1966, the following is a tabulation of all accidents in the United States causing temporary or permanent disability or death in 1964.

	Public		Other	
	Motor vehicle	Nonmotor vehicle	Home	Work
Fatal	47,000	18,000	28,500	14,200
Permanent disability (nonfatal)	140,000	50,000	110,000	80,000
Temporary disability	1,600,000	2,200,000	4,200,000	1,950,000

Let letters designate sets of accidents as follows.

S = all accidents, resulting in death or permanent or temporary disability
F = all fatal accidents
P = all public accidents
O = all nonpublic accidents
M = all motor vehicle accidents
PD = all permanent disability accidents
TD = all temporary disability accidents
W = all work accidents

How many accidents were there in each of the following sets?

(a) F (b) F^c (c) S

(d) $F \cap O$ (e) $F \cap M$ (f) $F \cap P$

(g) $F \cap M^c$ (h) $F \cap PD$ (i) $PD \cap TD$

(j) $W \cap F^c$ (k) $PD \cap O$ (l) $O - W$

21. A congressman, a candidate for reelection, polls his constituents on three important domestic issues as follows: Do you favor (a) increased taxes, (b) increased federal aid to education, and (c) a balanced budget. The replies he received and the numbers of each are tabulated below.

Increased taxes	Aid to education	Balanced budget	Number answering
Yes	Yes	Yes	2043
No	Yes	Yes	451
Yes	No	Yes	1024
No	No	Yes	3485
Yes	Yes	No	43
No	Yes	No	330
Yes	No	No	0
No	No	No	75

Let A be the set of voters who favor a tax increase, B, the set of voters who favor aid to education, and C, the set of voters who favor a balanced budget.

(a) How many voters are in each of the following sets? $A, A^c, B, B^c, C, C^c, A \cap B \cap C,$ $(A \cap B) \cup C$.

(b) If the congressman follows the wishes of the majority, how should he vote on each issue? How many voters will be pleased with his stand on all three?

CHAPTER 2

Relations and Functions

2.1 INTRODUCTION

The idea of a function appears, either explicitly or implicitly, throughout mathematics and other areas in which mathematics is used. This chapter will be devoted to a study of functions and, more generally, relations. We have already encountered relations; however, in this chapter we shall define a function mathematically as a special kind of relation; relations, in turn, will be defined in terms of ordered pairs. Although we have dealt rather extensively with ordered pairs, thus far we have only an intuitive idea of what an ordered pair is. Actually, the intuitive idea of an ordered pair is sufficient for many purposes, but to understand some mathematical constructions and proofs, it is helpful to have a precise definition.

The notion of an ordered pair, in particular, is extremely important and useful in mathematics, enabling us to make precise definitions of the concepts of relation and function within the framework of set theory. At one time in the fairly recent history of mathematics, the notion of an ordered pair was taken as a primitive notion on the same level as the notions of set and set membership. In 1921, however, Kuratowski showed that it was possible to define the notion of an ordered pair in terms of set and set membership.

We shall state a definition of the concept of ordered pair in terms of set and set membership, essentially as it was given by Kuratowski. We shall then state without proof the principal theorem concerning ordered pairs. At this stage the reader should not attempt to remember the definition, nor should he be confused by its apparent artificiality. He should only remember that such a definition is possible and that he can look it up if he wishes. The theorem, on the other hand, is quite important; the reader should remember it and learn how to use it.

Definition 2.1. If a and b are any objects, then the *ordered pair* of a and b, denoted by (a, b), is the doubleton

$$(a, b) = \{\{a\}, \{a, b\}\}.$$

In this case we say that a is the *first component* of (a, b) and that b is the *second component* of the ordered pair (a, b).

The main reason for adopting the above definition is that it enables us to prove the following theorem. This theorem is the basic characterization of ordered pair.

Theorem 2.1. For all a, b, c, and d,

$$(a, b) = (c, d) \qquad \text{if and only if both } a = c \text{ and } b = d.$$

The proof of this theorem is not difficult, and it is left as an exercise for the reader (see Exercise 6).

By induction we can extend the notion of ordered pair to the notion of ordered n-tuple, for $n \geq 3$. The extension is accomplished as follows. For any three objects, a, b, and c, we can define the ordered triple, (a, b, c), to be simply the ordered pair $((a, b), c)$; that is, $(a, b, c) = ((a, b), c)$.

For any four objects, a, b, c, and d, we can define the ordered quadruple, (a, b, c, d), to be the ordered pair $((a, b, c), d)$; that is, $(a, b, c, d) = ((a, b, c), d)$. In general, suppose that $n \geq 2$ and that we have already defined the notion of an ordered n-tuple. We can then define the notion of ordered $(n + 1)$-tuple as follows. For any $n + 1$ objects, $a_1, a_2, \ldots, a_n, a_{n+1}$, let a be the ordered n-tuple $(a_1, a_2, \ldots, a_n)$; then the ordered $(n + 1)$-tuple $(a_1, a_2, \ldots, a_n, a_{n+1})$ is defined as

$$(a_1, a_2, \ldots, a_n, a_{n+1}) = (a, a_{n+1}) = ((a_1, a_2, \ldots, a_n), a_{n+1}).$$

EXERCISES

1. Express each of the following ordered pairs in the set notation of Definition 2.1.
   - (a) (father, son)
   - (b) (pitcher, catcher)
   - (c) (1, 2)
   - (d) (2, 1)
   - (e) (1, 1)
   - (f) (employer, employee)

2. Each of the following sets represents an ordered pair. Write the corresponding ordered pair in the notation (a, b).
   - (a) $\{\{\text{mother}\}, \{\text{mother, daughter}\}\}$
   - (b) $\{\{\text{coach}\}, \{\text{coach, player}\}\}$
   - (c) $\{\{\text{player}\}, \{\text{coach, player}\}\}$
   - (d) $\{\{\text{player, coach}\}, \{\text{player}\}\}$
   - (e) $\{\{\emptyset\}, \{\emptyset, A\}\}$
   - (f) $\{\{1\}, \{1, 2\}\}$
   - (g) $\{\{1\}, \{1, 1\}\}$
   - (h) $\{\{1\}\}$ [See Exercise 1(e).]
   - (i) $\{\{A\}, \{A, \emptyset\}\}$
   - (j) $\{\{\emptyset\}, \{\emptyset, \{\emptyset\}\}\}$

3. Let a, b, c, d, e, and f be objects. Assuming Theorem 2.1, show that $(a, b, c) = (d, e, f)$ if and only if $a = d$, $b = e$, and $c = f$.

4. Let a, b, c, d, e, f, g, and h be objects. Using Theorem 2.1, show that $(a, b, c, d) = (e, f, g, h)$ if and only if $a = e$, $b = f$, $c = g$, and $d = h$.

5. Let n be a positive integer and suppose that $a_1, a_2, \ldots, a_n$, and $b_1, b_2, \ldots, b_n$ are objects. Assuming Theorem 2.1, prove by induction that $(a_1, a_2, \ldots, a_n) = (b_1, b_2, \ldots, b_n)$ if and only if $a_i = b_i$ for $1 \leq i \leq n$.

6. Prove Theorem 2.1.

2.2 CARTESIAN PRODUCTS

The reader is certainly familiar with the Euclidean plane and with coordinate systems (x-axis and y-axis) in that plane. Relative to a given coordinate system in the plane there is associated with each point p of the plane an ordered pair $(a(p), b(p))$, of real numbers, where $a(p)$ is the abscissa of p and $b(p)$ is the ordinate of p (see Fig. 2.1). In fact, a very useful way to think of the Euclidean plane is to consider each of its points p to be the ordered pair of real numbers $(a(p), b(p))$; the ordered pair $(a(p), b(p))$ of coordinates of p is usually denoted simply by (a, b). If we do so, we can treat the Euclidean plane as the set of all ordered pairs of real numbers. In a sense then, the reader has been familiar with ordered pairs for a long time.

The mathematician Descartes introduced coordinates into the Euclidean plane so that the analytic methods of algebra could be used in studying properties of geometric figures in the plane. When it is treated as the set of all ordered pairs of real numbers, the Euclidean plane is frequently called the *Cartesian plane* in his honor. This set of all ordered pairs of real numbers is sometimes denoted by $R^1 \times R^1$; the set $R^1 \times R^1$ is called the *Cartesian product of R^1 by R^1.* (Here and subsequently R^1 denotes the set of real numbers.) That is, we have defined $R^1 \times R^1$ as

$$R^1 \times R^1 = \{(a, b) \mid a \in R^1, b \in R^1\}. \quad (1)$$

The formula in Eq. (1) suggests an immediate generalization; we can let

$$A \times B = \{(a, b) \mid a \in A, b \in B\}, \quad (2)$$

where A and B are two sets. In fact, this is what we do in the following definition.

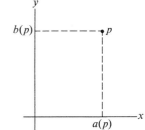

Fig. 2.1. Illustration of points in the plane as ordered pairs.

Definition 2.2. Let A and B be sets. Then the *Cartesian product of A by B*, denoted by $A \times B$, is the following set of ordered pairs:

$$A \times B = \{(a, b) \mid a \in A, b \in B\}. \quad (3)$$

EXAMPLE 1. Let us give a simple example to illustrate the definition. Let A and B be the sets: $A = \{1, 2, 3\}$ and $B = \{1, 2\}$. Note that the set A has three elements and that the set B has two elements. Let C be the Cartesian product of A and B,

$$C = A \times B = \{(1, 1), (1, 2), (2, 1), (2, 2), (3, 1), (3, 2)\}. \tag{4}$$

It often helps to think of the Cartesian product as a rectangular array, with rows corresponding to elements of one set and columns corresponding to those of the other set. Thus

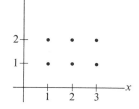

$$C = A \times B = \begin{pmatrix} (1, 1) & (1, 2) \\ (2, 1) & (2, 2) \\ (3, 1) & (3, 2) \end{pmatrix}.$$

Fig. 2.2. Graph of the Cartesian product $C = \{1, 2, 3\} \times \{1, 2\}$.

The set of points in C can be plotted in the Cartesian plane $R^1 \times R^1$; this set of points when plotted is called the *graph* of C. Figure 2.2 shows the graph of C.

It is evident from either (3) or Fig. 2.2 that the product set C has six elements. Suppose we let $N(A)$, $N(B)$, and $N(C) = N(A \times B)$ be the numbers of elements in the sets A, B, and $C = A \times B$, respectively. Then

$$N(A \times B) = N(A)N(B). \tag{5}$$

Equation (5) can easily be shown to hold for any finite sets A and B; this result is certainly a good reason for using the word "product" in the name "Cartesian product."

The idea of a Cartesian product can be generalized to the product of more than two sets. In fact, if n is an integer greater than 1 and if $A_1, A_2, \ldots, A_n$ are sets, then the *Cartesian product of $A_1, A_2, \ldots, A_n$*, denoted by

$$A_1 \times A_2 \times \cdots \times A_n, \quad \text{or} \quad \prod_{i=1}^{n} A_i, \quad \text{or} \quad \prod_{1 \leq i \leq n} A_i$$

(read, product of A_i, i going from one to n), is the following set of ordered n-tuples:

$$\prod_{i=1}^{n} A_i = \prod_{1 \leq i \leq n} A_i = A_1 \times A_2 \times \cdots \times A_n$$
$$= \{(a_1, a_2, \ldots, a_n) \mid a_i \in A_i \text{ for } 1 \leq i \leq n\}. \tag{6}$$

If all the sets A_i in (6) happen to be the same set A, then the product is denoted by A^n:

$$A^n = A \times A \times \cdots \times A \quad \text{(n factors)}. \tag{7}$$

EXAMPLE 2. The Cartesian plane is the Cartesian product

$$R^2 = R^1 \times R^1.$$

EXAMPLE 3. If we think of ordinary three-dimensional space as being co-ordinatized by a rectangular coordinate system (three mutually perpendicular axes), it is the Cartesian product

$$R^3 = R^1 \times R^1 \times R^1.$$

EXAMPLE 4. The *unit square Q*, defined by

$$Q = \{(x, y) \mid x, y \in R^1, |x| \leq 1, |y| \leq 1\},$$

is the Cartesian product $T \times T$, where T is the *unit interval:*

$$T = \{x \mid x \in R^1, |x| \leq 1\}. \qquad (8)$$

(See Fig. 2.3 for a graph of Q.)

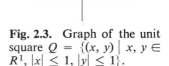

Fig. 2.3. Graph of the unit square $Q = \{(x, y) \mid x, y \in R^1, |x| \leq 1, |y| \leq 1\}$.

EXAMPLE 5. The *unit cube C* in three-dimensional Cartesian space,

$$C = \{(x, y, z) \mid x, y, z \in R^1, |x| \leq 1, |y| \leq 1, |z| \leq 1\},$$

is the Cartesian product $T^3 = T \times T \times T$:

$$C = T^3,$$

where T is given by Eq. (8). The graph of this unit cube C is shown in Fig. 2.4.

It should be noted that $A \times B$ and $B \times A$ need not be the same set. Compare the graphs of $\{1, 2, 3\} \times \{1, 2\}$ and $\{1, 2\} \times \{1, 2, 3\}$ shown in Figs. 2.2 and 2.5, respectively.

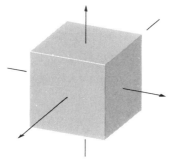

Fig. 2.4. Graph of the unit cube in 3-dimensional space.

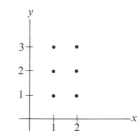

Fig. 2.5. Graph of $\{1, 2\} \times \{1, 2, 3\}$.

EXERCISES

1. Let $A = \{1, 2\}$, $B = \{2, 3, 5\}$, and $C = A \times B$.
   (a) Write all the ordered pairs in C.
   (b) Graph C.

2. Let $A = \{-1, 1\}$, $B = \{-1, 1\}$, and $C = A \times B$.
   (a) Write all the elements of C.
   (b) Graph C.

3. Which of the following sets C of ordered pairs are Cartesian products of sets A and B? If a set C is a Cartesian product, find the corresponding sets A and B such that $C = A \times B$.
   (a) $\{(1, 0)\}$ (b) $\{(1, 0), (0, 1)\}$
   (c) $\{(1, 0), (0, 1), (1, 1)\}$ (d) $\{(1, 0), (0, 1), (1, 1), (0, 0)\}$
   (e) $\{(-1, 2), (1, 2), (2, 2)\}$
   (f) $\{(11, 1), (11, -1), (7, -1), (7, 1), (8, 1), (8, -1)\}$
   (g) $\{(\text{mother, daughter}), (\text{daughter, mother}), (\text{father, son}), (\text{son, father})\}$

4. Let $A = \{\text{yes, no}\}$ and let $B = A^3 = A \times A \times A$.
   (a) Write all the elements of B.
   (b) Explain the physical meaning of the set B in terms of a business executive faced with making three decisions.

5. Draw a graph of $\{x \mid x \in R^1, 0 \leq x \leq 1\} \times \{x \mid x \in R^1, 0 \leq x \leq 1\}$.

6. Let $A = \emptyset$ and $B = \{1, 2\}$. What are the elements of the set $A \times B$? Check your answer by using the formula in Eq. (5).

7. Show that for any set A, $\emptyset \times A = A \times \emptyset = \emptyset$.

8. Let A and B be nonempty sets. Prove that $A \times B = B \times A$ if and only if $A = B$.

9. If A is a finite set, use Eq. (5) to show that $N(A^2) = N(A \times A) = [N(A)]^2$.

10. Let n be an integer greater than 1 and suppose that $A_1, A_2, \ldots, A_n$ are finite sets which have $N(A_1), N(A_2), \ldots, N(A_n)$ members, respectively. Give an argument which makes it plausible that the number of elements in the Cartesian product

$$\prod_{i=1}^{n} A_i = A_1 \times A_2 \times \cdots \times A_n$$

is given by

$$N\left(\prod_{i=1}^{n} A_i\right) = \prod_{i=1}^{n} N(A_i),$$

where $\prod_{i=1}^{n} N(A_i)$ means $N(A_1) \cdot N(A_2) \cdot \ldots \cdot N(A_n)$.

11. Show that $(A_1 \cup A_2) \times B = (A_1 \times B) \cup (A_2 \times B)$.

12. Prove or disprove that $(A_1 \cap A_2) \times B = (A_1 \times B) \cap (A_2 \times B)$.
    [*Hint:* Draw a Venn diagram as though $A_1 \times B$ and $A_2 \times B$ were subsets of $R^1 \times R^1$.]

2.3 RELATIONS

We have frequently talked about relations between objects. Some examples are the relations "father of," "subset of," "speaks to," and many others. Most of these were expressed either in words or in symbols by placing the two objects being related on either side of the words or symbols denoting the relation. For instance, we write $A \subset B$ for A is a subset of B, and we use an arrow $A \to B$ to indicate that A speaks to B. If we are speaking of only one fixed relation, as is usually the case, symbols or words between the two objects are not really necessary; we need only the names of the objects in some fixed order. If we agree always to write the object on the left first and the object on the right second, then (A, B) makes a very convenient name for this sentence: A is related to B. Thus we see that ordered pairs can be used rather nicely to indicate when two objects are in a specified relation.

EXAMPLE 1. Let M denote the set of all living men and W the set of all living women. Then $M \times W$ is the set of all possible living couples, each consisting of exactly one man and one woman. For certain of these pairs (x, y), $x \in M$, $y \in W$, it will be the case that the man is married to the woman, and for all other pairs it will not be the case. Let R be the set of all ordered pairs $(x, y) \in M \times W$ such that x is married to y. Then we see that the relation "married to" defines a subset R of $M \times W$.

Conversely, by selecting other subsets of $M \times W$ we can give other relations between men and women (some of which may not be meaningful).

Since we would like a definition of a relation and since all the apparent relations between two objects lead to a set of ordered pairs, it seems reasonable to define a (binary) relation as a set of ordered pairs. (The word binary merely means that *two* objects are being related.) Thus we have the following definition.

Definition 2.3. A *(binary) relation* is a set R of ordered pairs.

Often, if R is a relation, it is convenient to express the fact that $(x, y) \in R$ by writing xRy (read, x is in the relation R to y).

EXAMPLE 2. Let R be the set:

$$R = \{(A, B) \mid A, B \text{ are sets and } A \subset B\}.$$

Then R is exactly the relation $\subset$.

EXAMPLE 3. Let R be the set:

$$R = \{(a, A) \mid a \text{ is an object}, A \text{ is a set, and } a \in A\}.$$

Then R is exactly the relation "belongs to."

In Example 1, the relation "married to" is a subset of a Cartesian product. It is convenient to know that any relation R is a subset of some Cartesian product. To show this, we need the concepts of the domain and range of a relation.

Definition 2.4. Let R be a relation. Then the *domain of R*, denoted by dom R, is the set

$$\text{dom } R = \{x \mid \text{for some } y, (x, y) \in R\}.$$

The *range of R*, denoted by ran R, is the set

$$\text{ran } R = \{y \mid \text{for some } x, (x, y) \in R\}.$$

This definition asserts that the set of first components of a relation R is the domain of R and that the set of second components of R is the range of R. Once we have these sets, it is clear that

$$R \subset (\text{dom } R) \times (\text{ran } R).$$

Thus every relation R is a subset of a Cartesian product. On the other hand, if $R \subset A \times B$, does this relation mean that $A = \text{ran } R$ and $B = \text{dom } R$? No, in fact it seems clear that this will not, in general, be the case. What is true is that dom $R \subset A$ and ran $R \subset B$. The following examples help illustrate this point.

EXAMPLE 4. In Example 1 we considered the marriage relation, so that xRy means x is a man, y is a woman and x and y are married. The domain of R is

$$\text{dom } R = \{x \mid x \text{ is a married man}\},$$

and the range of R is

$$\text{ran } R = \{y \mid y \text{ is a married woman}\}.$$

Since neither every man nor every woman is married, it is the case that

$$\text{dom } R \underset{\neq}{\subset} M \quad \text{and} \quad \text{ran } R \underset{\neq}{\subset} W.$$

EXAMPLE 5. Let R be the relation whose graph is shown in Fig. 2.6. (The graph of a relation which is a subset of $R^1 \times R^1$ can be considered as the plot of the ordered pairs in R^2.) The domain of R is

$$\text{dom } R = \{1, 2, 3\},$$

and the range of R is

$$\text{ran } R = \{1, 2\}.$$

Observe that $R \underset{\neq}{\subset} (\text{dom } R) \times (\text{ran } R)$, since $(2, 1) \in (\text{dom } R) \times (\text{ran } R)$ and $(2, 1) \notin R$ (the same is true of $(3, 2)$).

Every subset of a Cartesian product $A \times B$ is, by definition, a set of ordered pairs and hence a relation. Thus for given sets A and B, there are as many relations as there are subsets of $A \times B$. A relation R which is a subset of $A \times B$ is called a *relation between* A and B; if $A = B$, then R is called a *relation on* A. In this case, $R \subset A \times A$.

Our rather artificial definition of a relation is useful for the following reasons. (i) Sets are relatively easy to work with. (ii) The definition is an abstraction into which all (binary) relations fit; thus any theorems about relations in general can be applied to any particular relation.

It is evident that we can define the concept of an *n-ary relation*, for every positive integer n, using the notion of ordered n-tuples. More explicitly, an *n-ary relation* is a set of ordered n-tuples.

EXAMPLE 6. The set $\{(a, b, c) \mid a$ is a man, b is a woman, and a and b are the parents of $c\}$ is a ternary relation on the set of people.

EXAMPLE 7. The set $\{(a, b, c, d) \mid a, b, c, d$ are people, d is a parent of c, and a and b are parents of $d\}$ is the quaternary relation on the set of people which is best described by the following sentence: a and b are grandparents of c on d's side.

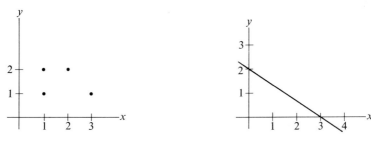

Fig. 2.6. Graph of the relation R of Example 5.

Fig. 2.7. Graph of the line whose equation is $2x + 3y = 6$.

The next examples are more analytic in nature and will serve as a connecting link to the idea of a function, which will be defined in the next section.

EXAMPLE 8. Let L be the line whose equation is

$$2x + 3y = 6. \tag{1}$$

This line L is really the solution set of Eq. (1), namely, a set of ordered pairs:

$$L = \{(x, y) \mid x, y \in R^1, \quad 2x + 3y = 6\}. \tag{2}$$

Thus L is a relation on the real numbers R^1. The graph of L is shown in Fig. 2.7.

EXAMPLE 9. Let C be the curve whose equation is

$$x^2 + y^2 = 1. \tag{3}$$

The curve C is actually the circle of radius 1 (*unit circle*) centered at the *origin*, $(0, 0)$, of the Cartesian plane. This circle C is the solution set of Eq. (3).

$$C = \{(x, y) \mid x, y \in R^1 \quad \text{and} \quad x^2 + y^2 = 1\}. \tag{4}$$

Thus C is a relation on R^1; its graph is shown in Fig. 2.8.

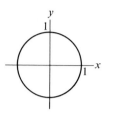

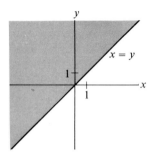

Fig. 2.8. Graph of the circle whose equation is $x^2 + y^2 = 1$.

Fig. 2.9. Graph of the solution set of the inequality $x \leq y$.

EXAMPLE 10. A familiar inequality whose graph is not so familiar is

$$x \leq y. \tag{5}$$

Let L be the solution set of inequality (5):

$$L = \{(x, y) \mid x, y \in R^1, \ x \leq y\}.$$

Thus L is a relation; its graph is shown in Fig. 2.9.

EXERCISES

1. Let $A = \{1, 2\}$, $B = \{2, 3, 5\}$, and $C = A \times B$.
   (a) Write all relations R such that $R \subset C$.
   (b) Graph each such relation R.
   (c) Determine dom R and ran R for each such relation R.
   (d) For each such R, determine whether or not R is a Cartesian product.

2. Find those relations R in Exercise 1 which have the following property: for all a, b, and c, if both $(a, b) \in R$ and $(a, c) \in R$, then $b = c$, that is, for each first element $a \in$ dom R there is only one second element $b \in$ ran R.

3. Let P be the set of all living people, and let $\hat{R}$ be the subset of $P \times P$ defined by

   $$\hat{R} = \{(x, y) \mid x, y \in P, \quad x \text{ and } y \text{ are married}\}.$$

   (a) Explain how the relation $\hat{R}$ differs from the relation R in Example 1.
   (b) Find dom $\hat{R}$ and ran $\hat{R}$.

4. Graph the following relation:

   $$I = \{(x, y) \mid x, y \in R^1, x = y\}.$$

   Does this relation have the property given in Exercise 2?

5. Find the graph of the relation,

$$T = \{(x, y) \mid x, y \in R^1, x < y\}.$$

Show that $T \cup I = L$, where I is the relation of Exercise 4, and L is the relation of Example 10.

6. Graph the following relation:

$$S = \{(x, y) \mid x, y \in R^1, x \geq y\}.$$

Show that $S \cup T = R^2$, where T is the relation of Exercise 5.

7. Graph each of the following relations Q. (Compute a small table of coordinate pairs to aid your plotting of points.)
   (a) Q is the solution set of $x^2 = y$.
   (b) Q is the solution set of $x^2 \leq y$.
   (c) Q is the solution set of $x^2 \leq y + 1$.
   (d) Q is the solution set of $x^2 + y^2 \leq 1$.
   (e) Q is the solution set of $x^2 + y^2 > 1$.
   (f) Q is the solution set of $9x^2 + 4y^2 \leq 36$.
   (g) Q is the solution set of $|x| + |y| \leq 1$.

8. Let A be a set and R be a relation on A (that is, $R \subset A \times A$). Then
   (i) R is said to be *reflexive* on A if and only if for all $a \in A$, aRa.
   (ii) R is said to be *symmetric* on A if and only if for all $a, b \in A$, if aRb, then bRa.
   (iii) R is said to be *transitive* on A if and only if for all $a, b, c \in A$, if both aRb and bRc, then aRc.
   (a) Using these definitions, show that the subset relation, $\subset$, is reflexive, not symmetric, and transitive.
   (b) Using the above definitions, show that the relation "father of" is not reflexive, not symmetric, and not transitive.

9. (Continuation of Exercise 8) Let A and R be as above and write $a\mathrel{\rlap{/}R}b$ (read, a is not in relation to b) for $(a, b) \notin R$. Then
   (iv) R is said to be *nonreflexive* on A if and only if for some $a \in A$, $a\mathrel{\rlap{/}R}a$.
   (v) R is said to be *nonsymmetric* on A if and only if for some $a, b \in A$, aRb but $b\mathrel{\rlap{/}R}a$.
   (vi) R is said to be *nontransitive* on A if and only if for some $a, b, c \in A$, it is true that both aRb and bRc but $a\mathrel{\rlap{/}R}c$.
   (a) Show that the relation "subset of," $\subset$, is nonsymmetric.
   (b) Show that the relation "less than or equal," $\leq$, is nonreflexive, symmetric, and transitive on R^1.
   (c) Show that the relation "brother of" is nonreflexive, nonsymmetric, and transitive on the set P of living people.
   (d) Show that the relation "brother of" is nonreflexive, symmetric, and transitive on the set M of living men.

10. (Continuation of Exercises 8 and 9) Let A and R be as above. Then
    (vii) R is said to be *antireflexive* on A if and only if for all $a \in A$, $a\mathrel{\rlap{/}R}a$.
    (viii) R is said to be *antisymmetric* on A if and only if for all $a, b \in A$, if aRb, then $b\mathrel{\rlap{/}R}a$.
    (ix) R is said to be *antitransitive* on A if and only if for all $a, b, c \in A$, if both aRb and bRc, then $a\mathrel{\rlap{/}R}c$.

(a) For each nonreflexive relation in Exercises 8 and 9, determine whether the relation is antireflexive.

(b) For each nonsymmetric relation in Exercises 8 and 9, determine whether the relation is antisymmetric.

(c) For each nontransitive relation in Exercises 8 and 9, determine whether the relation is antitransitive.

(d) Give an example of a relation which is antireflexive, antisymmetric, and anti-transitive.

11. (Continuation of Exercise 8) Let A and R be as above. Then R is an *equivalence relation* on A if and only if R is reflexive, symmetric, and transitive on A.

(a) Show that equality, $=$, is an equivalence relation on R^1, the set of real numbers.

(b) Let $A = \{a, b\}$ be a set containing two distinct elements. Write all equivalence relations on A; that is, find all subsets R of $A \times A$ which are reflexive, symmetric, and transitive on A.

12. Show that if R and T are equivalence relations on a set A, then $R \cap T$ is an equivalence relation on A.

13. Suppose R is a transitive antireflexive relation on a set A. Show that R is also anti-symmetric on A.

14. Prove the following propositions.

(a) If A is a relation and $B \subset A$, then B is a relation.

(b) If A and B are relations, then $A \cup B$ and $A \cap B$ are relations.

(c) If S is a nonempty set of relations, than $\cup_{A \in S} A$ and $\cap_{A \in S} A$ are relations.

2.4 FUNCTIONS

The reader has undoubtedly seen a definition of a function similar to the following one.

If there is a rule which associates one and only one value of a variable y with each value of a variable x in a range of values, then y is called a function of x. One writes

$$y = f(x)$$

for each x.

This definition of a function is a good heuristic starting point, but it is rather vague. Furthermore it may lead to the belief that a function is given by a formula; this is true in many cases, but there are very important cases in which this is not true.

However, before proceeding, let us look at the above idea from a slightly different point of view. The x can be thought of as an input to a deterministic machine, and the y can be thought of as the machine's output. Viewed this way, a function is a deterministic machine which yields a definite output for each of the various inputs it can accept. For example, consider the machine shown in

Fig. 2.10.   This machine accepts as input any real number x; having accepted as input a certain real number x, it then yields as output the number x^2. Thus it seems reasonable to call this a real-number-squaring machine.   To know completely what the machine does, we must know what the output is for each acceptable input.   A convenient way of designating this is by ordered pairs: (input, output). This point of view leads to the idea that a function is a set of ordered pairs, that is, a *function is a relation*.   But can a function be just any relation?   Evidently not!   The heuristic definition indicates that there must be one and only one output for each acceptable input.

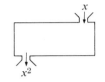

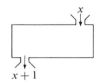

Fig. 2.10. The real-number-
squaring machine.

Fig. 2.11. The add-one-to-a-
real-number machine.

Let us consider a second example of a machine—the add-one-to-a-real-number machine.   This machine is shown in Fig. 2.11.   It can accept as input any real number.   For example, having received as input a particular real number x, the machine yields as output the number $x + 1$.   Thus the set of all pairs of inputs and outputs, $(x, x + 1)$, is the set

$$\{(x, x + 1) \mid x \in R^1\},$$

and hence it is a relation.   Again this relation has the property that there is one and only one output for every acceptable input.

These examples indicate that we should think of a function as a relation with the following special property: for each first component (input) of the relation there is one and only one second component (output).   If f is such a relation, and if $(a, b) \in f$ and $(a, c) \in f$, then we must have $b = c$; otherwise for the first component a we would have two second components.   We have thus arrived at the following formal definition of a function.

Definition 2.5. A *function f* is a relation such that for all a, b, c, if both $(a, b) \in f$ and $(a, c) \in f$, then $b = c$.

EXAMPLE 1.   Let $f = \{(x, x^2) \mid x \in R^1\}$.   Then f is a function.

EXAMPLE 2.   Let $g = \{(x, x + 1) \mid x \in R^1\}$.   Then g is a function.

The definition stated above appears to be far removed from our original heuristic definition of a function.   Let us return to our machine interpretation and show that this is really not the case.   As we observed before, we may think of a function as a machine with provisions for inputs and outputs. Let f be a function; the machine interpretation of f that we have in mind is indicated in Fig. 2.12. It would be convenient to have a concise notation for the output of the function f which would correspond to the input of a member of the domain of f. Fortunately, such a notation is available and has been in common use in mathematics for a very long time. The name given to the output of the function f corresponding to an acceptable input x is $f(x)$ (read, f of x). The symbol $f(x)$ is called *the value of f at x* or *the image of x by f*. Thus we see that the quantity $y = f(x)$ referred to in the heuristic definition is the value of the function f at the point x.

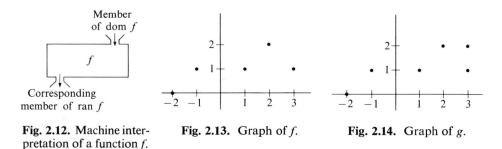

Fig. 2.12. Machine inter-   **Fig. 2.13.** Graph of f.   **Fig. 2.14.** Graph of g.
pretation of a function f.

Instead of calling $f(x)$ a function of x, we call it, more correctly, the value of the function f at the point x. Further, a function f may be thought of as the rule for associating with each value x another value $f(x)$ in such a way that for each x there is associated one and only one value.

Of course, it is necessary to specify the acceptable inputs for a function. However, once a function f is given, these inputs are automatically given: the acceptable inputs are the elements of the domain of f (since f is a relation, it has a domain). Also, the set of all possible outputs is just the range of f (since f is a relation, it has a range). Thus we see that for any function f,

$$f = \{(x, f(x)) \mid x \in \operatorname{dom} f\}, \tag{1}$$

and

$$f = \{(x, y) \mid x \in \operatorname{dom} f, \ y = f(x)\}. \tag{2}$$

The set in Eq. (2) exhibits the strong connection between the heuristic definition and the formal definition of a function: to specify a function one need only give the domain and the value $y = f(x)$ for each point x in the domain.

EXAMPLE 3.   Let f and g be the relations whose graphs are given in Figs. 2.13 and 2.14. From the figures, we see that f is a function, but that g is not a function, since (3, 1) and (3, 2) both belong to g. The domain of f is

$$\operatorname{dom} f = \{-2, -1, 1, 2, 3\},$$

and the range of f is

$$\operatorname{ran} f = \{0, 1, 2\}.$$

In fact, f is the following set of ordered pairs:

$$f = \{(-2, 0), (-1, 1), (1, 1), (2, 2), (3, 1)\}.$$

EXAMPLE 4. Let f be the set $\{(x, c) \mid x \in R^1, c \in R^1, c \text{ fixed}\}$. Then the graph of f is as given in Fig. 2.15. For this function we see that $f(x) = c$ for all x; such a function is usually called a *constant function*. We obtain a different constant function for each choice of c.

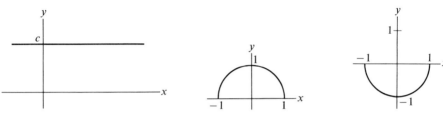

Fig. 2.15. Graph of the function $\{(x, c) \mid x \in R^1, c \in R^1, c \text{ fixed}\}$

Fig. 2.16. Graph of C_u.

Fig. 2.17. Graph of C_l.

EXAMPLE 5. Consider the relation C defined in Example 9 of Section 2.3:

$$C = \{(x, y) \mid x, y \in R^1, x^2 + y^2 = 1\}.$$

The graph of C is shown in Fig. 2.8. From the graph, it is evident that C is not a function; in fact, every x, except 1 and -1, in the domain of C has associated with it two values of y, namely, $\sqrt{1 - x^2}$ and $-\sqrt{1 - x^2}$. (The symbol $\sqrt{a}$ means the nonnegative square root of a nonnegative number a.) However, there is commonly associated with C a pair of functions. Let

$$C_u = \{(x, y) \mid x, y \in R^1, y = \sqrt{1 - x^2}\},$$
$$C_l = \{(x, y) \mid x, y \in R^1, y = -\sqrt{1 - x^2}\}.$$

Both C_u and C_l are functions; their graphs are shown in Figs. 2.16 and 2.17. C_u is the upper half of C and C_l is the lower half of C.

The example above points out that it is sometimes possible to obtain a function from a relation by restricting the range of the relation. We obtained C_u from C by requiring that the range of C_u be nonnegative real numbers; we obtained C_l by requiring that its range consist of nonpositive real numbers. Thus we see that it is necessary at times to restrict the range of a relation to obtain a function. Note also that if we restrict the range of a function, we obtain another function (with a different domain).

Another interesting variation on this idea is to restrict the domain of a function. For instance, the relation g of Fig. 2.14 is not a function. If we remove the element 3 from the domain, however, we obtain a new relation $\hat{g}$ which is a function; the graph of $\hat{g}$ is shown in Fig. 2.18. The domain of the function $\hat{g}$ is dom $\hat{g} = \{-2, -1, 1, 2\}$. Note that the relation $\hat{g}$ is not the same as the relation g; the two sets are unequal. Thus we see that by restricting the domain of a relation we obtain another relation. In some cases this new relation is a function. On the other hand, if we restrict the domain of a function, we always obtain a function, but one which is different from the original function.

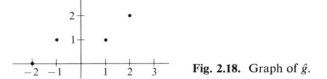

Fig. 2.18. Graph of $\hat{g}$.

It should be pointed out that domain and range restrictions occur rather naturally. For many physical situations, negative numbers are not meaningful. For such situations it is natural to restrict both the domain and the range of any function under consideration to the nonnegative real numbers.

Also, it should be pointed out that two functions, f_1 and f_2, are equal if and only if they have the same domain and if, for every x in the common domain, $f_1(x) = f_2(x)$.

EXAMPLE 6. A common way of specifying a function f is to give its domain and its value $f(x)$ for each x in its domain. For instance,

$$f(x) = x^2 \quad \text{for} \quad 0 \le x \le 1$$

and

$$g(x) = x^2 \quad \text{for} \quad x \in R^1$$

are specifications of functions. In the ordered-pair notation,

$$f = \{(x, x^2) \mid 0 \le x \le 1\},$$
$$g = \{(x, x^2) \mid x \in R^1\}.$$

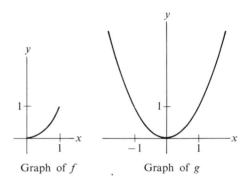

Graph of f Graph of g

Fig. 2.19. Graphs of the functions f and g in Example 6.

The graphs of these two functions appear in Fig. 2.19. These are, of course, different functions with different domains (and different ranges).

It sometimes happens that a function is defined incompletely by specifying its values but not its domain. When this happens, it is customary to take for the domain the largest set on which the formula giving the function values makes sense. Hopefully such situations will not occur in this book.

We add one final remark. We shall say that f is a *function defined on* a set A if dom $f = A$. For example, the function f in Example 6 is defined on $A = \{x \mid 0 \le x \le 1\}$.

EXERCISES

1. Let f be the function defined as
$$f = \{(x, x^3 + 1) \mid x \in R^1\}.$$

   (a) Find $f(0)$.   (b) Find $f(1)$.   (c) Find $f(-1)$.   (d) Graph the function f.

2. Let g be the function defined as
$$g = \{(x, y) \mid 0 \leq x \leq 2, y = x^3 + 1\}.$$

   (a) Graph the function g.
   (b) Explain how this function is related to the function f of Exercise 1.

3. Let L be the relation
$$L = \{(x, y) \mid x, y \in R^1, \quad 2x + 3y = 6\}.$$

   (a) Show that L is a function.
   (b) What is $L(x)$, the value of the function at the point x?
   (c) Express L in the form given in Eq. (1).

4. Let f be defined by $f(x) = \sqrt{x}$ for $x \geq 0$. Graph the function f. What is its domain? Its range? Express f in the form of Eq. (2).

5. Suppose that $f = \{(1, 1), (2, 1), (3, 2), (4, 2)\}$.
   (a) Graph f.   (b) Is f a function?

6. Let the functions f and g be defined as follows:
$$f(x) = \frac{x^2 - 1}{x - 1}, \qquad x \in R^1, \quad x \neq 1;$$
$$g(x) = x + 1, \qquad x \in R^1.$$

   Is $f = g$? Explain your answer.

7. Let the functions h and g be defined as
$$h = \left\{\left(x, \frac{x^2 - 1}{x - 1}\right) \;\middle|\; x \in R^1, \quad x \neq 1\right\} \cup \{(1, 2)\},$$
$$g = \{(x, x + 1) \mid x \in R^1\}.$$

   Is $h = g$? Explain your answer.

8. Let P be the set of all living people and define a relation H as
$$H = \{(p, h) \mid p \in P, h \text{ is the height of } p \text{ to the nearest inch} \quad \text{(round half inches}$$
$$\text{up to the next inch)}\}.$$

   (a) Is H a function?   (b) Find dom H.   (c) Explain what $H(p)$ denotes.

9. Let $S = \{a_1, a_2, \ldots, a_n\}$ be a set containing n distinct objects, $n \geq 1$. Define a function N on $\Pi(S)$, the power set of S, as follows:
$$N = \{(A, N(A)) \mid A \subset S, N(A) \text{ is the number of distinct elements in } A\}.$$

   (a) Find $N(\emptyset)$ and $N(S)$.
   (b) If $A \cap B = \emptyset$, explain why $N(A \cup B) = N(A) + N(B)$.

10. (Continuation of Exercise 9) Let S and N be as above. Define a function P on $\Pi(S)$ by

$$P = \left\{ \left(A, \frac{N(A)}{n} \right) \,\Big|\, A \subset S \right\}.$$

(a) Find $P(\emptyset)$ and $P(S)$.
(b) What is the domain of P? The range of P?
(c) Use part (b) of Exercise 9 to show that, if $A \cap B = \emptyset$, then $P(A \cup B) = P(A) + P(B)$.

11. Is the relation

$$V = \{(1, y) \mid y \in R^1\}$$

a function? Graph the relation V.

12. Define a relation C by

$$C = \{(x, y) \mid x, y \in R^1, \quad x \geq 0, \quad y^2 = x\}.$$

(a) Find the domain of C.
(b) Show that C is not a function.
(c) Show that by restricting the range of C to either the nonnegative real numbers or to the nonpositive real numbers, we obtain a new relation which is a function.

13. Let A be the set $\{a, b\}$, in which a and b are distinct objects. Determine all subsets of $A \times A$ which are functions.

14. Suppose that A is a set containing three distinct objects. How many subsets of $A \times A$ are functions?

15. A function f is said to be *one-to-one* (1-1) if and only if for all a, b, c, if both $(b, a) \in f$ and $(c, a) \in f$, then $b = c$, that is, if and only if for each output a there is only one input which results in a.
(a) Show that the function $f = \{(x, x) \mid x \in R^1\}$ is a one-to-one function.
(b) Show that the constant function $g = \{(x, 1) \mid x \in R^1\}$ is not a one-to-one function.
(c) Is the function f of Exercise 5 a one-to-one function? Explain.

16. A function f is said to be a *mapping from a set A into a set B*, denoted by $f : A \to B$, if and only if dom $f = A$ and ran $f \subset B$. (This is often expressed by saying f is a function defined on A mapping A into B.)
(a) Let f be defined by

$$f(x) = \frac{x^2}{x^2 + 1}$$

for $x \in R^1$. Show that f is a mapping of R^1 into R^1.
(b) Show that the function f in (a) is also a mapping of R^1 into B, $B = \{y \mid 0 \leq y\}$. What is the range of f?

17. A function f is said to be a *mapping from a set A onto a set B* if and only if dom $f = A$ and ran $f = B$. (This is often expressed by saying that f is a function defined on A mapping A onto B.)
(a) Show that the function f in Exercise 16 (a) is a mapping of R^1 onto $B = \{y \mid 0 \leq y < 1\}$.

(b) Let f be the function defined in Exercise 5. Show that f is a mapping of $A = \{1, 2, 3, 4\}$ onto $B = \{1, 2\}$.

(c) Show that the function f in Exercise 15 (a) is a one-to-one function mapping R^1 onto R^1.

(d) Explain why any function f is a mapping of its domain onto its range.

2.5 COMPOSITION OF FUNCTIONS

In the previous section we constructed machines which corresponded to the following functions:

$$f = \{(x, x^2) \mid x \in R^1\}, \tag{1}$$

$$g = \{(x, x + 1) \mid x \in R^1\}. \tag{2}$$

Now suppose that we wish to construct a function machine which corresponds to the following function h:

$$h = \{(x, x^2 + 1) \mid x \in R^1\}. \tag{3}$$

A little thought should reveal that such a machine can easily be built from the machines for f and g which we already have available. We need only to connect them in series in the order shown in Fig. 2.20 and treat the resulting composite machine as a single machine.

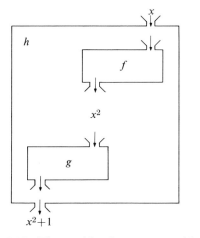

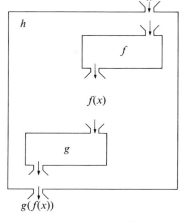

Fig. 2.20. The machine h as a composition of f and g.

Fig. 2.21. The machine h of the composition of f and g.

More generally, if f and g are functions represented by the machines shown in Fig. 2.21, the result of connecting them in series as shown in Fig. 2.21 is the machine representing a function h. For each x entering the machine, the output is $h(x) = g(f(x))$. Before proceeding further, a word of caution is in order.

For the machine g to function, the input must be acceptable; that is, $f(x)$ must belong to the domain of g. This will be the case if

$$\operatorname{ran} f \subset \operatorname{dom} g. \tag{4}$$

For two functions f and g such that condition (4) is satisfied, we can define a new function, h, called the *composition of f and g*, by letting

$$h(x) = g(f(x)) \qquad \text{for each} \quad x \in \operatorname{dom} f,$$

or equivalently,

$$h = \{(x, h(x)) \mid x \in \operatorname{dom} f, \ h(x) = g(f(x))\}.$$

We now give a formal definition.

Definition 2.6. Let f and g be functions such that

$$\operatorname{ran} f \subset \operatorname{dom} g. \tag{5}$$

Then the *composition of f and g* is the function

$$h = \{(x, g(f(x))) \mid x \in \operatorname{dom} f\}. \tag{6}$$

The function h is called the *composite* of f and g. A standard notation for the composite of f and g is $g \circ f$; thus

$$g \circ f = \{(x, g(f(x))) \mid x \in \operatorname{dom} f\}. \tag{7}$$

It should be observed that the value of $g \circ f$ at a point $x \in \operatorname{dom} f$ is

$$(g \circ f)(x) = g(f(x)). \tag{8}$$

This follows immediately from the definition of the value of a function at a point, and from Eq. (7).

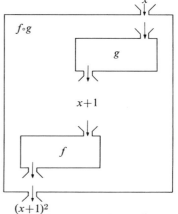

EXAMPLE 1. Let f and g be the functions defined in Eqs. (1) and (2). What is the composition of g and f, that is, what is $f \circ g$? Note that the order here is the opposite of that given earlier.

Let us build the composite machine for $f \circ g$. This machine is shown in Fig. 2.22. From this machine we see that the output, for an input x, is $(x + 1)^2$. Thus

$$f \circ g = \{(x, (x + 1)^2) \mid x \in R^1\}.$$

Further, note that $f \circ g \neq g \circ f$. For example, $(f \circ g)(1) = (1 + 1)^2 = 4$, but $(g \circ f)(1) = 1^2 + 1 = 2$.

Fig. 2.22. The machine of the composition $f \circ g$ of g and f.

The previous example shows that we should not expect $f \circ g$ and $g \circ f$ to be the same function; usually they are different functions.

EXAMPLE 2. Let $f(x) = 2x$ for $x \in R^1$ define a function f, and let $g(x) = 3x^2 + 1$ for $x \in R^1$ define another function g. Find $g \circ f$ and $f \circ g$.
By Eq. (7)

$$(g \circ f)(x) = g(f(x)) = 3(f(x))^2 + 1 = 3(2x)^2 + 1 = 12x^2 + 1$$

for each $x \in R^1$, and

$$(f \circ g)(x) = f(g(x)) = 2(g(x)) = 2(3x^2 + 1) = 6x^2 + 2$$

for each $x \in R^1$. Thus

$$g \circ f = \{(x, 12x^2 + 1) \mid x \in R^1\},$$

and

$$f \circ g = \{(x, 6x^2 + 2) \mid x \in R^1\}.$$

The reader should note carefully how we obtained the function values for $g \circ f$ and $f \circ g$.

EXAMPLE 3. Let $f = \{(3, 2), (4, 3), (5, 7)\}$ and let $g = \{(2, 0), (3, 11), (7, 1), (8, 2)\}$. Then

$$(g \circ f)(3) = g(f(3)) = g(2) = 0,$$

since $f(3) = 2$. Also

$$(g \circ f)(4) = g(f(4)) = g(3) = 11, \qquad (g \circ f)(5) = g(f(5)) = g(7) = 1.$$

Thus

$$g \circ f = \{(3, 0), (4, 11), (5, 1)\}.$$

Note that $\operatorname{ran} f = \{2, 3, 7\} \subsetneq \operatorname{dom} g = \{2, 3, 7, 8\}$, and that $\operatorname{ran}(g \circ f) = \{0, 11, 1\} \subsetneq \operatorname{ran} g = \{0, 11, 1, 2\}$.

In general, we have $\operatorname{ran}(g \circ f) \subset \operatorname{ran} g$. This statement is easy to verify, and it is left as an exercise (see Exercise 4). Finally, in probability theory, the composition of f and g, $g \circ f$, is commonly denoted by $g(f)$. Since we shall treat probability theory later in this text, the reader should note this fact carefully.

EXERCISES

1. Let $f = \{(0, 2), (1, 2), (2, 3)\}$ and $g = \{(2, 0), (3, 5), (6, 7)\}$. Determine $g \circ f$.

2. Let $h = \{(x, x^2 + 1) \mid x \in R^1\}$ and let $u = \{(x, \sqrt{x}) \mid x \in R^1, x \geq 0\}$.
   (a) Determine $u \circ h$. What is $(u \circ h)(1)$?
   (b) Determine $h \circ u$. What is the domain of $h \circ u$? The range?

3. Let $u = \{(x, \sqrt{x}) \mid x \in R^1, x \geq 0\}$ and let $v = \{(x, 1 - x^2) \mid x \in R^1, -1 \leq x \leq 1\}$.
   (a) Find $u \circ v$.
   (b) What is $u(v(x))$ for $-1 \leq x \leq 1$?
   (c) Graph $u \circ v$.
   (d) Find $(u \circ v)(\frac{1}{2})$, $(u \circ v)(-1)$, and $(u \circ v)(0)$.

4. (a) Show that ran $g \circ f \subset$ ran g, where f and g are functions such that ran $f \subset$ dom g.
   (b) Give an example of a pair of functions f and g such that ran $g \circ f =$ ran g.

5. Let f, g, and h be functions such that ran $f \subset$ dom g and ran $g \subset$ dom h.
   (a) Use the machine representation to illustrate each of the following compositions:
   $h \circ (g \circ f)$ and $(h \circ g) \circ f$. [*Hint:* To illustrate $h \circ (g \circ f)$, first make the composition
   machine for $g \circ f$ and then compose this machine with h.]
   (b) Show that $h \circ (g \circ f) = (h \circ g) \circ f$. (This result asserts that the operation of composition is an associative operation.)

6. It is possible to define the composition $S \circ R$ of two relations R and S. To do so, set

   $$S \circ R = \{(x, y) \mid \text{there exists } z \text{ such that } (x, z) \in R \text{ and } (z, y) \in S\}.$$

   (a) Given that R and S are functions with ran $R \subset$ dom S, show that this definition
   of the composition of R and S as relations agrees with the definition of the
   composition of R and S as functions.
   (b) Find the composition $S \circ R$ of the following pair of relations:
   $S = \{(2, 0), (3, 11), (7, 1), (8, 2)\}$, $R = \{(3, 2), (4, 3), (5, 7)\}$.

7. If R is a relation, then the inverse relation of R, denoted by R^{-1}, is the set of reverses
   of the ordered pairs in R; that is,

   $$R^{-1} = \{(y, x) \mid (x, y) \in R\}.$$

   (a) Find f^{-1} and g^{-1} where f and g are the functions (relations) of Exercise 1. Are
   f^{-1} and g^{-1} functions?
   (b) Find $f \circ f^{-1}$ and $g \circ g^{-1}$, where again f and g are the functions of Exercise 1.
   (c) Find $f^{-1} \circ f$ and $g^{-1} \circ g$.
   (d) Which of the relations $f \circ f^{-1}$, $g \circ g^{-1}$, $f^{-1} \circ f$, and $g^{-1} \circ g$ are functions?

8. (Continuation of Exercise 7) Let f be a one-to-one function.
   (a) Show that f^{-1} is a function whose domain is the range of f and whose range is
   the domain of f.
   (b) Show that $(f \circ f^{-1})(y) = f(f^{-1}(y)) = y$ for each $y \in$ ran f and that $(f^{-1} \circ f)(x)$
   $= f^{-1}(f(x)) = x$ for each $x \in$ dom f.
   (c) Show that f^{-1} is a one-to-one function.

9. (Continuation of Exercise 7)   If R and S are relations, show that $(S \circ R)^{-1} =$
   $R^{-1} \circ S^{-1}$.

2.6 SUMS AND PRODUCTS OF FUNCTIONS

In this section we shall restrict our attention to *real-valued functions;* that is,
we shall consider only functions whose ranges are subsets of R^1, the set of real
numbers. Such functions are the most common, and it is possible to add, subtract,
and multiply their values. For instance, if f and g are two real-valued functions

and x is a point in the domain of each function, then

$$f(x) + g(x) \qquad\qquad (1)$$

is the sum,

$$f(x) - g(x) \qquad\qquad (2)$$

is the difference, and

$$f(x) \cdot g(x) \qquad\qquad (3)$$

is the product of two real numbers.

The above discussion suggests that given two real-valued functions f and g, we can form new functions h_1, h_2, and h_3 by letting

$$h_1(x) = f(x) + g(x), \qquad\qquad (4)$$

$$h_2(x) = f(x) - g(x), \qquad\qquad (5)$$

$$h_3(x) = f(x) \cdot g(x). \qquad\qquad (6)$$

A natural name for h_1 is $f + g$, the *sum of f and g;* a name for h_2 is $f - g$, the *difference of f and g;* and a name for h_3 is $f \cdot g$ (note that this is *not* composition), the *product of f and g.* In fact, we do define the sum, difference, and product of two functions in essentially the manner indicated in Eqs. (4), (5), and (6) and give them the names $f + g$, $f - g$, and $f \cdot g$; the formal definitions are given below. However, before giving the formal definitions, it is apparent that certain restrictions are necessary. Equations (1), (2), and (3) are meaningless unless the point x is in both the domain of f and the domain of g. So we will be able to define the sum, difference, and product of two functions only on the set $(\text{dom } f) \cap (\text{dom } g)$. With this restriction in mind, we proceed to the definition.

Definition 2.7. Let f and g be real-valued functions and let $D = (\text{dom } f) \cap (\text{dom } g)$. Then we define
(a) the *sum of f and g,* denoted by $f + g$, by

$$(f + g)(x) = f(x) + g(x) \qquad \text{for each} \quad x \in D;$$

(b) the *difference of f and g,* denoted by $f - g$, by

$$(f - g)(x) = f(x) - g(x) \qquad \text{for each} \quad x \in D;$$

(c) the *product of f and g,* denoted by $f \cdot g$, by

$$(f \cdot g)(x) = f(x) \cdot g(x) \qquad \text{for each} \quad x \in D.$$

Expressing $f + g$, $f - g$, and $f \cdot g$ in the ordered-pair notation, we have

$$f + g = \{(x, f(x) + g(x)) \mid x \in D\},$$
$$f - g = \{(x, f(x) - g(x)) \mid x \in D\},$$
$$f \cdot g = \{(x, f(x) \cdot g(x)) \mid x \in D\}.$$

EXAMPLE 1. If $f(x) = x^2$ and $g(x) = x$ for $x \in R^1$, then

$$(f + g)(x) = x^2 + x,$$
$$(f - g)(x) = x^2 - x,$$
$$(f \cdot g)(x) = x^2 x = x^3.$$

Thus

$$f + g = \{(x, x^2 + x) \mid x \in R^1\},$$
$$f - g = \{(x, x^2 - x) \mid x \in R^1\},$$
$$f \cdot g = \{(x, x^3) \mid x \in R^1\}.$$

EXAMPLE 2. Let $f(x) = x$ for $x \in R^1$, and let $g(x) = \sqrt{1 - x^2}$ for $-1 \le x \le 1$. Then $D = (\text{dom} f) \cap (\text{dom} g) = \{x \mid -1 \le x \le 1\}$. Thus the sum, difference, and product of f and g are defined on the set D, and, for $x \in D$,

$$(f + g)(x) = x + \sqrt{1 - x^2},$$
$$(f - g)(x) = x - \sqrt{1 - x^2},$$
$$(f \cdot g)(x) = x\sqrt{1 - x^2}.$$

In Definition 2.7 we treated sums, differences, and products of functions, but not quotients of functions. The reason for this omission is that quotients do not behave so nicely. Suppose that we were to consider

$$\frac{f(x)}{g(x)}. \tag{7}$$

This expression makes sense provided $x \in (\text{dom} f) \cap (\text{dom} g)$ *and* $g(x) \ne 0$ (division by zero is not defined). Thus we see that an additional restriction is necessary in order to be able to define the quotient of two functions.

Definition 2.8. Let f and g be real-valued functions, let $D = (\text{dom} f) \cap (\text{dom} g)$, and let $Z = \{x \mid g(x) = 0\}$. Then we define the *quotient of f and g*, denoted by f/g, by

$$\left(\frac{f}{g}\right)(x) = \frac{f(x)}{g(x)} \qquad \text{for each} \quad x \in D - Z.$$

Expressing f/g in the ordered-pair notation, we have

$$\frac{f}{g} = \left\{\left(x, \frac{f(x)}{g(x)}\right) \;\middle|\; x \in D - Z\right\}.$$

EXAMPLE 3. Let $f(x) = 1$ for $x \in R^1$, and let $g(x) = x$ for $x \in R^1$. Then f/g is called the *reciprocal* of g and

$$\frac{f(x)}{g(x)} = \frac{1}{x} \qquad \text{for} \quad x \in R^1 - \{0\}.$$

Instead of writing $R^1 - \{0\}$, we usually write $x \neq 0$. Thus

$$\frac{f(x)}{g(x)} = \frac{1}{x} \quad \text{for} \quad x \neq 0.$$

More generally, we can define the reciprocal of any function g by letting $f(x) = 1$ for $x \in \text{dom } g$. Then

$$\frac{f(x)}{g(x)} = \frac{1}{g(x)} \quad \text{for} \quad x \in \text{dom } g - Z,$$

where, as before, $Z = \{x \mid g(x) = 0\}$.

EXAMPLE 4. Let $f(x) = 1 - x^2$ for $x \in R^1$ and let $g(x) = 1 - x$ for $x \in R^1$. Then $Z = \{1\}$ and

$$\frac{f(x)}{g(x)} = \frac{1 - x^2}{1 - x} = 1 + x \quad \text{for} \quad x \in R^1 - \{1\},$$

or

$$\frac{f(x)}{g(x)} = 1 + x \quad \text{for} \quad x \neq 1. \tag{8}$$

Note that the expression $1 + x$ on the right-hand side in Eq. (8) is meaningful even when $x = 1$; however, f/g is *not* defined when $x = 1$. We could extend the definition of f/g so that the formula (8) would be true even for $x = 1$, but, in doing so, we would obtain a new function. To be more explicit, the functions

$$h(x) = 1 + x, \quad x \in R^1,$$

and

$$\left(\frac{f}{g}\right)(x) = 1 + x, \quad x \neq 1,$$

are distinct functions—they have different domains.

Another common operation on functions is called *scalar multiplication*. If c is a real number and f is a real-valued function, we can multiply the value $f(x)$ of f by c:

$$c \cdot f(x)$$

for each x in the domain of f. In this way we can form a new function, called the *scalar multiple of f by c*. This function is usually denoted by cf.

Definition 2.9. Let f be a real-valued function and let c be a real number. Then we define the *scalar multiple of f by c*, denoted by cf, by

$$(cf)(x) = c \cdot f(x) \quad \text{for each} \quad x \in \text{dom } f.$$

Expressing cf in the ordered-pair notation, we have

$$cf = \{(x, c \cdot f(x)) \mid x \in \operatorname{dom} f\}.$$

EXAMPLE 5. Let $c = 5$ and $f(x) = x^2$ for each $x \in R^1$. Then

$$(cf)(x) = 5x^2 \qquad \text{for} \quad x \in R^1$$

and

$$cf = \{(x, 5x^2) \mid x \in R^1\}.$$

EXAMPLE 6. Let $c = -1$ and $f(x) = x^2 - x$ for each $x \in R^1$. Then

$$(cf)(x) = -1(x^2 - x) = x - x^2 \qquad \text{for each} \quad x \in R^1.$$

Note that $f + (-1)g = f - g$ since $((-1)g)(x) = -1 \cdot g(x) = -g(x)$, and hence $(f + (-1)g)(x) = f(x) - g(x) = (f - g)(x)$. Thus scalar multiplication and addition of functions yields subtraction of functions. In a similar manner, we can show that division of two functions can be accomplished by using the reciprocal and multiplication.

The following theorem lists the basic properties of sums, products, and scalar multiples of functions. To simplify the notation we shall assume that $\operatorname{dom} f = \operatorname{dom} g = \operatorname{dom} h = D$; the reader should be able to state each result in the more general case without any difficulty.

Theorem 2.2. Let f, g, and h be functions each having D as its domain, and let a and b be real numbers. Then

(a) $f + g = g + f$ (addition of functions is commutative);
(b) $f + (g + h) = (f + g) + h$ (addition of functions is associative);
(c) $f \cdot g = g \cdot f$ (multiplication of functions is commutative);
(d) $f \cdot (g \cdot h) = (f \cdot g) \cdot h$ (multiplication of functions is associative);
(e) $f \cdot (g + h) = f \cdot g + f \cdot h$ (multiplication of functions is distributive over addition of functions);
(f) $(a + b)f = af + bf$ (addition of real numbers is distributive over scalar multiplication of functions);
(g) $a(f + g) = af + ag$ (scalar multiplication of functions is distributive over addition of functions);
(h) $a(bf) = (ab)f$.

We shall not give proofs for all parts of this theorem. Instead, we prove only parts (b) and (c); the reader should be able to produce proofs for the other parts easily by using the methods that we use to prove parts (b) and (c) (see Exercise 7).

Proof of (b). Let $x \in D$, the common domain of f, g, and h. Then

$$(g + h)(x) = g(x) + h(x),$$

and

$$(f + (g + h))(x) = f(x) + (g + h)(x) = f(x) + (g(x) + h(x))$$
$$= (f(x) + g(x)) + h(x). \tag{9}$$

The last equality above results from the fact that addition of real numbers is associative. Next,

$$(f + g)(x) = f(x) + g(x);$$

hence

$$((f + g) + h)(x) = (f + g)(x) + h(x) = (f(x) + g(x)) + h(x). \tag{10}$$

From Equations (9) and (10) we see that

$$(f + (g + h))(x) = ((f + g) + h)(x)$$

for each $x \in D$. Thus $f + (g + h) = (f + g) + h.$ ▲

Proof of (c). Let $x \in D$. Then

$$(f \cdot g)(x) = f(x) \cdot g(x) = g(x) \cdot f(x) = (g \cdot f)(x).$$

In the above argument we used the fact that $f(x) \cdot g(x) = g(x) \cdot f(x)$ which follows from the fact that multiplication of real numbers [and that is what $f(x)$ and $g(x)$ are] is commutative. Since $(f \cdot g)(x) = (g \cdot f)(x)$ for every $x \in D$, $f \cdot g = g \cdot f.$ ▲

EXERCISES

1. Find the sum $f + g$ for each of the following pairs of functions f and g.
   (a) $f = \{(2, 0), (1, 1), (3, 1)\}$; $g = \{(2, 1), (3, 3), (1, 2)\}$
   (b) $f = \{(2, 0), (1, 1), (3, 1)\}$; $g = \{(2, 1), (3, 3), (4, -1), (1, 2)\}$
   (c) $f(x) = x, -1 \leq x \leq 1; g(x) = x, 0 < x$
   (d) $f(x) = x, x \in R^1; g(x) = 0, x \in R^1$
   (e) $f(x) = 2x + 1/x, x \neq 0$, and $g(x) = -x + 3/(x - 1), x \neq 1$
   (f) f and $g = -f$
   (g) f and $g(x) = 0, x \in \text{dom } f$
   (h) f and $g(x) = 1, x \in \text{dom } f$

2. Find the product $f \cdot g$ for each pair of functions f and g in Exercise 1.

3. Give the domain for both $f + g$ and $f \cdot g$ for each pair of functions f and g in Exercise 1.

4. (a) Find the quotient f/g for each pair of functions in Exercise 1.
   (b) Find the domain of f/g for each function in part (a).

5. For each function g in Exercise 1, find the functions
   (a) $2g$ (b) $-3g$.

6. Show that $f/g = f \cdot (1/g)$; that is, show that f/g and $f \cdot (1/g)$ have the same domains and the same values for each x in their common domain.

7. (a) Prove Theorem 2.2(a).   (b) Prove Theorem 2.2(d).
   (c) Prove Theorem 2.2(e).   (d) Prove Theorem 2.2(f).
   (e) Prove Theorem 2.2(g).   (f) Prove Theorem 2.2(h).

The next four exercises require a knowledge of algebraic structures.

8. Let G be the set of real-valued functions defined on a set $D \neq \emptyset$. Show that this set together with the operation of sum of two functions forms a commutative group. [*Hint:* See parts (f) and (g) of Exercise 1.]

9. Explain why the set G in Exercise 8 together with the operation of product of two functions does not form a group. What would be the multiplicative identity element? What would be the multiplicative inverse element?

10. Show that the set G in Exercise 8 together with the two operations of sum and product of functions forms a commutative ring with unit.

11. Show that the set G of Exercise 8, together with the operations of sum and scalar multiplication of functions, forms a vector space over the real numbers. What is the zero vector?

2.7 SOME IMPORTANT FUNCTIONS

This section will be devoted to a discussion of some rather elementary functions, namely, the polynomial functions, the rational functions, the square-root function, and the absolute-value function. All these terms will be defined in the course of the section. Furthermore, all functions of this section will be real-valued functions defined on some subset of the real numbers.

Let us begin by considering three rather simple functions:

$$\{(x, 1) \mid x \in R^1\}, \tag{1}$$

$$\{(x, x) \mid x \in R^1\}, \tag{2}$$

$$\left\{\left(x, \frac{1}{x}\right) \,\middle|\, x \in R^1 - \{0\}\right\}. \tag{3}$$

The first is a constant function; it has the value 1 for every $x \in R^1$. Its graph appears in Fig. 2.23. The second is called the *identity function;* its value at each point x is x itself. A graph appears in Fig. 2.24. The third function above is the

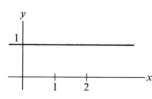

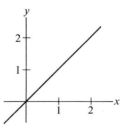

Fig. 2.23. The graph of $\{(x, 1) \mid x \in R^1\}$.   **Fig. 2.24.** The graph of $\{(x, x) \mid x \in R^1\}$.

reciprocal of the identity function; the value assigned to each nonzero point x is $1/x$. Its graph appears in Fig. 2.25.

Using these three functions we may create many new functions by forming the sums, products, quotients, and scalar multiples of these functions with each other and themselves. For example, the function

$$\{(x, x^2) \mid x \in R^1\}, \qquad (4)$$

(usually denoted simply by $y = x^2$) can be obtained by multiplying the identity function by itself

$$\{(x, x) \mid x \in R^1\} \cdot \{(x, x) \mid x \in R^1\}$$
$$= \{(x, x^2) \mid x \in R^1\}.$$

More generally, for any positive integer n the function

$$\{(x, x^n) \mid x \in R^1\} \qquad (5)$$

is constructed as follows:

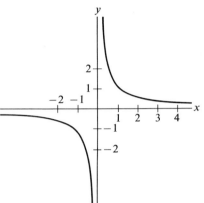

Fig. 2.25. The graph of $\{(x, 1/x) \mid x \neq 0\}$.

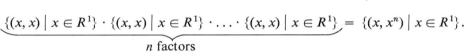

$$\underbrace{\{(x, x) \mid x \in R^1\} \cdot \{(x, x) \mid x \in R^1\} \cdot \ldots \cdot \{(x, x) \mid x \in R^1\}}_{n \text{ factors}} = \{(x, x^n) \mid x \in R^1\}.$$

The graphs of the functions whose values at x are x^2 and x^3 are shown in Figs. 2.26 and 2.27, respectively.

Using scalar multiplication and addition of functions, we can now form an important class of functions, the *polynomial functions*. These are all the functions that can be formed from a finite number of the functions $\{(x, x^n) \mid x \in R^1\}$ by

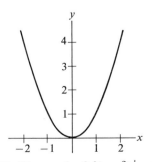

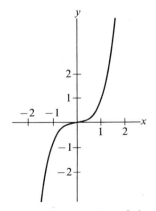

Fig. 2.26. The graph of $\{(x, x^2) \mid x \in R^1\}$.   **Fig. 2.27.** The graph of $\{(x, x^3) \mid x \in R^1\}$.

multiplying by scalars and adding. For instance, the function f given by

$$f(x) = 4 - x^2 \qquad \text{for} \quad x \in R^1$$

is such a function. In fact,

$$f = 4\{(x, 1) \mid x \in R^1\} + 0\{(x, x) \mid x \in R^1\} - 1\{(x, x^2) \mid x \in R^1\}.$$

(The graph of f is given in Fig. 2.28.)

Definition 2.10. Let $a_0, a_1, \ldots, a_n$ be $n + 1$ real numbers. Then the function p whose value at each point $x \in D \subset R^1$ is given by

$$p(x) = a_0 x^n + a_1 x^{n-1} + \cdots + a_{n-1} x + a_n$$

is called a *polynomial function on* D. (D may be R^1, or it may be a proper subset of R^1.)

Definition 2.11. If $a_0 \neq 0$, the polynomial function p whose values are given by

$$p(x) = a_0 x^n + a_1 x^{n-1} + \cdots + a_{n-1} x + a_n$$

is said to be *of degree n*.

EXAMPLE 1. The function f whose values are given by

$$f(x) = 4 - x^2$$

is a polynomial function of degree 2; $a_0 = -1, a_1 = 0, a_2 = 4$.

EXAMPLE 2. The function g whose values for each positive integer n are

$$g(n) = 3n^3 + 2n - 3$$

is a polynomial function of degree 3 on the set of positive integers J^+; $a_0 = 3$, $a_1 = 0, a_2 = 2, a_3 = -3$.

Another important class of functions, which actually contains the polynomial functions, is the class of rational functions. The rational functions are quotients of polynomial functions.

Definition 2.12. Let p and q be polynomial functions, let $D = \text{dom } p \cap \text{dom } q$, and let $Z = \{x \mid q(x) = 0\}$. Then the function r defined on $D - Z$ by

$$r(x) = \frac{p(x)}{q(x)}, \qquad x \in D - Z,$$

is called a *rational function*.

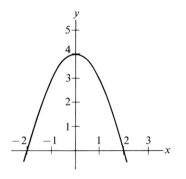

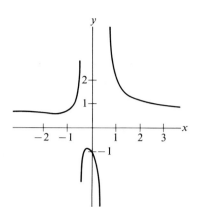

Fig. 2.28. The graph of $f(x) = 4 - x^2$.   **Fig. 2.29.** The graph of the function r of Example 4.

EXAMPLE 3. The reciprocal of the identity function $\{(x, 1/x) \mid x \neq 0\}$ is a rational function:

$$\frac{1}{x} = \frac{p(x)}{q(x)},$$

where $p(x) = 1$ and $q(x) = x$.

EXAMPLE 4. The function r defined by

$$r(x) = \frac{3x^2 + 2x + 1}{4x^2 - 1}, \qquad \text{when } 4x^2 - 1 \neq 0,$$

is a rational function. The domain of definition of r can be taken to be $R^1 - \{\frac{1}{2}, -\frac{1}{2}\}$. The graph of r is shown in Fig. 2.29.

Another very common function is the function whose values $f(x)$ are given by

$$f(x) = \sqrt{x}.$$

For the above formula to be meaningful, we must require that x be greater than or equal to zero. Thus the function we are now considering is

$$f = \{(x, \sqrt{x}) \mid x \geq 0\}.$$

This function can be called the *square-root function;* its graph appears in Fig. 2.30. The reader may have seen the relation

$$y^2 = x, \qquad x \geq 0, \qquad (6)$$

and may be wondering how it differs from the square-root function. In terms of ordered pairs, the relation (6) is

$$R = \{(x, y) \mid x \geq 0, \ y^2 = x\}.$$

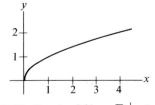

Fig. 2.30. Graph of $\{(x, \sqrt{x}) \mid x \geq 0\}$.

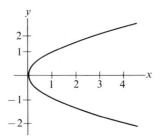

Fig. 2.31. The graph of the relation
$$R = \{(x, y) \mid x \geq 0, y^2 = x\}.$$

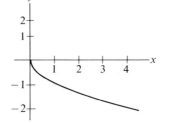

Fig. 2.32. The graph of
$$\{(x, -\sqrt{x}) \mid x \geq 0\}.$$

Its graph appears in Fig. 2.31. Inspection reveals that the square-root function is obtained from the relation R by restricting the range of R to the nonnegative real numbers. If we restrict the range of R to the nonpositive real numbers, we obtain from R the function

$$g = \{(x, -\sqrt{x}) \mid x \geq 0\}.$$

The graph of g is shown in Fig. 2.32. Thus we see that the relation R is the union of the two functions f and g:

$$R = f \cup g.$$

If we compose the square-root function with a polynomial function or a rational function, we can obtain functions whose values are given by

$$\sqrt{p(x)}, \tag{7}$$

$$p(\sqrt{x}), \tag{8}$$

$$\sqrt{\frac{p(x)}{g(x)}}, \tag{9}$$

$$\frac{p(\sqrt{x})}{q(\sqrt{x})}, \tag{10}$$

depending on the order in which the composition is taken. We must be careful in selecting a suitable domain, however. The expression (7) for example, is meaningful only for $x \in R^1 - N$, where $N = \{x \mid p(x) < 0\}$.

EXAMPLE 5. The function h, whose values are given by

$$h(x) = \sqrt{4x^2 - 1},$$

is the composition of the function g, whose values are $g(x) = 4x^2 - 1$, and the square-root function f:

$$h = f \circ g.$$

The domain of h is $R^1 - N$, where $N = \{x \mid 4x^2 - 1 < 0\}$. A little inspection reveals that

$$N = \{x \mid 4x^2 - 1 < 0\} = \{x \mid -\tfrac{1}{2} < x < \tfrac{1}{2}\}.$$

Thus the domain of h is $\{x \mid x \geq \tfrac{1}{2}\} \cup \{x \mid x \leq -\tfrac{1}{2}\}$.

EXAMPLE 6. The function h whose values are given by

$$h(x) = 3x^{3/2} + x + \sqrt{x}$$

is the composition of the square-root function f and the function g whose values are given by $g(x) = 3x^3 + x^2 + x$; $h = g \circ f$. The domain of h is $\{x \mid x \geq 0\}$.

Another important function which is frequently encountered is the *absolute-value function f* whose values are given by

$$f(x) = |x|$$

[read, $f(x)$ is the absolute value of x], where $|x|$ is defined by

$$|x| = \begin{cases} x & \text{if } x > 0, \\ 0 & \text{if } x = 0, \\ -x & \text{if } x < 0. \end{cases}$$

For example, some of the elements of the set f are $(2, 2)$, $(-2, 2)$, $(0, 0)$, $(8, 8)$, $(-10, 10)$. The graph of the absolute-value function is given in Fig. 2.33.

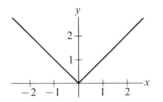

Fig. 2.33. The graph of the absolute-value function $\{(x, |x|) \mid x \in R^1\}$.

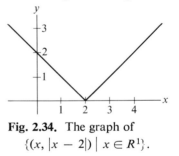

Fig. 2.34. The graph of $\{(x, |x - 2|) \mid x \in R^1\}$.

We may, of course, compose the absolute-value function with other functions. The following example illustrates the idea.

EXAMPLE 7. Let f be the absolute-value function, and let g be the function defined by

$$g(x) = x - 2.$$

Then the composition h of g and f, $f \circ g$, has values

$$h(x) = |g(x)| = |x - 2|.$$

Figure 2.34 shows the graph of h.

EXERCISES

1. Which of the following define polynomial functions? Give the degree of each polynomial function.

   (a) $f(x) = \sqrt{x}$

   (b) $f(x) = x^3 - x$

   (c) $f(x) = 2$

   (d) $f(x) = \sqrt{x^2}$ (Be careful!)

   (e) $f(x) = x - \dfrac{x^2}{6} + \dfrac{x^3}{120}$

   (f) $f(x) = \dfrac{2x}{x-1}$

2. Which of the following define rational functions?

   (a) $f(x) = \dfrac{3}{x}$

   (b) $f(x) = |x - 2|$

   (c) $f(x) = \dfrac{2x}{x-1}$

   (d) $f(x) = \dfrac{\sqrt{2x} + 1}{x^2 + 2x + 3}$

   (e) $f(x) = \dfrac{\sqrt{2x} + 1}{x^2 + 2x + 3}$

   (f) $f(x) = x$

   (g) $f(x) = \dfrac{|x|^2}{3x^2 + 4x}$

   (h) $f(x) = x^{1/3}$

3. Find the domain of each rational function in Exercise 2.

4. (a) Express the function f defined by $f(x) = |x|^2$, $x \in R^1$, as a composition of the absolute-value function and another function.

   (b) Show that the function f in part (a) is

$$f = \{(x, x^2) \mid x \in R^1\}.$$

5. (a) Express the function g defined by $g(x) = |x|^3$, $x \in R^1$, as a composition of the absolute-value function and another function.

   (b) Is the function g the same as the function $\{(x, x^3) \mid x \in R^1\}$? Explain.

   (c) Graph the function g.

6. Graph the functions f whose values are given below.

   (a) $f(x) = x + 1$

   (b) $f(x) = 1 - x^2$

   (c) $f(x) = x^2 + 1$

   (d) $f(x) = 1 - 2x$

   (e) $f(x) = x^3 + 4x^2$

   (f) $f(x) = |1 - x^2|$

   (g) $f(x) = |4x + 3|$

7. Find suitable domains for each of the functions in Eqs. (8), (9), and (10).

8. In the text we stated that every polynomial function is a rational function. Explain why this is true. [*Hint:* You may need to make use of the fact that $\{(x, 1) \mid x \in D\}$ is a polynomial function of degree zero.]

9. Show that the composition of the function $\{(x, x^2) \mid x \in R^1\}$ and the square-root function is the absolute-value function; that is, show that

$$\{(x, \sqrt{x}) \mid x \geq 0\} \circ \{(x, x^2) \mid x \in R^1\} = \{(x, x) \mid |x| \in R^1\}.$$

10. Show that the sum of two polynomial functions is a polynomial function. What can be said about the degree of the sum?

11. Show that if $c \neq 0$ is a real number and p is a polynomial function, then cp is a polynomial function. What is the degree of cp?

12. Show that the product of two polynomial functions is a polynomial function. What is the degree of the product?

13. Show that the sum $r_1 + r_2$ of two rational functions, r_1 and r_2, is a rational function. Express the domain of the sum $r_1 + r_2$ in terms of the domains of r_1 and r_2.

14. Show that the product $r_1 r_2$ and the quotient r_1/r_2 of two rational functions r_1 and r_2 are rational functions. Express the domain of $r_1 r_2$ in terms of the domains of r_1 and r_2. Find an expression for the domain of r_1/r_2.

15. Show that the reciprocal $1/r$ of a rational function r is again a rational function. What is the domain of $1/r$?

16. Show that the composition of two polynomials is a polynomial.

2.8 PICTURES AND GRAPHS

The functions studied in this chapter have their domains and ranges in many different types of sets. In some cases, both their domains and their ranges are in arbitrary sets. In other cases, either the domain or the range (or both!) is in a special set. For example, the range of the functions in Section 2.6 is a subset of R^1, and both the domains and ranges of the functions in Section 2.7 are in R^1.

In this section we shall investigate another special class of functions. The domain of these functions is R^2, or a subset of R^2, and their range is in R^1. The set of ordered pairs

$$\{((x, y), z) \mid (x, y) \in R^2, \ z = x^2 + y^2\}$$

is a function of this type. Let f be a real-valued function whose domain is R^2; we write

$$f = \{((x, y), f(x, y)) \mid (x, y) \in R^2, \ f(x, y) \in R^1\} \tag{1}$$

and

$$f = \{((x, y), z) \mid (x, y) \in R^2, \ z = f(x, y)\}. \tag{2}$$

The function f in Eqs. (1) and (2) is usually pictured as a surface which lies above the domain of the function in the xy-plane. We place a point $(x, y, z) = ((x, y), z)$ at a distance $z = f(x, y)$ above the point (x, y) in the domain of f. The collection of all these points (x, y, z) forms a surface.

In this section we shall study a special class of functions of the type indicated in Eqs. (1) and (2), and we shall describe an important application of these functions.

Definition 2.13. The function

$$p = \{((x, y), p(x, y)) \mid (x, y) \in R^2, \ 0 \leq p(x, y) \leq 1\} \tag{3}$$

will be called a *picture function*. The function q such that

$$q = \{((x, y), q(x, y)) \mid (x, y) \in R^2, \; q(x, y) = 1 - p(x, y)\} \qquad (4)$$

will be called the *negative* of the picture function p. A sheet of paper (considered as the xy-plane R^2) printed so that $p(x, y)$ is a measure of the blackness at the point (x, y) is called the *picture* of the picture function p.

A picture is white at a point (x, y) where $p(x, y) = 0$, black at a point (x, y) where $p(x, y) = 1$, and gray with intensity $p(x, y)$ at a point (x, y) where $0 < p(x, y) < 1$.

A picture can be placed in many different positions in the xy-plane, and it can be drawn to many different scales (the same picture can be printed either large or small). Thus the first problem is to classify pictures—to determine which pictures are the same and which are different.

Definition 2.14. Let p_1 and p_2 be two picture functions [see Eq. (3)]. Let C_1 be the set of points (configuration) in R^2 on which $p_1(x, y) > 0$, and let C_2 be the configuration in R^2 on which $p_2(x, y) > 0$. Then the pictures of the picture functions p_1 and p_2 are the *same* picture if and only if there exists a similarity transformation T such that the following two conditions are satisfied: (a) the configuration C_1 and C_2 are similar, that is, the similarity transformation T transforms C_1 into C_2; (b) if (x, y) in C_1 and (x', y') in C_2 are corresponding points under the similarity transformation T, then $p_1(x, y) = p_2(x', y')$.

If the picture of two picture functions p_1 and p_2 are the same according to this definition, then these pictures show the same scene in the everyday meaning of this statement.

Let f be a function defined on R^2 [see Eq. (1)]. Define a function g on R^2 by

$$\begin{aligned} g(x, y) &= 0 && \text{if } f(x, y) \neq 0, \\ g(x, y) &= 1 && \text{if } f(x, y) = 0. \end{aligned} \qquad (5)$$

Definition 2.15. The function g defined in equations (5) is a special type of picture function which is called a *graph function; g* is the graph function of the equation $f(x, y) = 0$. The picture of the graph function g is the *graph* of the equation $f(x, y) = 0$.

The transmission of pictures by telegraph, radio, and television, and the analysis of pictures by computing machines are important activities in our civilization at the present time. The pictures transmitted or analyzed are usually not infinite in extent; they are, in fact, usually printed on some standard rectangle. A picture function in these applications is thus a function of the following form:

$$p = \{((x, y), p(x, y)) \mid a \leq x \leq b, \; c \leq y \leq d, \; 0 \leq p(x, y) \leq 1\}. \qquad (6)$$

The transmission of pictures and their analysis is greatly simplified by the fact that a recognizable picture of the picture function p can be printed with far less information than that provided by the complete function p in Eq. (6). Choose a standardized set of points $G = \{(x_i, y_j) \mid 1 \leq i \leq m, 1 \leq j \leq n\}$ in the rectangle $\{(x, y) \mid a \leq x \leq b, c \leq y \leq d\}$ which are uniformly spaced in m rows and n columns. Choose also a positive integer r; this constant of the transmission system determines the discrete number of intensities of blackness in the transmitted picture. We shall now define a picture function p_a which approximates the picture function p in such a way that the picture of p_a is recognizable as the picture of p. The function p_a is defined as follows:

$$p_a(x_i, y_j) = \frac{[rp(x_i, y_j)]}{r} \qquad \text{if } (x_i, y_j) \in G,$$

$$p_a(x, y) = \quad 0 \qquad \text{if } (x, y) \notin G. \tag{7}$$

Here $[rp(x_i, y_j)]$ denotes the greatest integer in the number $rp(x_i, y_j)$. Since p is a picture function, it is clear that the only possible values for $p_a(x_i, y_j)$ are

$$0, \frac{1}{r}, \frac{2}{r}, \ldots, \frac{k}{r}, \ldots, \frac{r-1}{r}, \frac{r}{r} = 1. \tag{8}$$

Thus p_a is also a picture function (see Definition 2.13).

The function p_a is completely determined by the integer r and the values of the function p at the mn points in G. The essential information for the definition of p_a is contained in the following matrix:

$$\begin{Vmatrix} p_a(x_1, y_1) & p_a(x_1, y_2) & \cdots & p_a(x_1, y_n) \\ p_a(x_2, y_1) & p_a(x_2, y_2) & \cdots & p_a(x_2, y_n) \\ \vdots & & & \vdots \\ p_a(x_m, y_1) & p_a(x_m, y_2) & \cdots & p_a(x_m, y_n) \end{Vmatrix}. \tag{9}$$

In a standardized transmission system, r is a fixed constant for the system, and the matrix can be simplified still further. Each entry in the matrix is one of the numbers k/r in Eq. (8), and it is sufficient to transmit the numerator k. Thus, if $p_a(x_i, y_j) = k_{ij}/r$ [see Eqs. (7) and (9)], the matrix in Eq. (9) can be replaced by the following simpler matrix of integers:

$$\begin{Vmatrix} k_{11} & k_{12} & \cdots & k_{1n} \\ k_{21} & k_{22} & \cdots & k_{2n} \\ \vdots & & & \vdots \\ k_{m1} & k_{m2} & \cdots & k_{mn} \end{Vmatrix}. \tag{10}$$

The function p_a can be transmitted by transmitting the mn integers k_{ij} in the matrix in Eq. (10). A recognizable picture of the picture function p can be obtained by printing a picture of the picture function p_a. The intensity of blackness is discrete rather than continuous; at each point it is possible to have white ($k = 0$), black ($k = r$), and $r - 1$ shades of gray. The parameters of the transmission system are m, n, and r. These parameters determine the *quality* of the transmitted picture. The quality is *high* if m, n, and r are large, and the quality is *low* if m, n, and r are small.

EXERCISES

1. Define a picture function p_1 in R^2 as follows (see Definition 2.13). On the boundary lines of the nine squares in Fig. 2.35, set $p_1(x, y) = 1$; outside the nine squares, set $p_1(x, y) = 0$; inside each of the nine squares, set $p_1(x, y)$ equal to the value shown. Prove that p_1 is a picture function and draw a picture of p_1.

2. A picture function p_2 is defined as in Exercise 1. Figure 2.36 shows the location of the nine squares and the value of $p_2(x, y)$ for (x, y) in each of them. Prove that p_2 is a picture function and draw a picture of p_2.

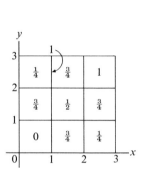

Fig. 2.35. Definition of the picture function p_1 in Exercise 1.

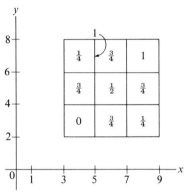

Fig. 2.36. Definition of the picture function p_2 in Exercise 2.

3. Prove that the picture of the picture function p_1 in Exercise 1 and the picture of the picture function p_2 in Exercise 2 are the same picture. Describe in detail how the two pictures differ and why they are classified as the same picture.

4. The pictures of two picture functions are classified as the same picture. Each picture shows a certain triangle. What can you say about the two triangles: are they congruent or similar in the sense of plane geometry?

A knowledge of linear transformations is required in order to work Exercises 5, 7, 8, 9, 11.

5. The elements in each row of the matrix in Eq. (10) can be treated as the coordinates of a point in n-dimensional coordinate space R^n. The approximate picture function p_a can be represented as a configuration C consisting of m points in R^n. In this form the picture function can be transformed and processed in various ways. Explain how the picture function p_a can be enciphered so that only those with instructions for deciphering it can read its picture.

6. Describe a mathematical procedure for deciding when two pictures are nearly the same. Explain how to define a measure of how nearly the same two pictures are.

7. A picture function p_1 is positive on a configuration C_1. A nonsingular transformation T transforms C_1 into a configuration C_2, and it transforms (x, y) in C_1 into (x', y') in C_2. Define a second picture function p_2 so that $p_2(x', y') = p_1(x, y)$ for (x', y') in C_2 and $p_2(x', y') = 0$ elsewhere. Under what circumstances would you say that the picture of p_2 is a distortion of the picture of p_1? Define a *reflection* of a picture. Define a *distorted reflection* of a picture.

8. Draw a picture which is a reflection of the picture of the picture function p_1 in Exercise 1.

9. Draw a picture which is a distortion of the picture of the picture function p_1 in Exercise 1.

10. Construct the graphs of the following equations as pictures of an appropriate picture function.

(a) $x^2 + y^2 = 25$ (b) $\dfrac{x^2}{36} + \dfrac{y^2}{25} = 1$ (c) $\dfrac{x^2}{36} - \dfrac{y^2}{25} = 1$

11. Show that the graph of the equation in Exercise 10(b) is a distortion of the graph of the equation in Exercise 10(a), but that the graph of the equation in part (c) is not a distortion of the graph in part (a).

12. Let q be the negative of the picture function p [see Eq. (4)]. Explain how the pictures of p and q are related. Describe an application of the negative q of a picture function p.

CHAPTER 3

Difference Equations and Growth Functions

3.1 SEQUENCES

In this chapter we shall study certain functions called *sequences* and some of their important applications.

Each of the following expressions describes the same *finite sequence:*

$$\{(0, u(0)),\ (1, u(1)),\ \ldots,\ (k, u(k)),\ \ldots,\ (n, u(n))\}, \tag{1}$$

$$u(0),\ u(1),\ \ldots,\ u(k),\ \ldots,\ u(n), \tag{2}$$

$$u_0,\ u_1,\ \ldots,\ u_k,\ \ldots,\ u_n. \tag{3}$$

Similarly, each of the following expressions describes the same *infinite sequence:*

$$\{(0, u(0)),\ (1, u(1)),\ \ldots,\ (k, u(k)),\ \ldots\}, \tag{4}$$

$$u(0),\ u(1),\ \ldots,\ u(k),\ \ldots, \tag{5}$$

$$u_0,\ u_1,\ \ldots,\ u_k,\ \ldots \tag{6}$$

In each case $u(k)$ or u_k is called a *term* of the sequence; furthermore, $u(0)$ or u_0 is called the *first term* of the sequence, $u(1)$ or u_1 is called the *second term*, etc. In this chapter $u(k)$ and u_k will denote numbers.

If a certain quantity is counted or measured at a succession of times, the numbers obtained form a sequence. Let $u(0)$ represent the value of the count or measurement at time zero, and let $u(1)$, $u(2)$, ... denote the values obtained at succeeding times. This process of counting or measuring the same quantity at a succession of times yields the values $u(0)$, $u(1)$, $u(2)$, ... of a sequence. Since many counts and measurements are made at regular time intervals in business, industry, science, and government, sequences are among the most common mathematical tools used in everyday life.

EXAMPLE 1. On September 1, 1967 a family moved into a new house. On the same day the local public utility read the electric meter and turned on the current. On the first day of each month thereafter, the meter was read again. The successive readings form a sequence $u(0)$, $u(1)$, $u(2)$, . . .

EXAMPLE 2. A certain alumnus of State University contributed $10 to the endowment association of his alma mater on the day of his graduation. In addition, he promised to make a contribution at commencement time each year thereafter and to increase the amount of his contribution by $10 each year. Thus he contributed $10 the year he graduated, $20 at the time of his first annual class reunion, $30 at his second class reunion, etc. His gifts form the sequence 10, 20, 30, . . . Two types of problems arise in connection with this sequence. First, find a formula for the amount of the contribution the alumnus will make at his nth annual class reunion. Second, find the sum of all of his contributions from the time of his graduation up to and including his nth annual class reunion. The solutions of these two problems will be given in the next section of this chapter.

EXAMPLE 3. A microbiologist places 10^4 bacteria in a beaker of nutrient fluid at time zero. From experimentally determined information about the growth of these bacteria, the microbiologist predicts that the number of bacteria in the beaker at the end of 1, 2, 3, 4, 5, and 6 hours will be 1.1×10^4, 1.2×10^4, 1.3×10^4, 1.4×10^4, 1.5×10^4, and 1.6×10^4. The six numbers are the six values of a finite sequence with six terms.

EXAMPLE 4. A certain investor deposits $1000 in a savings bank which pays 4% interest compounded annually. One year later the deposit has increased in value to $1040; two years later, to $1081.60, etc. The successive values of the deposit form the terms of a sequence. The investor desires to have a formula which will give the value of his investment n years after the original deposit. This formula will be derived in Section 3.3.

EXAMPLE 5. A certain investor deposits $1000 each year for five years in a savings bank which pays 4% interest compounded annually. The investor wishes to determine the total value of his five deposits at the time of the fifth deposit.

The solution of this problem requires the solution of two problems as follows. First, it is necessary to find the sequences whose terms are the successive values of each deposit. Second, it is necessary to find the sum of the values of the five deposits at the time of the fifth deposit. We shall show later that the successive values of the first deposit are given by the sequence

$$1000, \ 1000(1.04), \ 1000(1.04)^2, \ 1000(1.04)^3, \ 1000(1.04)^4. \tag{7}$$

Thus the fifth term, $1000(1.04)^4$, of (7) gives the value of the first deposit at the time of the fifth deposit. Similarly, the fourth term of (7) gives the value of the second deposit at the time of the fifth deposit, etc., and the first term of (7) gives the value of the fifth deposit at the time of the fifth deposit. Thus the sum of the five terms in (7) is the value of the five deposits at the time of the fifth deposit. The solution of the second problem described above requires us to find the sum of the terms of the sequence (7). A formula for this sum will be derived in Section 3.3.

The five examples presented above lead to the following observations.

1. Sequences occur in connection with many problems in everyday life.
2. In many cases a sequence is defined by giving the following two types of information: (a) its first term, $u(0)$, or its first two terms, $u(0)$ and $u(1)$, and (b) certain additional information or relations which enable us to calculate later terms of the sequence from earlier ones. The problem is to find a formula for all terms of the sequence from the information given. The later sections of this chapter will treat this problem in a number of special cases.
3. Many problems require us to find the sum of the terms of a sequence.

3.2 ARITHMETIC PROGRESSIONS

Many readers of this book already know about arithmetic progressions. For this reason, the study of progressions forms an appropriate introduction to a new chapter—a chapter which contains new problems and requires new methods for their solution. The study of progressions will provide an opportunity to introduce and fix the notation and terminology in a familiar mathematical setting. Furthermore, progressions will be treated from a new point of view, namely, that of difference equations. The subject of difference equations, their solutions, and their applications forms the central theme of the chapter.

Let a and d be two numbers. The sequence

$$a, \; a + d, \; a + 2d, \; \ldots \tag{1}$$

is called an *arithmetic progression*. Each term in the sequence is formed from the preceding term by adding d, the *common difference*, to it. The sequence (1) is completely described by the following two statements:

$$u(k) = u(k - 1) + d, \quad k = 1, 2, \ldots, \tag{2}$$

$$u(0) = a. \tag{3}$$

Equation (2) is called a *difference equation*. Equation (3) specifies the *initial value* a of the sequence which satisfies the difference equation (2).

The first problem we encounter is to find a formula for the term $u(k)$ in the sequence (1). Equations (2) and (3) can be used to solve this problem. From Eq. (2) with $k = 1$ and from Eq. (3) we have

$$u(1) = u(0) + d, \qquad u(0) = a. \tag{4}$$

From these two equations we have

$$u(1) = a + d. \tag{5}$$

From Eq. (2) with $k = 2$ and from Eq. (5) we have

$$u(2) = u(1) + d, \qquad u(1) = a + d, \tag{6}$$

or

$$u(2) = (a + d) + d = a + 2d. \tag{7}$$

Continuing in this same manner we compute

$$\begin{aligned} u(3) &= a + 3d, \\ u(4) &= a + 4d, \\ u(5) &= a + 5d, \\ &\vdots \end{aligned} \tag{8}$$

We say that (2) is a *recurrence relation* which can be used to compute successively as many terms of the sequence $u(0)$, $u(1)$, $u(2)$, . . . as may be desired.

The values which we have obtained in Eqs. (3), (5), (7), and (8) strongly suggest that

$$u(n) = a + nd, \qquad n = 0, 1, 2, \ldots \tag{9}$$

The formula in (9) can be established by the method known as mathematical induction. First, we have already shown that the formula in Eq. (9) is true for $n = 0, 1$, and 2. Second, assume that Eq. (9) is true for any integer $n = k$. Then $u(k) = a + kd$, and from Eq. (2) (with k replaced by $k + 1$) we have

$$u(k + 1) = u(k) + d, \qquad u(k) = a + kd,$$

or

$$u(k + 1) = (a + kd) + d = a + (k + 1)d.$$

This result is Eq. (9) with n replaced by $k + 1$. We have thus shown that the set of integers for which Eq. (9) is true has the following two properties: (a) the set contains the number 1, (b) if the set contains the integer k, it also contains the integer $k + 1$. The principle of mathematical induction states that any set of integers having these two properties consists of all positive integers. Thus $u(n) = a + nd$ for $n = 0, 1, 2, \ldots$, and Eq. (9) is true as stated. The reader should observe that formula (9) gives, not the nth term, but rather the $(n + 1)$st term of the sequence.

We shall now show that Eq. (9) can be established by solving a system of linear equations. The sequence in Eq. (1) is completely described by Eqs. (2) and (3). Equation (3) gives the value of $u(0)$, but $u(1)$, $u(2)$, ..., $u(n)$ are unknowns. These unknown values satisfy the system of linear equations obtained by writing Eq. (2) for $k = 1, 2, \ldots, n$. These equations are the following:

$$
\begin{aligned}
u(1) &= a + d, \\
-u(1) + u(2) &= d, \\
-u(2) + u(3) &= d, \\
&\quad\quad\quad\quad\quad\quad\quad (10) \\
-u(n-3) + u(n-2) &= d, \\
-u(n-2) + u(n-1) &= d, \\
-u(n-1) + u(n) &= d.
\end{aligned}
$$

The system of linear equations in (10) can be solved easily; add the first equation in (10) to the second equation; then add the second equation to the third equation; and so on. The resulting system is the following:

$$
\begin{aligned}
u(1) &= a + d, \\
u(2) &= a + 2d, \\
u(3) &= a + 3d, \\
u(n-2) &= a + (n-2)d, \\
u(n-1) &= a + (n-1)d, \\
u(n) &= a + nd.
\end{aligned}
$$

From the form of this system, we draw three conclusions: (a) the original system of equations in (10) has a solution, (b) the solution of the system of equations in (10) is unique, and (c) the solution of the system of equations in (10) is

$$
\begin{aligned}
u(1) &= a + d, \\
u(2) &= a + 2d, \\
u(3) &= a + 3d, \\
&\;\;\vdots \\
u(n-2) &= a + (n-2)d, \\
u(n-1) &= a + (n-1)d, \\
u(n) &= a + nd.
\end{aligned}
$$

Thus, $u(n) = a + nd$ for every n as stated in Eq. (9). The results obtained by employing systems of linear equations agree with those obtained by other methods.

We shall now find the sum of the first n terms of the arithmetic progression (1). We shall show that

$$a + (a + d) + (a + 2d) + \cdots + [a + (n - 1)d] = \frac{n}{2}[2a + (n - 1)d]. \qquad (11)$$

Let S denote the sum on the left in (11). Then, since addition is commutative, we can write S in the following two ways:

$$S = \quad a \quad + \quad (a + d) \quad + \cdots + [a + (n - 1)d],$$
$$S = [a + (n - 1)d] + [a + (n - 2)d] + \cdots + \quad a.$$

Add these two equations; the result is

$$2S = [2a + (n - 1)d] + [2a + (n - 1)d] + \cdots + [2a + (n - 1)d]$$
$$= n[2a + (n - 1)d].$$

Thus

$$S = \frac{n}{2}[2a + (n - 1)d],$$

and the proof of the formula in (11) is complete.

EXAMPLE 1. Find the sum of the first n integers.
The first n integers are

$$1, 2, 3, \ldots, k, \ldots, (n - 1), n. \qquad (12)$$

These integers form an arithmetic progression for which $a = 1$ and $d = 1$. Then by the formula in (11) we have

$$1 + 2 + 3 + \cdots + k + \cdots + n =$$

$$\frac{n}{2}[2 + (n - 1)] = \frac{n(n + 1)}{2}. \qquad (13)$$

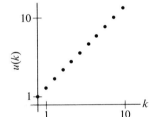

Fig. 3.1. Graph of the arithmetic progression for which $u(k) = k + 1$, $k = 0, 1, 2, \ldots, 10$.

Figure 3.1 illustrates the fact that the graph of an arithmetic progression is a set of points which lie on a straight line.

EXAMPLE 2. Find the sum of the first n odd integers.
The first n odd integers are

$$1, 3, 5, \ldots, (2k + 1), \ldots, (2n - 1). \qquad (14)$$

They form an arithmetic progression in which $a = 1$ and $d = 2$. Then by the formula in (11) we have

$$1 + 3 + 5 + \cdots + (2k + 1) + \cdots + (2n - 1) = \frac{n}{2}[2 + 2(n - 1)] = n^2. \qquad (15)$$

Figure 3.2 shows that the graph of the
arithmetic progression (14) consists of
points on a straight line, but the straight
line is steeper than the line on which the
graph of the arithmetic progression (12)
lies (see Fig. 3.1).

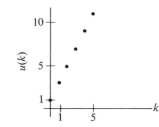

Fig. 3.2. Graph of the arithmetic progression for which $u(k) = 2k + 1$, $k = 0$, $1, 2, \ldots, 5$.

EXAMPLE 3. Consider again the alumnus in Example 2 in Section 3.1 who contributes to the endowment association of his alma mater at commencement each
year. His gifts form an arithmetic progression for which $a = 10$ and $d = 10$.
The gift he makes at his nth class reunion is the term $u(n)$ in the arithmetic progression $u(0), u(1), \ldots, u(n)$. By formula (9),

$$u(n) = 10 + n(10) = 10(n + 1).$$

Thus the alumnus contributes $10(n + 1)$ dollars at his nth annual class reunion.
His contribution at this class reunion is the $(n + 1)$st term of the arithmetic
progression with $a = 10$ and $d = 10$. By formula (11) the sum of the first $(n + 1)$
terms is

$$\frac{(n + 1)}{2}[20 + n(10)] = (n + 1)(5n + 10).$$

Thus his gifts up to and including the 25th annual class reunion amount to
$(25 + 1)(5 \cdot 25 + 10)$, or 3510 dollars.

EXAMPLE 4. The terms between any two terms of an arithmetic progression
are called *arithmetic means* between these two terms.   Find the six arithmetic
means between 5 and 26.

　　To solve this problem, we observe that we have an arithmetic progression
$u(0), u(1), \ldots, u(7)$. Since there are six means, the total number of terms is 8.
We know that $a = 5$; the common difference d is not known. By formula (9),
however, $u(7) = a + 7d = 5 + 7d$, and it is given that $u(7) = 26$.   Then
$5 + 7d = 26$ and $d = 3$. The six required arithmetic means are 8, 11, 14, 17,
20, and 23.

EXAMPLE 5. A woman deposits P dollars in a savings bank which promises
to pay simple interest at the rate of $100i\%$ annually. The interest on the deposit
for the first year is iP dollars, and the total value of the investment is $P + iP$ dollars
at the end of the first year. Since the bank pays simple interest, the interest for
the second year is also iP dollars, and the total value of the investment at the
end of the second year is $(P + iP) + iP$, or $P + 2iP$ dollars. The succession
of values of the investment forms the arithmetic progression

$$P, P + iP, P + 2iP, P + 3iP, \ldots$$

The value of the investment k years after the deposit is $P + kiP$ dollars. Figure 3.3 shows the growth in value of $100 invested at 4% simple interest. We say that the investment grows *linearly* since the points which represent its values lie on a straight line.

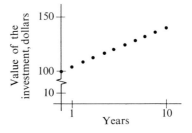

Fig. 3.3. Graph of the value of $100 invested at 4% simple interest.

EXERCISES

1. Find the tenth term and the sum of the first ten terms of each of the following arithmetic progressions.
   (a) 2, 4, 6, ...   (b) −5, −4, −3, ...   (c) 9, 8, 7, ...
   (d) 5, 10, 15, ...   (e) 25, 23, 21, ...   (f) 0, −3, −6, ...

2. For each of the sequences in Exercise 1, give the difference equation for the sequence and the initial value of the sequence [see Eqs. (2) and (3)].

3. Draw the graph of each of the sequences in Exercise 1. Comment on the significance of $u(0)$ and d for each of the graphs.

4. If a clock strikes only the hours, how many times does it strike in a day?

5. An engineer accepts a position with an aircraft firm. His starting salary is $9500, and he is promised a raise of $300 at the end of each six-month period. What is his annual salary at the end of ten years, and what are his total earnings during his first ten years with the firm?

6. Find the 5 arithmetic means between 17 and −1.

7. Find the 7 arithmetic means between −5 and 27.

8. Find the 125 arithmetic means between 43 and 421. Give a formula for these 125 arithmetic means.

9. Find one arithmetic mean between 16 and 48. The one arithmetic mean is called *the arithmetic mean* of the two numbers.

10. Show that the arithmetic mean of two numbers a and b is $(a + b)/2$.

11. Let $u(0), u(1), u(2), \ldots$ be an arithmetic progression with initial value a and common difference d. If c is any number, show that $cu(0), cu(1), cu(2), \ldots$ is also an arithmetic progression. Then find the initial value and common difference of this arithmetic progression.

12. Let $u_1(0), u_1(1), u_1(2), \ldots$ be an arithmetic progression with initial value a_1 and common difference d_1, and let $u_2(0), u_2(1), u_2(2), \ldots$ be an arithmetic progression with initial value a_2 and common difference d_2. Show that the sequence $u_1(0) + u_2(0), u_1(1) + u_2(1), u_1(2) + u_2(2), \ldots$ is also an arithmetic progression, and find its initial value and common difference. The new sequence is called the *sum* of the two given sequences. Write the difference equation for each of the given arithmetic progressions, and find the difference equation for the sum of these progressions.

13. Show that the set of all arithmetic progressions forms a group under the operation of addition described in Exercise 12. What is the identity element of this group? What is the inverse element of a given element of the group?

14. How many numbers between 250 and 500 are exactly divisible by 7?

15. A man bought a house at the beginning of 1950 for $20,000. If it increased in value $800 each year, how much was it worth at the end of 1958? Draw a graph to show the values of the house at the beginning of 1950 and at the end of each year thereafter through 1958.

16. A student bought a Series E bond for $750 and ten years later redeemed it for $1000. If the income on the investment of $750 is computed at simple interest, find the annual rate of interest.

17. A man bought an automobile for $4000. The depreciation in value of the automobile amounted to 16% of its original value during the first year, 14.5% of its original value during the second year, 13% of its original value during the third year, etc. Find the value of the automobile at the end of ten years.

3.3 GEOMETRIC PROGRESSIONS

Let a and r be two numbers. The sequence

$$a, \; ar, \; ar^2, \; \ldots \tag{1}$$

is called a *geometric progression*. Each term after the first one is formed by multiplying the preceding term by r. The number r is called the *common ratio*. The sequence (1) is completely described by the following two statements:

$$u(k) = ru(k - 1), \quad k = 1, 2, \ldots, \tag{2}$$

$$u(0) = a. \tag{3}$$

Equation (2) is the difference equation satisfied by the geometric progression (1), and Eq. (3) specifies the initial value of the sequence which satisfies the difference equation (2).

The first problem here is to find a formula for the term $u(k)$ in the sequence (1). Equations (2) and (3) can be used to solve this problem. From Eq. (2) with $k = 1$ and from Eq. (3) we have

$$u(1) = ru(0), \quad u(0) = a. \tag{4}$$

From these two equations we obtain

$$u(1) = ar. \tag{5}$$

From Eq. (2) with $k = 2$ and from Eq. (5) we have

$$u(2) = ru(1), \quad u(1) = ar, \tag{6}$$

or
$$u(2) = ar^2. \tag{7}$$

Continuing in this manner, we compute

$$u(3) = ar^3,$$
$$u(4) = ar^4, \tag{8}$$
$$u(5) = ar^5,$$
$$\vdots$$

We have used Eq. (2) as a recurrence relation to compute the successive terms of the geometric progression determined by Eqs. (2) and (3).

The values which we have obtained in Eqs. (3), (5), and (8) strongly suggest that

$$u(n) = ar^n, \qquad n = 0, 1, 2, \ldots \tag{9}$$

The formula (9) can be established by mathematical induction. First, we have already shown that the formula in Eq. (9) is true for $n = 0$, 1, and 2. Second, we assume that Eq. (9) is true for any integer $n = k$. Then $u(k) = ar^k$, and from Eq. (2) (with k replaced by $k + 1$) we have

$$u(k + 1) = ru(k), \qquad u(k) = ar^k,$$

or

$$u(k + 1) = r(ar^k) = ar^{k+1}.$$

This result is Eq. (9) with n replaced by $k + 1$. We have thus shown that the set of integers for which Eq. (9) is true has the following two properties: (a) the set contains the number 1; and (b) if the set contains the integer k, it also contains the integer $k + 1$. The principle of mathematical induction states that any set of integers with these two properties consists of all positive integers. Thus $u(n) = ar^n$ for $n = 0, 1, 2, \ldots$, and Eq. (9) is true as stated. The reader should observe once more that formula (9) gives, not the nth term, but rather the $(n + 1)$st term of the sequence.

We shall now show that Eq. (9) can be established by solving a system of linear equations. The sequence in Eq. (1) is completely described by Eqs. (2) and (3). Equation (3) gives the value of $u(0)$, but $u(1), u(2), \ldots, u(n)$ are unknowns. These unknown values satisfy the system of linear equations obtained by writing Eq. (2) for $k = 1, 2, \ldots, n$. These equations are the following:

$$
\begin{aligned}
u(1) &&&&= ar, \\
-ru(1) + u(2) &&&&= 0, \\
-ru(2) + u(3) &&&&= 0, \\
&\rule{8cm}{0.4pt} && \tag{10} \\
-ru(n-3) + u(n-2) &&&&= 0, \\
-ru(n-2) + u(n-1) &&&&= 0, \\
-ru(n-1) + u(n) &&&&= 0.
\end{aligned}
$$

The system of equations in (10) can be solved easily. Multiply the first equation in (10) by r and add it to the second equation; then multiply the second equation by r and add it to the third equation; etc. The resulting system is the following:

$$
\begin{aligned}
u(1) &= ar, \\
u(2) &= ar^2, \\
u(3) &= ar^3, \\
&\;\;\vdots \\
u(n-2) &= ar^{n-2}, \\
u(n-1) &= ar^{n-1}, \\
u(n) &= ar^n.
\end{aligned}
$$

From the form of this system, we draw three conclusions: (a) the original system of equations in (10) has a solution, (b) the solution of the system of equations in (10) is unique, and (c) the solution of the system of equations in (10) is

$$
\begin{aligned}
u(1) &= ar, \\
u(2) &= ar^2, \\
u(3) &= ar^3, \\
&\;\vdots \\
u(n-2) &= ar^{n-2}, \\
u(n-1) &= ar^{n-1}, \\
u(n) &= ar^n.
\end{aligned}
$$

Thus $u(n) = ar^n$ for $n = 0, 1, 2, \ldots$ as stated in Eq. (9). The results obtained by employing systems of linear equations agree with those obtained by other methods.

Next, let $u(0)$, $u(1)$, $\ldots$, $u(k)$, $\ldots$ denote once more the geometric progression (1) which is determined by Eqs. (2) and (3). We shall now find the sum of the first n terms of the geometric progression (1). We shall show that

$$
u(0) + u(1) + \cdots + u(n-1) = \frac{u(0) - u(n)}{1-r}, \qquad r \neq 1, \tag{11}
$$

or

$$
a + ar + ar^2 + \cdots + ar^{n-1} = \frac{a - ar^n}{1-r}, \qquad r \neq 1. \tag{12}
$$

Subtract $u(k-1)$ from each side of Eq. (2); the result is $u(k) - u(k-1) = (r-1)u(k-1)$. Write this equation for $k = 1, 2, \ldots, n$ as follows:

$$
\begin{aligned}
u(n) - u(n-1) &= (r-1)u(n-1), \\
u(n-1) - u(n-2) &= (r-1)u(n-2), \\
u(n-2) - u(n-3) &= (r-1)u(n-3), \\
&\;\vdots \\
u(2) - u(1) &= (r-1)u(1), \\
u(1) - u(0) &= (r-1)u(0).
\end{aligned}
$$

Add these equations. All terms on the left cancel except $u(n)$ and $-u(0)$, and the result is

$$u(n) - u(0) = (r - 1)[u(0) + u(1) + \cdots + u(n - 2) + u(n - 1)].$$

If $r \neq 1$, Eq. (11) follows from this equation by dividing both sides by $r - 1$. Equation (12) is a restatement of (11), and the proof of (12) is complete. If $r = 1$, the sequence is a special geometric progression which is also an arithmetic progression with $d = 0$; it can be treated by the methods developed in Section 3.2.

EXAMPLE 1. Study the geometric progression with $a = 1$ and $r = -1$. Formula (9) shows that the terms of this progression are $1, -1, 1, -1, 1, \ldots$. Formula (12) shows that the sum of an even number of terms is 0, and that the sum of an odd number of terms is 1. Figure 3.4 contains a graph of this progression. Since the terms are alternately positive and negative, we say the progression is an *alternating* progression.

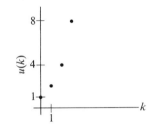

Fig. 3.4. Graph of the geometric progression $u(k) = (-1)^k$.

Fig. 3.5. Graph of the geometric progression $u(k) = 2^k$.

EXAMPLE 2. Study the geometric progression which has $a = 1$ and $r = 2$. Formula (9) shows that the terms of this progression are

$$1, 2, 2^2, 2^3, \ldots, \tag{13}$$

and formula (12) shows that the sum of the first n terms is $2^n - 1$. Figure 3.5 contains a graph of this progression.

The reader should compare the geometric progression in this example with the arithmetic progression in Example 2 in Section 3.2. The arithmetic progression has $a = 1$ and $d = 2$; the geometric progression has $a = 1$ and $r = 2$. The arithmetic progression grows *linearly*, but the geometric progression grows *exponentially*. Comparing the graphs in Figs. 3.2 and 3.5 we see that the points on the graph of the arithmetic progression lie on a straight line, but the points on the graph of the geometric progression lie on an exponential curve which rises much more rapidly than the straight line.

EXAMPLE 3. A woman deposits P dollars in a bank which promises to pay compound interest at the rate of $100i\%$ annually. The interest on the deposit for the first year is iP dollars, and the total value of the investment at the end of the first year is $P + iP$, or $P(1 + i)$, dollars. During the second year interest is paid on $P(1 + i)$ dollars, and the interest for the second year is $P(1 + i)i$ dollars. Then the value of the investment at the end of the second year is $P(1 + i) + P(1 + i)i$, or $P(1 + i)^2$, dollars. Continuing in this manner, we see that the successive values of the deposit are given by the terms of the geometric progression,

$$P, P(1 + i), P(1 + i)^2, \ldots, P(1 + i)^k, \ldots$$

The value of the investment k years after the deposit is $P(1 + i)^k$. Tables are available which give the value of $(1 + i)^k$ for extensive ranges of values of i and k. Figure 3.6 shows the values, at two year intervals, of \$100 invested at 4% simple interest and at 4% interest compounded annually. The values of the geometric progression (compound interest) grow much more rapidly than those of the corresponding arithmetic progression (simple interest).

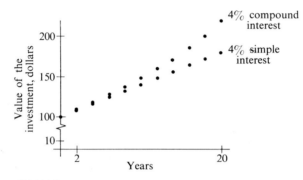

Fig. 3.6. Values of \$100 invested at 4% simple interest and at 4% interest compounded annually.

EXAMPLE 4. An investor deposits \$100 each year for five years in a savings bank which pays 4% interest compounded annually. Find the sum of the values of the five deposits at the time of the fifth deposit (see Example 5 in Section 3.1).

Example 3 has shown that the successive values of the first deposit are those given in the top row of Fig. 3.7; the other rows give the values of the other four deposits. The table shows that the total value of the five deposits at the time of the fifth deposit is the sum of the entries in the last column of Fig. 3.7. The entries in the last column form a geometric progression of five terms with $a = 100$ and $r = 1.04$. By formula (12) the sum of the terms of this progression is

$$\frac{100 - 100(1.04)^5}{1 - (1.04)} = 100 \frac{(1.04)^5 - 1}{0.04}.$$

Evaluation of the last expression shows that the value of the five deposits at the time of the fifth deposit is \$541.63.

A succession of n equal and equally spaced payments is called an *annuity*. If each payment is P, and if the compound interest rate is $100i\%$ per time period,

First deposit	100	100(1.04)	100(1.04)²	100(1.04)³	100(1.04)⁴
Second deposit		100	100(1.04)	100(1.04)²	100(1.04)³
Third deposit			100	100(1.04)	100(1.04)²
Fourth deposit				100	100(1.04)
Fifth deposit					100

Fig. 3.7. Values of the five deposits in Example 4.

then the value of the annuity at the time of the last payment is

$$P \frac{(1 + i)^n - 1}{i}.$$

Annuity tables give the value of $[(1 + i)^n - 1]/i$ for extensive ranges of values of n and i.

A geometric progression $a, ar, ar^2, \ldots$ with $|r| < 1$ has important special properties. We have shown in Eq. (12) that

$$a + ar + ar^2 + \cdots + ar^{n-1} = \frac{a - ar^n}{1 - r}, \qquad r \neq 1. \tag{14}$$

If $|r| < 1$, then $\lim_{n \to \infty} r^n = 0$, and the expression on the right-hand side in (14) approaches a limit as n increases without limit. We write

$$a + ar + ar^2 + \cdots + ar^{n-1} + \cdots = \lim_{n \to \infty} \frac{a - ar^n}{1 - r} = \frac{a}{1 - r}, \qquad |r| < 1. \tag{15}$$

The expression on the left-hand side in (15) is called an *infinite series* or, more precisely, an *infinite geometric* series. The infinite geometric series *converges*, or has a *sum*, if and only if the limit on the right in (15) exists, and the *sum* is the value of this limit when it exists. The infinite geometric series converges and has a sum if and only if $|r| < 1$; furthermore, the value of the sum is $a/(1 - r)$ when it exists. The infinite geometric series has important applications as illustrated in the next examples.

EXAMPLE 5. Physicists investigate the decay of radioactive substances. Experiments have shown, for example, that a certain fraction r, $0 < r < 1$, of a radioactive substance decays each hour. The value of r depends on the substance. If a grams of the substance are given at time $t = 0$, then the amount which decays between $t = 0$ and $t = 1$ is ar, and the amount which remains at $t = 1$ is $a - ar$, or $a(1 - r)$. The amount which decays between $t = 1$ and $t = 2$ is $a(1 - r)r$, and the amount which remains at $t = 2$ is $a(1 - r) - a(1 - r)r = a(1 - r)^2$. Continuing in this manner, we obtain the following two geometric progressions:

$$a, a(1 - r), a(1 - r)^2, \ldots, a(1 - r)^n, \ldots, \tag{16}$$

$$ar, ar(1 - r), ar(1 - r)^2, \ldots, ar(1 - r)^{n-1}, \ldots \tag{17}$$

The term $a(1 - r)^n$ in (16) is the amount of the radioactive substance which remains at time $t = n$, and the term $ar(1 - r)^{n-1}$ in (17) is the amount of the radioactive substance which decays between $t = n - 1$ and $t = n$. Since

$$\lim_{n \to \infty} a(1 - r)^n = 0, \qquad 0 < r < 1, \tag{18}$$

the amount of the substance which remains approaches zero as n increases indefinitely. We should be able to check this statement by determining how much of the substance has decayed. The total amount which has decayed up to time $t = n$ is

$$ar + ar(1 - r) + \cdots + ar(1 - r)^{n-1} = \frac{ar - ar(1 - r)^n}{1 - (1 - r)} = a[1 - (1 - r)^n]. \tag{19}$$

The total amount which decays as the time increases without limit is

$$ar + ar(1 - r) + \cdots + ar(1 - r)^{n-1} + \cdots = \lim_{n \to \infty} a[1 - (1 - r)^n] = a. \tag{20}$$

Equation (18) shows that, as time increases, the amount of the radioactive substance which remains approaches zero. Equation (20) shows that the total amount of the substance which decays approaches a, the amount of the substance with which we started. These two statements agree, as they should.

Consider a specific example in which $a = 16$ and $r = \frac{1}{2}$. The progression (16) becomes

$$16, \ 16(\tfrac{1}{2}), \ 16(\tfrac{1}{2})^2, \ \ldots, \ 16(\tfrac{1}{2})^n, \ \ldots, \tag{21}$$

and $16(\tfrac{1}{2})^n$ is the amount of the substance which remains at time $t = n$. The graph of the geometric progression (21) in Fig. 3.8 shows an example of *exponential decay*. Equation (19) shows that the total amount of the substance which has decayed up to time $t = n$ is

$$16[1 - (\tfrac{1}{2})^n]. \tag{22}$$

Figure 3.9 contains a graph of the function whose values are given by (22).

The value of the time n at which the amount $a(1 - r)^n$ of the substance which remains is $a/2$ is called the *half-life* of the substance. Equation (19) shows that, at this same time, one-half the substance has decayed. The half-life of the radioactive substance which has $r = \frac{1}{2}$ is one hour [see (21) and Figs. 3.8 and 3.9].

EXAMPLE 6. A chemistry student washes a precipitate on a filter paper to remove a certain water-soluble impurity. He fills the filter paper with distilled water and allows one-fourth of the water to run through, carrying one-fourth of the impurity with it. He then refills the filter paper with distilled water and allows one-fourth to run through again. He repeats this process indefinitely. Let $u(0) = a$, the amount of the impurity in the precipitate initially. Compute the amount $u(k)$ of the impurity which remains in the precipitate after one-fourth of the water has run through k times.

Since $u(k) = \frac{3}{4}u(k-1)$ and $u(0) = a$, we have $u(k) = (\frac{3}{4})^k a$. When one-fourth of the filter paper full of water has run through four times (making one filter paper full), there remains in the filter paper $(\frac{3}{4})^4 a = \frac{81}{256}a$, or almost one-third, of the original impurity. If all the water had been allowed to run through the filter paper once, it would (theoretically) have carried all the impurity with it.

This example explains why the chemistry laboratory manual specifies that all the water should be allowed to run through the filter paper before more is added.

EXAMPLE 7. A bacteriologist wants to count the number N of bacteria in a certain solution S_0. He proceeds as follows. He takes one-tenth of the solution S_0 and dilutes it to form a new solution S_1; he takes one-tenth of S_1 and dilutes it to form a new solution S_2; etc. By a laboratory counting procedure, the bacteriologist finds that the solution S_4 contains ten bacteria. Find N, the number of bacteria in S_0.

Let $u(0) = N$, and let $u(k)$ be the number of bacteria in the solution S_k. Then $u(k) = \frac{1}{10}u(k-1)$, and $u(k) = (\frac{1}{10})^k N$. Since $u(4) = 10$, we find that $(\frac{1}{10})^4 N = 10$, or $N = 10^5 = 100,000$.

This example illustrates a practical method employed by bacteriologists for counting the number of bacteria in a solution when the number is large.

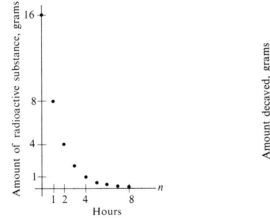

Fig. 3.8. Graph of $16(\frac{1}{2})^n$, the amount of a certain radioactive substance which remains at time $t = n$.

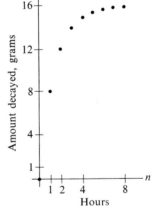

Fig. 3.9. Graph of $16[1 - (\frac{1}{2})^n]$, the total amount of the radioactive substance in Fig. 3.8 which has decayed up to time $t = n$.

EXERCISES

1. Find the tenth term and the sum of the first ten terms of each of the following geometric progressions.
   (a) 2, 6, 18, ...   (b) $3, 3^2, 3^3, \ldots$
   (c) $1, -\frac{1}{2}, \frac{1}{4}, \ldots$ (d) 2, -2, 2, ...
   (e) 2, -6, 18, ...   (f) $1, \frac{2}{3}, \frac{4}{9}, \ldots$

2. Draw a graph of each of the progressions in Exercise 1.

3. Find the sixth term and the sum of the first six terms for the geometric progressions determined by each of the following difference equations and initial conditions:

(a) $u(k) = 2u(k - 1)$, $u(0) = 1$;   (b) $u(k) = -2u(k - 1)$, $u(0) = 1$;

(c) $u(k) = 2u(k - 1)$, $u(0) = 3$;   (d) $u(k) = -2u(k - 1)$, $u(0) = 3$;

(e) $u(k) = -2u(k - 1)$, $u(0) = -3$;   (f) $u(k) = \dfrac{u(k - 1)}{2}$, $u(0) = 4$;

(g) $u(k) = -\dfrac{u(k - 1)}{2}$, $u(0) = 4$.

4. Draw the graph of each of the geometric progressions determined by the difference equations and initial conditions in Exercise 3.

5. Find the sum of each of the following infinite geometric series if the sum exists. Solve each problem by finding the sum of the first n terms of the series and then finding the limit (if it exists) as the number of terms increases without limit.

(a) $1 + \frac{1}{2} + \frac{1}{4} + \cdots$

(b) $\frac{2}{3} + \frac{4}{9} + \frac{8}{27} + \cdots$

(c) $\dfrac{3}{10} + \dfrac{3}{10^2} + \dfrac{3}{10^3} + \cdots$

(d) $1 + \frac{3}{2} + \frac{9}{4} + \cdots$

(e) $2 + 2^2 + 2^3 + \cdots$

(f) $9 + \dfrac{9}{10} + \dfrac{9}{10^2} + \cdots$

6. The infinite decimal 0.777 . . . is merely another way of writing the infinite geometric series

$$\frac{7}{10} + \frac{7}{10^2} + \frac{7}{10^3} + \cdots$$

Find the value of the infinite decimal 0.777 . . .

7. The terms between any two terms of a geometric progression are called the *geometric means* between these two terms. Find five geometric means between 3 and 192.

8. Find one geometric mean between 4 and 16. The single geometric mean between two numbers is called *the geometric mean* of the numbers.

9. If a and b are any two positive numbers, show that their geometric mean is $\sqrt{ab}$.

10. Let a and b be any two positive numbers such that $a \neq b$. Show that the arithmetic mean of a and b is greater than their geometric mean. (See Exercise 9 above and Exercise 10 in Section 3.2.)

11. One-tenth of a certain radioactive substance disintegrates each hour. Assume that ten milligrams of the substance are present at time $t = 0$. Compute the amount of the substance which remains at times $t = 1, 2, \ldots, 10$. Compute also the total amount of the substance which has disintegrated from time $t = 0$ to $t = 1, 2, \ldots, 10$. Draw graphs to show the amount of the substance which remains and the total amount which has disintegrated. Find approximately the half-life of the substance.

12. A man buys an automobile for $4000. The value of the automobile depreciates 10% each year. Compute the value of the automobile at the end of $1, 2, \ldots, 10$ years.

Compute also the total loss in value of the automobile at the end of 1, 2, . . . , 10 years. Find approximately how old the automobile is when its value is one half of the original purchase price.

13. At the beginning of each year for ten years an investor deposits $500 in a savings bank which pays 5% interest compounded annually. Prepare a table similar to the one in Fig. 3.7 to show the value of each payment at the beginning of each succeeding year. Find a formula for the total value of all payments at the beginning of year $k(k = 1, 2, . . . , 10)$. Draw a graph of the function whose value is given by the formula.

14. A certain city had a population of 10,000 in 1950, and the population has increased by 5% each year since that time. Find a geometric progression whose terms give the population of the city in successive years beginning with 1950. Draw a graph which shows the population of the city in successive years. Does the population of the city "grow exponentially"? Explain the significance of this term.

15. A bacteriologist desires to count the number N of bacteria in a certain solution S_0. He proceeds as follows. He takes one-fifth of the solution S_0 and dilutes it to form a new solution S_1; he takes one-fifth of S_1 and dilutes it to form a new solution S_2; etc. The bacteriologist finds, by a laboratory counting procedure, that the solution S_6 contains eight bacteria. Find N, the number of bacteria in S_0.

3.4 DIFFERENCE EQUATIONS AND GROWTH FUNCTIONS

A hardware store keeps an inventory of its light bulbs by counting the number $u(k)$ of bulbs in stock at time $t = k$, $k = 0, 1, 2, . . .$ The store checks its inventory count against shipments received and sales as follows. Let $v(k - 1)$ and $w(k - 1)$ denote respectively the number of incoming bulbs received and the number sold between $t = k - 1$ and $t = k$. Then

$$u(k) = u(k - 1) + v(k - 1) - w(k - 1). \tag{1}$$

This equation will be called the *inventory equation*. If $u(0)$ and the sequences $v(0), v(1), v(2), . . .$ and $w(0), w(1), w(2), . . .$ are given, the inventory counts $u(1), u(2), u(3), . . .$ can be calculated by using Eq. (1).

The inventory equation is the basic equation for the study of growth and decay phenomena. The difference equations for many important growth and decay functions can be obtained by specifying the values of, or the form of, the functions $v(k - 1)$ and $w(k - 1)$ in Eq. (1).

If a sum of money is invested at $100i\%$ simple interest, then

$$u(0) = P, \quad v(k - 1) = iP, \quad w(k - 1) = 0, \quad k = 1, 2, . . . \tag{2}$$

The inventory equation (1) shows that the growth of the investment is determined by

$$u(k) = u(k - 1) + iP, \quad k = 1, 2, . . . , \tag{3}$$

$$u(0) = P. \tag{4}$$

Equation (3) may be called the *simple interest equation;* its solution is an arithmetic progression (see Section 3.2).

   If a sum of money is invested at $100i\%$ compound interest, then

$$u(0) = P, \quad v(k - 1) = iu(k - 1), \quad w(k - 1) = 0, \quad k = 1, 2, \ldots \quad (5)$$

The inventory equation (1) shows that the growth of the investment is determined by

$$u(k) = (1 + i)u(k - 1), \quad k = 1, 2, \ldots, \quad (6)$$

$$u(0) = P. \quad (7)$$

Equation (6) may be called the *compound interest equation;* its solution is a geometric progression (see Section 3.3) in which the common ratio is greater than one.

   If a quantity a of radioactive material decays at the rate of $100i\%$ per time
period, then

$$u(0) = a, \quad v(k - 1) = 0, \quad w(k - 1) = iu(k - 1), \quad k = 1, 2, \ldots \quad (8)$$

The inventory equation (1) shows that the decay of the radioactive substance
is determined by

$$u(k) = (1 - i)u(k - 1), \quad k = 1, 2, \ldots, \quad (9)$$

$$u(0) = a. \quad (10)$$

Equation (9) may be called the *exponential decay equation;* its solution is a geometric progression (see Section 3.3) in which the common ratio is less than one.

   Consider an annuity with annual payments P which draw compound interest
at the rate of $100i\%$ annually. Then

$$u(0) = P, \quad v(k - 1) = iu(k - 1) + P, \quad w(k - 1) = 0, \quad k = 1, 2, \ldots \quad (11)$$

The inventory equation (1) shows that the growth of the annuity is determined by

$$u(k) = (1 + i)u(k - 1) + P, \quad k = 1, 2, \ldots, \quad (12)$$

$$u(0) = P. \quad (13)$$

Equation (12) may be called the *annuity equation.*

   If a sum of money P is invested at $100i\%$ compound interest, and if a sum W
is withdrawn at the end of each time period, then

$$u(0) = P, \quad v(k - 1) = iu(k - 1), \quad w(k - 1) = W, \quad k = 1, 2, \ldots \quad (14)$$

The inventory equation (1) shows that the successive values of the investment are
determined by

$$u(k) = (1 + i)u(k - 1) - W, \quad k = 1, 2, \ldots, \quad (15)$$

$$u(0) = P. \quad (16)$$

Equation (15) may be called the *harvest equation.*

Each of the growth and decay problems described above has led to a difference equation with initial condition of the form

$$u(k) = ru(k-1) + d, \quad k = 1, 2, \ldots, \tag{17}$$

$$u(0) = a. \tag{18}$$

In these equations, r, d, and a are given constants. This system can be solved by the methods which have been used for special cases of the system in Sections 3.2 and 3.3.

In many problems it is important to determine the behavior of $u(n)$ as n increases. For example, does $u(n)$ increase without limit, decrease to zero, oscillate, or what? The following example indicates the importance for the applications of the answer to this question.

EXAMPLE 1. Find the solution of Eq. (15) which has the initial value (16), and determine the behavior of $u(n)$ as n increases.

The methods used in Sections 3.2 and 3.3 show that the solution of Eq. (15) which has the initial value (16) is

$$u(n) = P(1 + i)^n - W[1 + (1 + i) + \cdots + (1 + i)^{n-1}]$$

$$= P(1 + i)^n - W\frac{1 - (1 + i)^n}{1 - (1 + i)}$$

$$= \frac{(iP - W)(1 + i)^n + W}{i}. \tag{19}$$

There are three cases as follows.

(a) $iP > W$. In this case, $u(n)$ increases exponentially as n increases.

(b) $iP = W$. In this case, $u(n) = P$ for $n = 0, 1, 2, \ldots$

(c) $iP < W$. In this case, $u(n)$ decreases exponentially and soon becomes negative as n increases.

These results are intuitively correct. If $W = iP$, then the investor withdraws the interest iP each time, and the value $u(n)$ of the investment has the constant value P. If the investor withdraws more than the interest iP each time, the value of the investment decreases and the expression in Eq. (19) eventually is negative. If $u(n) \geq 0$ but $u(n + 1) < 0$, then the difference equation

$$u(k) = (1 + i)u(k-1) - W$$

is not a meaningful description of the investment problem for $k > n$, and formula (19) does not apply for $k > n$. If the investor withdraws less than the interest, the value of the investment increases exponentially.

EXAMPLE 2. As a final example, consider a growth problem for which

$$v(k-1) = iu(k-1), \quad w(k-1) = u(k-2), \quad k = 2, 3, \ldots, \tag{20}$$

$$u(0) = a, \quad u(1) = b. \tag{21}$$

The inventory equation (1) shows that

$$u(k) = (1 + i)u(k - 1) - u(k - 2), \tag{22}$$

$$u(0) = a, \quad u(1) = b. \tag{23}$$

Equation (22) is called a *second-order difference equation*. The first two values, $u(0)$ and $u(1)$, of the solution can be chosen arbitrarily as indicated in Eq. (23), and Eq. (22) is a recurrence relation which determines successively $u(2)$, $u(3)$, $u(4)$, . . .

In the next section we shall investigate some applications of systems of linear difference equations to the study of the growth of two interacting populations. The applications of difference equations are important in the biological, manage-ment, and social sciences. Many problems in these fields lead to sequences which must be determined. Frequently it can be shown that the sequence satisfies a difference equation. In these cases the difference equation can be solved, and the sequence which is the answer to the problem can be found. In other cases the principles which describe economic forces or the interactions between two or more populations can be formulated as a system of linear difference equations. In these cases, information about economic behavior or the growth of the inter-acting populations can be obtained by solving the system of linear difference equations which contains the statement of basic principles.

EXERCISES

1. A difference equation and an initial value are given in each of parts (a) through (g) of this exercise. In each case compute $u(1)$, $u(2)$, . . . , $u(5)$. Draw a graph of $u(0)$, $u(1)$, . . . , $u(5)$. Give an interpretation of the difference equation and its initial condition.

   (a) $u(k) = 1.06u(k - 1),$ $k = 1, 2, \ldots ,$
        $u(0) = 500$

   (b) $u(k) = u(k - 1) + 30,$ $k = 1, 2, \ldots ,$
        $u(0) = 500$

   (c) $u(k) = 0.94u(k - 1),$ $k = 1, 2, \ldots ,$
        $u(0) = 500$

   (d) $u(k) = 1.06u(k - 1) + 500,$ $k = 1, 2, \ldots ,$
        $u(0) = 500$

   (e) $u(k) = 1.06u(k - 1) - 30,$ $k = 1, 2, \ldots ,$
        $u(0) = 500$

   (f) $u(k) = 1.06u(k - 1) - 50,$ $k = 1, 2, \ldots ,$
        $u(0) = 500$

   (g) $u(k) = 1.06u(k - 1) - 10,$ $k = 1, 2, \ldots ,$
        $u(0) = 500$

2. A fisheries expert stocks a certain lake with 100,000 fish. Experience has shown that the fish in this particular lake double in number each year. Fishing is permitted in the lake, and the total number of fish removed from the lake each year is N. The

number of fish in the lake in succeeding years is determined by the difference equation $u(k) = 2u(k-1) - N$ and the initial value $u(0) = 100{,}000$.

(a) If $N = 75{,}000$, find $u(1), u(2), \ldots, u(5)$. Plot $u(0), u(1), \ldots, u(5)$. Describe the behavior of $u(k)$ as k increases. As the number of fish in the lake continues to increase, crowding occurs eventually. When this happens, the difference equation $u(k) = 2u(k-1) - 75{,}000$ no longer describes the growth of the fish population.

(b) If $N = 125{,}000$, find $u(1), u(2), u(3)$. Plot $u(0), u(1), u(2), u(3)$, and describe the behavior of $u(k)$ as k increases. Show that before the end of the third year there will be no fish left in the lake. In this case the fish population is wiped out completely because the annual harvest of fish is too large.

(c) Find the annual harvest N of fish that will keep the fish population of the lake constant, that is, find N so that $u(k) = 100{,}000$ for $k = 0, 1, 2, \ldots$

3. Each neutron which is released in a certain fissionable material releases two more neutrons in turn. Let $u(0) = N$, the number of neutrons released initially, and let $u(k)$ denote the number of neutrons released at the kth stage. Show that the difference equation $u(k) = 2u(k-1)$ and the initial condition $u(0) = N$ determine the number of neutrons released at the successive stages of the nuclear reaction, and find $u(k)$. Find also the total number

$$\sum_{k=0}^{99} u(k)$$

of neutrons released during the first one hundred stages of the reaction.

4. A student starts a chain letter by writing to four of his friends and asking that each of them write to four others, etc. Let $u(k)$ denote the number of letters written at the kth stage of the chain letter. Show that

$$u(0) = 4, \qquad u(1) = 16,$$

and that

$$u(k) = 4u(k-1)$$

for $k = 1, 2, \ldots$ Find the solution of this difference equation for which $u(0) = 4$. Find the number

$$\sum_{k=0}^{49} u(k)$$

of letters written during the first fifty stages of the chain letter. Show that at least one person has written the four letters more than once during the first fifty stages of the chain letter.

5. Find the solution of the difference equation $u(k) = ku(k-1)$ for which $u(0) = 1$. Show that $u(n) = n(n-1)(n-2) \cdots 3 \cdot 2 \cdot 1$. This expression for $u(n)$ is called *n factorial*, and it is denoted by $n!$.

6. Let $u(k)$ in Example 2 denote the number of bacteria in a culture at time $t = k$. Show that the values of $v(k-1)$ and $w(k-1)$ in Eq. (20) can be given the following inter-

pretation. Between $t = k - 1$ and $t = k$, the number of new bacteria added to the culture as a result of growth is $iu(k - 1)$. Furthermore, between $t = k - 1$ and $t = k$, all those bacteria in the culture at time $t = k - 2$ die.

7. Consider the following special case of Eqs. (22) and (23):

$$u(k) = 2u(k - 1) - u(k - 2), \qquad u(0) = 100, \qquad u(1) = 200.$$

Show that $u(n) = 100(n + 1)$ for $n = 0, 1, 2, \ldots$

8. Consider the following special case of Eqs. (22) and (23) obtained by setting $i = 1$ in Eq. (22):

$$u(k) = 2u(k - 1) - u(k - 2), \qquad u(0) = a, \qquad u(1) = b.$$

Show that the solution of this system is $u(n) = (b - a)n + a$. Investigate the behavior of $u(n)$ as n increases.

9. Consider the following difference equation and initial values:

$$u(k) - 5u(k - 1) + 6u(k - 2) = 0, \qquad k = 2, 3, \ldots,$$
$$u(0) = a, \qquad u(1) = b.$$

Show that $u(k) = 2^k$ and $u(k) = 3^k$ are two special solutions of this difference equation, and that $u(k) = c_1 2^k + c_2 3^k$ is also a solution for every choice of the constants c_1 and c_2. Determine c_1 and c_2 so that the solution $u(k) = c_1 2^k + c_2 3^k$ satisfies the given initial conditions. Show that the solution of the difference equation which satisfies the given initial conditions is

$$u(k) = (3a - b)2^k + (b - 2a)3^k.$$

3.5 GROWTH FUNCTIONS FOR INTERACTING POPULATIONS

In the preceding section we investigated growth functions for a single population or quantity. In many cases, we found that such growth functions are solutions of simple difference equations. Frequently we are concerned with a growth function for each of two associated populations. The growth of one population may affect the growth of the other population either favorably or unfavorably. For example the two populations may compete for food, or one population may prey on the other, or each population may prey on the other, etc. In many of these cases, also, the growth functions for the two interacting populations can be found as the solutions of difference equations. Two examples will illustrate the nature of the problems and their solutions.

EXAMPLE 1 (The Lanchester Equations of Combat). Two armies engage in combat. Each army counts the number of its men still in combat at the end of each day. Let $x_1(0)$ and $x_2(0)$ denote the number of men in the first and second armies respectively before combat begins, and let $x_1(k)$ and $x_2(k)$ denote the number of men in the two armies at the end of the kth day. Thus the numbers of men in combat at the ends of successive days can be represented as the column vectors $X(k)$,

$$X(k) = \begin{Vmatrix} x_1(k) \\ x_2(k) \end{Vmatrix}, \qquad k = 0, 1, 2, \ldots \tag{1}$$

A mathematical model has been proposed for determining the (column vector) growth function $X(k)$ and thus the ultimate winner in the combat. The model is known as the Lanchester Equations of Combat. According to these equations,

$$\begin{aligned} x_1(k + 1) - x_1(k) &= -a_2 x_2(k), \\ x_2(k + 1) - x_2(k) &= -a_1 x_1(k). \end{aligned} \tag{2}$$

Equations (2) state that the decrease in the number of men in each army is proportional to the number of men in the other army. The (positive) constants a_1 and a_2 are measures of the effectiveness of the weapons of the first and second armies, respectively. The problem is to determine the course of the combat, that is, to use equations (2) to find $X(k)$ for $k = 1, 2, \ldots$

Observe that equations (2) can be written in the form,

$$\begin{aligned} x_1(k + 1) &= x_1(k) - a_2 x_2(k), \\ x_2(k + 1) &= -a_1 x_1(k) + x_2(k). \end{aligned} \tag{3}$$

If we set

$$A = \begin{Vmatrix} 1 & -a_2 \\ -a_1 & 1 \end{Vmatrix},$$

then equations (3) can be written as the matrix equation

$$X(k + 1) = A * X(k). \tag{4}$$

Thus the Lanchester Equations of Combat can be written as a matrix difference equation.

A complete treatment of the solution of matrix difference equations is beyond the scope of this book. As a result, we shall not be able to obtain a complete solution of Eq. (4). We must be content with computing $X(k)$ for several values of k in some typical cases to exhibit the nature of the solutions of the equation $X(k + 1) = A * X(k)$.

From Eq. (4) we compute the following:

$$\begin{aligned} X(1) \quad &= A * X(0), \\ X(2) \quad &= A * X(1) = A * (A * X(0)) \quad = A^2 * X(0), \\ X(3) \quad &= A * X(2) = A * (A^2 * X(0)) = A^3 * X(0), \\ &\vdots \\ X(k + 1) &= A * X(k) = A * (A^k * X(0)) = A^{k+1} * X(0), \\ &\vdots \end{aligned} \tag{5}$$

Equations (5) show that $X(k)$, $k = 1, 2, 3, \ldots$, is completely determined by the difference equation (4) and the initial value $X(0)$. Furthermore, the difference equation (4) can be used as a recurrence relation and $X(k)$ can be computed as shown in equations (5) for any finite number of values of k.

We shall illustrate these methods by computing several solutions of Eq. (4) for a special choice of the matrix A. Set

$$A = \begin{Vmatrix} 1 & -0.1 \\ -0.1 & 1 \end{Vmatrix}. \tag{6}$$

A straightforward calculation gives the following values for $A^2, A^3, \ldots, A^6$:

$$A^2 = \begin{Vmatrix} 1.010 & -0.200 \\ -0.200 & 1.010 \end{Vmatrix},$$

$$A^3 = \begin{Vmatrix} 1.030 & -0.301 \\ -0.301 & 1.030 \end{Vmatrix},$$

$$A^4 = \begin{Vmatrix} 1.060 & -0.404 \\ -0.404 & 1.060 \end{Vmatrix},$$

$$A^5 = \begin{Vmatrix} 1.101 & -0.510 \\ -0.510 & 1.101 \end{Vmatrix},$$

$$A^6 = \begin{Vmatrix} 1.152 & -0.620 \\ -0.620 & 1.152 \end{Vmatrix}.$$

A solution of $X(k + 1) = A * X(k)$ can now be computed by assuming a value for $X(0)$ and using these values for the powers of A in equations (5). The successive values $X(1), X(2), \ldots$ are found by multiplying $X(0)$ by the successive powers of A. Figure 3.10 contains a table which gives the first seven values of $X(k)$ for three solutions obtained in this manner. The graphs of the three solutions are shown in Fig. 3.11.

Solution 1 (see Figs. 3.10 and 3.11) describes a combat in which the first army initially has twice as many men as the second army. As the combat proceeds, the second army loses men rapidly but the first army loses men slowly. Eventually, the second army loses all its men [$x_2(k)$ is negative for $k = 6$], but the first army still has more than eight-tenths of its original force. Clearly the first army wins. Solution 2 describes a combat in which the two armies have the same number of men initially and are equally effective in combat [$a_1 = a_2$ in Eqs. (2) and (3)]. The two armies lose men at the same rate, and hence they remain equal in strength. As time increases, the two armies are gradually destroyed and neither side wins. Solution 3 is similar to Solution 1 except that the second army is initially twice as large as the first army. The first army loses all its men before the end of the sixth day. The second army wins and more than eight-tenths of its men survive. If two armies are equally effective man-for-man, that is, if $a_1 = a_2$, then the larger army wins!

k	Solution 1		Solution 2		Solution 3	
	$x_1(k)$	$x_2(k)$	$x_1(k)$	$x_2(k)$	$x_1(k)$	$x_2(k)$
0	10.000	5.000	10.000	10.000	5.000	10.000
1	9.500	4.000	9.000	9.000	4.000	9.500
2	9.100	3.050	8.100	8.100	3.050	9.100
3	8.795	2.140	7.290	7.290	2.140	8.795
4	8.581	1.261	6.561	6.561	1.261	8.581
5	8.455	0.402	5.905	5.905	0.402	8.455
6	8.415	−0.443	5.314	5.314	−0.443	8.415

Fig. 3.10. Three solutions $X(k)$, $k = 0, 1, 2, \ldots, 6$, of the difference equation $X(k + 1) = A * X(k)$ for the matrix A in Eq. (6).

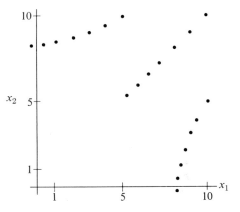

Fig. 3.11. Graphs of the three solutions $X(k)$ of $X(k + 1) = A * X(k)$ whose values are tabulated in Fig. 3.10.

EXAMPLE 2 (*A Simple Predator-Prey Model*). In an African game preserve the lions prey on the antelopes. At the beginning of a certain year there are $x_1(0)$ lions and $x_2(0)$ antelopes in the preserve. Let $x_1(k)$ and $x_2(k)$ denote the number of lions and antelopes, respectively, at the end of k years. As in Example 1 [see Eq. (1)], let $X(k)$ be the column vector whose elements are $x_1(k)$ and $x_2(k)$. Volterra, Lotka, and others have proposed mathematical models for determining the growth of two populations, one of which preys on the other. One simple model is based on the following equations:

$$x_1(k + 1) - x_1(k) = b_2[x_2(k) - c_2],$$
$$x_2(k + 1) - x_2(k) = -b_1[x_1(k) - c_1]. \tag{7}$$

Here b_1, b_2, c_1, c_2 are four positive constants. The first equation states that the increase $x_1(k + 1) - x_1(k)$ in the number of lions is proportional to $x_2(k) - c_2$. The number of lions increases if $x_2(k) > c_2$ and decreases if $x_2(k) < c_2$. The second equation states that the increase $x_2(k + 1) - x_2(k)$ in the number of antelopes is proportional to, but opposite in sign to, $x_1(k) - c_1$; thus the number of antelopes decreases if this quantity is positive (the number of lions is large) and increases if it is negative. The equations are, to a first approximation, a statement of the interaction of the two populations. As in Example 1, the growth of the two populations is described by a system of linear difference equations with constant coefficients [see equations (7)]. The problem is to determine the growth of the two populations, that is, to use equations (7) to calculate $X(k)$ for $k = 1, 2, \ldots$

To solve equations (7), observe first that they can be written in the following form:

$$[x_1(k + 1) - c_1] - [x_1(k) - c_1] = b_2[x_2(k) - c_2],$$
$$[x_2(k + 1) - c_2] - [x_2(k) - c_2] = -b_1[x_1(k) - c_1].$$

Then

$$[x_1(k + 1) - c_1] = [x_1(k) - c_1] + b_2[x_2(k) - c_2],$$
$$[x_2(k + 1) - c_2] = -b_1[x_1(k) - c_1] + [x_2(k) - c_2].$$

Set

$$C = \left\| \begin{matrix} c_1 \\ c_2 \end{matrix} \right\|. \tag{8}$$

Then the equations can be written as a matrix difference equation:

$$X(k + 1) - C = B * [X(k) - C], \tag{9}$$

where

$$B = \left\| \begin{matrix} 1 & b_2 \\ -b_1 & 1 \end{matrix} \right\|. \tag{10}$$

In Eq. (9) set

$$Y(k) = X(k) - C. \tag{11}$$

Then

$$X(k) = Y(k) + C, \tag{12}$$

and Eq. (9) takes the simple form

$$Y(k + 1) = B * Y(k). \tag{13}$$

If Eq. (13) can be solved for $Y(k)$, then $X(k)$ can be found from Eq. (12). Thus the problem can be solved by first solving Eq. (13).

From Eq. (13) we compute the following [see equations (5)]:

$$
\begin{aligned}
Y(1) \quad &= B * Y(0), \\
Y(2) \quad &= B^2 * Y(0), \\
Y(3) \quad &= B^3 * Y(0), \\
&\vdots \\
Y(k + 1) &= B^{k+1} * Y(0), \\
&\vdots
\end{aligned}
\tag{14}
$$

It is possible to express the solution $Y(k)$ of Eq. (13), and hence the solution $X(k)$ of Eq. (9), in terms of elementary functions, but the derivation of these forms of the solutions is beyond the scope of this book. We shall, however, compute enough values of $Y(k)$, and hence of $X(k)$, to show significant features of the solution of Eq. (9) in a special numerical example. The equations (14) show that $Y(k)$, $k = 1, 2, 3, \ldots$, is completely determined by the difference equation (13) and the initial value $Y(0)$. The difference equation (13) can be used as a recurrence relation to compute $Y(k)$ for any finite number of values of k.

To illustrate the nature of the results obtained from the predator-prey model in the equations (7), we shall compute a few values of $X(k)$ for the following choices of B and C:

$$B = \begin{Vmatrix} 1.00 & 0.10 \\ -0.20 & 1.00 \end{Vmatrix}, \quad C = \begin{Vmatrix} 20.00 \\ 40.00 \end{Vmatrix}. \tag{15}$$

The following powers of the matrix B were computed with a desk calculator. To avoid round-off errors, they were calculated to eight decimal places, and the results were rounded off to three decimal places.

$$B^2 = \begin{Vmatrix} 0.980 & 0.200 \\ -0.400 & 0.980 \end{Vmatrix} \qquad B^3 = \begin{Vmatrix} 0.940 & 0.298 \\ -0.596 & 0.940 \end{Vmatrix}$$

$$B^4 = \begin{Vmatrix} 0.880 & 0.392 \\ -0.784 & 0.880 \end{Vmatrix} \qquad B^5 = \begin{Vmatrix} 0.802 & 0.480 \\ -0.960 & 0.802 \end{Vmatrix}$$

$$B^6 = \begin{Vmatrix} 0.706 & 0.560 \\ -1.120 & 0.706 \end{Vmatrix} \qquad B^{10} = \begin{Vmatrix} 0.182 & 0.770 \\ -1.540 & 0.182 \end{Vmatrix}$$

$$B^{15} = \begin{Vmatrix} -0.593 & 0.705 \\ -1.410 & -0.593 \end{Vmatrix} \qquad B^{20} = \begin{Vmatrix} -1.153 & 0.281 \\ -0.562 & -1.153 \end{Vmatrix}$$

$$B^{25} = \begin{Vmatrix} -1.194 & -0.328 \\ 0.656 & -1.194 \end{Vmatrix} \qquad B^{30} = \begin{Vmatrix} -0.643 & -0.836 \\ 1.672 & -0.643 \end{Vmatrix}$$

$$B^{35} = \begin{Vmatrix} 0.288 & -0.979 \\ 1.958 & 0.288 \end{Vmatrix} \qquad B^{40} = \begin{Vmatrix} 1.171 & -0.647 \\ 1.294 & 1.171 \end{Vmatrix}$$

$$B^{45} = \begin{Vmatrix} 1.560 & 0.043 \\ -0.086 & 1.560 \end{Vmatrix} \qquad B^{50} = \begin{Vmatrix} 1.210 & 0.783 \\ -1.567 & 1.210 \end{Vmatrix}$$

$$B^{55} = \begin{Vmatrix} 0.218 & 1.209 \\ -2.418 & 0.218 \end{Vmatrix}$$

A solution of the difference equation $X(k + 1) - C = B * [X(k) - C]$ [see Eq. (9)] can now be computed as follows. Assume a value for $Y(0)$ and then calculate $Y(1)$, $Y(2)$, ... by equations (14). Then substitute $Y(0)$, $Y(1)$, $Y(2)$, ... for $Y(k)$ in Eq. (12) to obtain $X(0)$, $X(1)$, $X(2)$, ... Figure 3.12 contains a table which gives seventeen values of $X(k)$ for three solutions obtained in this manner. The graphs of these three solutions are given in Fig. 3.13 and Fig. 3.14.

k	Solution 1		Solution 2		Solution 3	
	$x_1(k)$	$x_2(k)$	$x_1(k)$	$x_2(k)$	$x_1(k)$	$x_2(k)$
0	20.0	40.0	30.0	40.0	20.0	50.0
1	20.0	40.0	30.0	38.0	21.0	50.0
2	20.0	40.0	29.8	36.0	22.0	49.8
3	20.0	40.0	29.4	34.0	23.0	49.4
4	20.0	40.0	28.8	32.2	23.9	48.8
5	20.0	40.0	28.0	30.4	24.8	48.0
6	20.0	40.0	27.1	28.8	25.6	47.1
10	20.0	40.0	21.8	24.6	27.7	41.8
15	20.0	40.0	14.1	25.9	27.1	34.1
20	20.0	40.0	8.5	34.4	22.8	28.5
25	20.0	40.0	8.1	46.6	16.7	28.1
30	20.0	40.0	13.6	56.7	11.6	33.6
35	20.0	40.0	22.9	59.6	10.2	42.9
40	20.0	40.0	31.7	52.9	13.5	51.7
45	20.0	40.0	35.6	39.1	20.4	55.6
50	20.0	40.0	32.1	24.3	27.8	52.1
55	20.0	40.0	22.2	15.8	32.1	42.2

Fig. 3.12. Three solutions $X(k)$, $k = 0, 1, \ldots, 6, 10, 15, \ldots, 55$, of the difference equation $X(k + 1) - C = B * [X(k) - C]$ for the values of B and C given in Eq. (15).

Solution 1 (see Figs. 3.12 and 3.13) is a constant solution. If

$$X(0) = \left\| \begin{matrix} 20.00 \\ 40.00 \end{matrix} \right\| = C,$$

then

$$X(k) = \left\| \begin{matrix} 20.00 \\ 40.00 \end{matrix} \right\| = C$$

satisfies the difference equation (9) for $k = 0, 1, 2, \ldots$ The lion and antelope populations are in equilibrium, and the model predicts that they will remain constant in size indefinitely.

Solutions 2 and 3 have an oscillatory character as shown in Figs. 3.13 and 3.14. As shown in Fig. 3.13, Solution 2 starts with the number of lions greater than the equilibrium number and the number of antelopes equal to the equilibrium

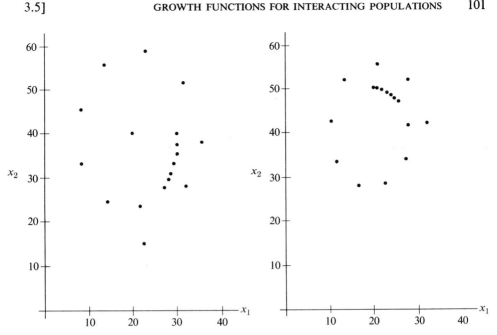

Fig. 3.13. Graphs of Solution 1 and Solution 2 in Fig. 3.12.

Fig. 3.14. Graph of Solution 3 in Fig. 3.12.

number. Because of the excess number of lions, the antelope population diminishes rapidly. This shrinkage in the antelope population is followed in turn by a shrinkage in the lion population. Then, because there are fewer lions, the antelopes recover and their number increases. This increase in the number of antelopes is followed by an increase in the number of lions. And thus the cycles continue. Solution 3 also is an oscillatory solution similar to Solution 2; the two solutions differ only in starting at different points in the cycle.

The model is an unstable one as shown in the graphs. The oscillations in the sizes of the two populations become larger and larger with the passage of time, and the model predicts that one of the two populations will be reduced to zero eventually. The initial value $X(0)$ determines which population (lions or antelopes) is eliminated. Since we know that two populations, one a predator and the other the prey, can live together indefinitely, we are led to question the validity of the model in equations (7). As we have stated already, however, equations (7) are a first approximation only, and many refinements in them are possible in order to obtain closer agreement with the real world.

Example 2 provides an example of one of the problems studied in mathematical biology. There is now extensive mathematical literature which treats the growth of two interacting populations. The predator-prey interaction is only one of many types of interaction. Many of the mathematical models used in these studies employ differential equations rather than difference equations, but the two types of models have many similarities.

EXERCISES

1. Let A be the matrix given in Eq. (6). Compute the solution $X(k)$, $k = 1, 2, \ldots, 6, 7,$ 8, of the Lanchester Equations of Combat [see Eq. (4)] corresponding to each of the following values for the initial condition $X(0)$.

(a) $\left\| \begin{matrix} 10 \\ 6 \end{matrix} \right\|$ (b) $\left\| \begin{matrix} 10 \\ 7 \end{matrix} \right\|$ (c) $\left\| \begin{matrix} 10 \\ 8 \end{matrix} \right\|$ (d) $\left\| \begin{matrix} 10 \\ 9 \end{matrix} \right\|$

(e) $\left\| \begin{matrix} 9 \\ 10 \end{matrix} \right\|$ (f) $\left\| \begin{matrix} 8 \\ 10 \end{matrix} \right\|$ (g) $\left\| \begin{matrix} 7 \\ 10 \end{matrix} \right\|$ (h) $\left\| \begin{matrix} 6 \\ 10 \end{matrix} \right\|$

[*Hint:* Use the values of $A^2, A^3, \ldots, A^6$ given on p. 96.]

2. Let B and C be the matrices given in Eq. (15). Extend the table in Fig. 3.12 to provide solutions of the Predator-Prey Model equation [see Eq. (9)] corresponding to each of the following values for the initial condition $X(0)$.

(a) $\left\| \begin{matrix} 21 \\ 40 \end{matrix} \right\|$ (b) $\left\| \begin{matrix} 25 \\ 40 \end{matrix} \right\|$ (c) $\left\| \begin{matrix} 20 \\ 41 \end{matrix} \right\|$ (d) $\left\| \begin{matrix} 20 \\ 45 \end{matrix} \right\|$

(e) $\left\| \begin{matrix} 21 \\ 41 \end{matrix} \right\|$ (f) $\left\| \begin{matrix} 25 \\ 45 \end{matrix} \right\|$ (g) $\left\| \begin{matrix} 19 \\ 39 \end{matrix} \right\|$ (h) $\left\| \begin{matrix} 15 \\ 35 \end{matrix} \right\|$

[*Hint:* Use the values for the powers of B given on p. 99.]

3. Compute Solutions 2 and 3 in the table in Fig. 3.12 for $k = 60, 65, \ldots, 100$. [*Hint:* To compute $X(k)$, first compute $Y(k)$ by equations (14) and then find $X(k)$ by Eq. (12). Observe that

$$Y(k + 50) = B^{k+50} * Y(0) = B^k * [B^{50} * Y(0)], \qquad k = 10, 15, \ldots, 50.$$

But $B^{50} * Y(0)$ can be found from the table in Fig. 3.12 since $X(50) - C = Y(50) = B^{50} * Y(0)$ by Eqs. (11) and (14). Use the values of $B^5, B^{10}, \ldots, B^{50}$ given on p. 99.]

The following exercises require a knowledge of trigonometry and analytic geometry.

4. Consider the following special case of the Predator-Prey Model:

$$x_1(k + 1) - x_1(k) = \sin \theta[x_2(k) - c_2],$$
$$x_2(k + 1) - x_2(k) = -\sin \theta[x_1(k) - c_1]. \tag{16}$$

Here θ is a constant such that $0 < \theta < \pi/2$. In certain cases it is desirable to refine this model by adding a term on the right in equations (16) to account for the effect of crowding in the two populations; add the term $[\cos \theta - 1][x_1(k) - c_1]$ to the first equation and $[\cos \theta - 1][x_2(k) - c_2]$ to the second. These terms inhibit growth when the populations are large ($x_1(k) > c_1$ and $x_2(k) > c_2$) and promote it when the populations are small. Equations (16) are replaced by the following more refined model:

$$x_1(k + 1) - x_1(k) = [\cos \theta - 1][x_1(k) - c_1] + \sin \theta[x_2(k) - c_2],$$
$$x_2(k + 1) - x_2(k) = -\sin \theta[x_1(k) - c_1] + [\cos \theta - 1][x_2(k) - c_2]. \tag{17}$$

(a) Show that Eqs. (17) can be written in the form

$$x_1(k + 1) - c_1 = \cos \theta [x_1(k) - c_1] + \sin \theta [x_2(k) - c_2],$$
$$x_2(k + 1) - c_2 = -\sin \theta [x_1(k) - c_1] + \cos \theta [x_2(k) - c_2]. \tag{18}$$

In matrix form, these equations are

$$X(k + 1) - C = D * [X(k) - C], \tag{19}$$

where

$$D = \left\| \begin{array}{cc} \cos \theta & \sin \theta \\ -\sin \theta & \cos \theta \end{array} \right\|.$$

(b) Set $Y(k) = X(k) - C$ [see Eq. (8)] and show that Eq. (19) becomes

$$Y(k + 1) = D * Y(k). \tag{20}$$

(c) Show that

$$D^k = \left\| \begin{array}{cc} \cos k\theta & \sin k\theta \\ -\sin k\theta & \cos k\theta \end{array} \right\|.$$

(d) Set

$$Y(k) = \left\| \begin{array}{c} r \cos (k\theta + \omega) \\ r \sin (k\theta + \omega) \end{array} \right\|. \tag{21}$$

Show that this function $Y(k)$ is a solution of Eq. (20) for every r and ω. Let

$$\left\| \begin{array}{c} y_1(0) \\ y_2(0) \end{array} \right\|$$

be any given initial value. Show that r and ω can be chosen so that

$$Y(0) = \left\| \begin{array}{c} r \cos \omega \\ r \sin \omega \end{array} \right\| = \left\| \begin{array}{c} y_1(0) \\ y_2(0) \end{array} \right\|.$$

(e) Show that $X(k) = Y(k) + C$, where $Y(k)$ is the function defined in Eq. (21), is a solution of Eq. (19). Thus the most general solution of Eq. (19) is

$$X(k) = \left\| \begin{array}{c} r \cos (k\theta + \omega) + c_1 \\ r \sin (k\theta + \omega) + c_2 \end{array} \right\|. \tag{22}$$

(f) The column vector $X(k)$ in Eq. (22) can be plotted in a rectangular coordinate plane as the point whose coordinates are $(x_1(k), x_2(k))$. Show that the distance from the point $(x_1(k), x_2(k))$ to the point (c_1, c_2) is constant and equal to r. Thus show that the graph of $X(k)$ in Eq. (22) consists of points on a circle whose center is (c_1, c_2) and whose radius is r.

(g) Show that the solution $X(k)$ in Eq. (22) is periodic if and only if $\theta = 2\pi/n$ for some integer n. If $\theta = 2\pi/n$, then $X(n) = X(0)$, and the period of the solution is n.

(h) Use equations (18) to show that

$$[x_1(k + 1) - c_1]^2 + [x_2(k + 1) - c_2]^2 = [x_1(k) - c_1]^2 + [x_2(k) - c_2]^2.$$

This result proves that the points $X(k)$, for any solution of Eqs. (18) and (19), have a constant distance from the point (c_1, c_2). Thus the graph of every solution consists of points on a circle whose center is (c_1, c_2).

5. Consider the following special case of the Lanchester Equations of Combat:

$$x_1(k + 1) - x_1(k) = -(\sinh \theta)x_2(k),$$
$$x_2(k + 1) - x_2(k) = -(\sinh \theta)x_1(k).$$
(23)

Here θ is a positive constant. In certain cases it is desirable to refine this model by adding a term on the right in equations (23) to account for the strength (favorable effect) which results from having a large force; add the term $[\cosh \theta - 1]x_1(k)$ to the first equation and $[\cosh \theta - 1]x_2(k)$ to the second. Since $\cosh \theta > 1$, these terms represent favorable influences which tend to lessen the decrease in size of the two armies. Equations (23) are replaced by the following more refined model:

$$x_1(k + 1) - x_1(k) = [\cosh \theta - 1]x_1(k) - (\sinh \theta)x_2(k),$$
$$x_2(k + 1) - x_2(k) = -(\sinh \theta)x_1(k) + [\cosh \theta - 1]x_2(k).$$
(24)

(a) Show that equations (24) can be written as

$$x_1(k + 1) = (\cosh \theta)x_1(k) - (\sinh \theta)x_2(k),$$
$$x_2(k + 1) = -(\sinh \theta)x_1(k) + (\cosh \theta)x_2(k).$$
(25)

Written as a matrix equation, these equations are

$$X(k + 1) = E * X(k),$$
(26)

where

$$E = \begin{Vmatrix} \cosh \theta & -\sinh \theta \\ -\sinh \theta & \cosh \theta \end{Vmatrix}.$$

(b) Show that

$$E^k = \begin{Vmatrix} \cosh k\theta & -\sinh k\theta \\ -\sinh k\theta & \cosh k\theta \end{Vmatrix}.$$

(c) Set

$$X_1(k) = \begin{Vmatrix} r \cosh (k\theta + \omega) \\ r \sinh (k\theta + \omega) \end{Vmatrix},$$
(27)

$$X_2(k) = \begin{Vmatrix} -r \cosh (k\theta + \omega) \\ r \sinh (k\theta + \omega) \end{Vmatrix},$$
(28)

$$X_3(k) = \begin{Vmatrix} -r \sinh (k\theta + \omega) \\ r \cosh (k\theta + \omega) \end{Vmatrix},$$
(29)

$$X_4(k) = \begin{Vmatrix} r \sinh (k\theta + \omega) \\ -r \cosh (k\theta + \omega) \end{Vmatrix}.$$
(30)

Show that $X_1(k)$, $X_2(k)$, $X_3(k)$, and $X_4(k)$ are solutions of Eq. (26) for every r and ω. Let

$$\begin{Vmatrix} x_1(0) \\ x_2(0) \end{Vmatrix}$$

be any given initial value. Show that r and ω can be chosen so that, for some $i(i = 1, 2, 3, \text{ or } 4)$,

$$X_i(0) = \begin{Vmatrix} x_1(0) \\ x_2(0) \end{Vmatrix}.$$

(d) Show that the graphs of $X_1(k)$ and $X_2(k)$ consist of sets of points on the right and left branches respectively of the hyperbola $x_1^2 - x_2^2 = r^2$. Show that the graphs of $X_3(k)$ and $X_4(k)$ consist of sets of points on the upper and lower branches respectively of the hyperbola $x_1^2 - x_2^2 = -r^2$.

(e) Use equations (25) to show that the solution

$$X(k) = \left\| \begin{matrix} x_1(k) \\ x_2(k) \end{matrix} \right\|$$

of Eq. (26) satisfies the equation

$$x_1(k+1)^2 - x_2(k+1)^2 = x_1(k)^2 - x_2(k)^2.$$

Use this result to show once more that the graph of any solution of Eq. (26) consists of a set of points on one or the other of the hyperbolas in part (d).

3.6 THE EVALUATION OF CERTAIN SUMS

Several formulas for finding the sum of the terms of a finite sequence have been established in this chapter. The methods used in proving them [see, for example, the proof of Eq. (11) in Section 3.3] suggest, correctly, the existence of a general theorem. We shall now prove this general theorem and indicate some of its applications.

Theorem 3.1. Let

$$u(0),\ u(1),\ u(2),\ \ldots,\ u(k),\ \ldots, \tag{1}$$

$$U(0),\ U(1),\ U(2),\ \ldots,\ U(k),\ \ldots \tag{2}$$

be two given sequences such that

$$u(k) = U(k) - U(k-1), \qquad k = 1, 2, \ldots \tag{3}$$

Then

$$\sum_{k=1}^{n} u(k) = U(n) - U(0) \tag{4}$$

for any positive integer n.

Proof. Write Eq. (3) for successive values of k as

$$
\begin{aligned}
u(1) &= U(1) & &- U(0), \\
u(2) &= U(2) & &- U(1), \\
u(3) &= U(3) & &- U(2), \\
&\ \vdots \\
u(n-1) &= U(n-1) & &- U(n-2), \\
u(n) &= U(n) & &- U(n-1).
\end{aligned} \tag{5}
$$

Add the equations in (5). Since all terms on the right cancel except $U(0)$ in the first equation and $U(n)$ in the last equation, the result is Eq. (4).▲

EXAMPLE 1.   Set

$$u(k) = 2k - 1, \qquad U(k) = k^2, \qquad k = 0, 1, 2, \ldots \qquad (6)$$

Then

$$u(k) = 2k - 1 = k^2 - (k - 1)^2 = U(k) - U(k - 1).$$

Thus the hypotheses of Theorem 3.1 are satisfied by the two sequences in (6), and it follows that $\sum_{k=1}^{n} (2k - 1) = n^2 - 0^2$ or

$$1 + 3 + 5 + \cdots + (2n - 1) = n^2. \qquad (7)$$

Equation (7) states that the sum of the first n odd integers is n^2.

At this point the reader will probably raise an objection and ask a question. First, he will object, Eq. (7) does not represent a new achievement, since the odd integers form an arithmetic progression and (7) can be established easily by Eq. (11) in Section 3.2. Second, the reader will ask, if a sequence $u(0), u(1), u(2), \ldots$ is given, how can a sequence $U(0), U(1), U(2), \ldots$ satisfying (3) be found? We shall deal with the objection in Example 2 and with the question in Example 3.

EXAMPLE 2.   Set

$$u(k) = k^2, \qquad U(k) = \frac{k(k + 1)(2k + 1)}{6}, \qquad k = 0, 1, 2, \ldots \qquad (8)$$

Then

$$U(k) - U(k - 1) = \frac{k(k + 1)(2k + 1)}{6} - \frac{(k - 1)k(2k - 1)}{6}$$

$$= \frac{k[(k + 1)(2k + 1) - (k - 1)(2k - 1)]}{6} = k^2 = u(k).$$

Thus the hypotheses of Theorem 3.1 are satisfied by the two sequences in (8), and it follows that

$$\sum_{k=1}^{n} k^2 = \frac{n(n + 1)(2n + 1) - 0}{6},$$

or

$$1^2 + 2^2 + 3^2 + \cdots + n^2 = \frac{n(n + 1)(2n + 1)}{6}. \qquad (9)$$

This formula cannot be established by any of the results obtained for arithmetic and geometric progressions in Sections 3.2 and 3.3, because $0^2, 1^2, 2^2, 3^2, \ldots$ is neither an arithmetic nor a geometric progression.

EXAMPLE 3.   If a sequence $u(0), u(1), u(2), \ldots$ is given, it is frequently possible to calculate a sequence $U(0), U(1), U(2), \ldots$ which satisfies hypothesis (3) in Theorem 3.1. An example will illustrate the procedure.

If $U(k)$ is any polynomial in k, it is easily shown that $U(k) - U(k - 1)$ is a polynomial in k of one lower degree. Thus, if $u(k) = k^2$ as in Example 2, we set $U(k) = ak^3 + bk^2 + ck + d$ and seek to determine the coefficients a, b, c, d so that $U(k) - U(k - 1) = k^2$. But

$$
\begin{aligned}
U(k) - U(k - 1) &= [ak^3 + bk^2 + ck + d] \\
&\quad - [a(k - 1)^3 + b(k - 1)^2 + c(k - 1) + d] \\
&= 3ak^2 + (-3a + 2b)k + (a - b + c).
\end{aligned}
$$

This polynomial reduces to k^2 if and only if

$$
\begin{aligned}
3a &= 1, \\
-3a + 2b &= 0, \\
a - b + c &= 0.
\end{aligned}
$$

This system of linear equations has the unique solution

$$
a = \tfrac{1}{3}, \qquad b = \tfrac{1}{2}, \qquad c = \tfrac{1}{6}.
$$

Choose $d = 0$ since no restriction is placed on the choice of d. These values for the four coefficients yield the function U in Eq. (8).

Thus we have shown that, at least when $u(k) = k^2$, it is possible to calculate the function $U(k)$ required for an application of Theorem 3.1. The following general theorem can be established, but the proof will not be given.

Theorem 3.2. Let

$$
u(0), \; u(1), \; u(2), \; \ldots, \; u(k), \; \ldots \tag{10}
$$

be a given sequence such that $u(k)$ is a polynomial in k of degree n. Then there exists a polynomial

$$
U(k) = a_0 k^{n+1} + a_1 k^n + \cdots + a_n k + a_{n+1} \tag{11}
$$

such that $u(k) = U(k) - U(k - 1)$. The coefficient a_{n+1} can be chosen arbitrarily, but $a_0, a_1, \ldots, a_n$ are uniquely determined as the solution of a system of linear equations.

EXAMPLE 4. The following example shows that Theorem 3.1 can be used in some cases to find the sum of an infinite series. Set

$$
u(k) = \frac{1}{k(k + 1)}, \qquad k = 1, 2, \ldots, \tag{12}
$$

$$
U(k) = -\frac{1}{k + 1}, \qquad k = 0, 1, 2, \ldots \tag{13}
$$

Then

$$U(k) - U(k - 1) = -\frac{1}{k + 1} - \frac{-1}{k} = \frac{1}{k(k + 1)} = u(k).$$

Thus the hypotheses of Theorem 3.1 are satisfied, and it follows from Eq. (4) that

$$\frac{1}{1 \cdot 2} + \frac{1}{2 \cdot 3} + \cdots + \frac{1}{n(n + 1)} = 1 - \frac{1}{n + 1}.$$

From the definition of the sum of an infinite series, it follows that

$$\frac{1}{1 \cdot 2} + \frac{1}{2 \cdot 3} + \cdots + \frac{1}{n(n + 1)} + \cdots = \lim_{n \to \infty} \left(1 - \frac{1}{n + 1}\right) = 1. \quad (14)$$

The infinite series on the left in Eq. (14) converges and its sum is 1.

EXAMPLE 5.   We shall now use Theorem 3.1 to find the value of

$$\sum_{k=1}^{n} \sin k\theta.$$

Set

$$u(k) = \sin k\theta, \quad k = 0, 1, 2, \ldots, \tag{15}$$

$$U(k) = \frac{\cos (k + \frac{1}{2})\theta}{-2 \sin (\theta/2)}, \quad \sin (\theta/2) \ne 0, \quad k = 0, 1, 2, \ldots \tag{16}$$

Then

$$U(k) - U(k - 1) = \frac{\cos (k + \frac{1}{2})\theta - \cos (k - \frac{1}{2})\theta}{-2 \sin (\theta/2)}. \tag{17}$$

By the addition formula for the cosine, we have

$$\cos (k + \tfrac{1}{2})\theta = \cos k\theta \cos \frac{\theta}{2} - \sin k\theta \sin \frac{\theta}{2},$$

$$\cos (k - \tfrac{1}{2})\theta = \cos k\theta \cos \frac{\theta}{2} + \sin k\theta \sin \frac{\theta}{2}.$$

If these values are substituted on the right in Eq. (17), we find that

$$U(k) - U(k - 1) = \sin k\theta.$$

Thus the hypotheses of Theorem 3.1 are satisfied, and, by Eq. (4),

$$\sum_{k=1}^{n} \sin k\theta = \frac{\cos (n + \frac{1}{2})\theta}{-2 \sin (\theta/2)} - \frac{\cos (\theta/2)}{-2 \sin (\theta/2)}$$

$$= \frac{\cos (\theta/2) - \cos (n + \frac{1}{2})\theta}{2 \sin (\theta/2)}$$

for every positive integer n if $\sin (\theta/2) \ne 0$.

EXERCISES

1. Use Theorems 3.1 and 3.2 to find the value of the following sum:

$$1 + 4 + 7 + \cdots + (3k - 2) + \cdots + (3n - 2).$$

Set $u(k) = 3k - 2$, and then use Theorem 3.2 to find a polynomial $U(k)$ of the second degree such that $U(k) - U(k - 1) = u(k)$. Use the method employed in Example 3 to show that $U(k) = [k(3k - 1)]/2$ is a function with the desired property. Then use Theorem 3.1 to find the value of the given sum. Check your answer by using the formula for the sum of an arithmetic progression in Eq. (11) in Section 3.2.

2. Set

$$u(k) = k^3, \qquad U(k) = \frac{k^2(k + 1)^2}{4}, \qquad k = 0, 1, 2, \ldots,$$

and use Theorem 3.1 to verify that

$$\sum_{k=1}^{n} k^3 = \frac{n^2(n + 1)^2}{4}$$

for every positive integer n.

3. Set

$$u(k) = k^4, \qquad U(k) = \frac{k(k + 1)(2k + 1)(3k^2 + 3k - 1)}{30}, \qquad k = 0, 1, 2, \ldots,$$

and use Theorem 3.1 to verify that

$$\sum_{k=1}^{n} k^4 = \frac{n(n + 1)(2n + 1)(3n^2 + 3n - 1)}{30}$$

for every positive integer n.

4. Set

$$u(k) = k(k + 1), \qquad U(k) = \frac{k(k + 1)(k + 2)}{3}, \qquad k = 0, 1, 2, \ldots,$$

and use Theorem 3.1 to verify that

$$\sum_{k=1}^{n} k(k + 1) = \frac{n(n + 1)(n + 2)}{3}$$

for every positive integer n.

5. Set

$$u(k) = (2k - 1)^3, \qquad U(k) = k^2(2k^2 - 1), \qquad k = 0, 1, 2, \ldots,$$

and use Theorem 3.1 to verify that

$$\sum_{k=1}^{n} (2k - 1)^3 = n^2(2n^2 - 1)$$

for every positive integer n.

6. Set

$$u(k) = \frac{1}{(3k - 2)(3k + 1)}, \qquad U(k) = \frac{-1}{3(3k + 1)}, \qquad k = 0, 1, 2, \ldots,$$

and use Theorem 3.1 to verify that

$$\sum_{k=1}^{n} \frac{1}{(3k - 2)(3k + 1)} = \frac{n}{3n + 1}$$

for every positive integer n.

7. Show that the following infinite series converges and that its sum has the value indicated:

$$\frac{1}{1 \cdot 4} + \frac{1}{4 \cdot 7} + \frac{1}{7 \cdot 10} + \cdots + \frac{1}{(3n - 2)(3n + 1)} + \cdots = \frac{1}{3}.$$

[*Hint:* Observe that, by Exercise 6, the sum of the first n terms of the infinite series is

$$\frac{1}{1 \cdot 4} + \frac{1}{4 \cdot 7} + \cdots + \frac{1}{(3n - 2)(3n + 1)} = \frac{n}{3n + 1} = \frac{1}{3 + (1/n)}.$$

The desired result is obtained by taking the limit as n tends to infinity.]

8. Set

$$u(k) = k2^k, \qquad U(k) = (k - 1)2^{k+1}, \qquad k = 0, 1, 2, \ldots,$$

and use Theorem 3.1 to verify that

$$\sum_{k=1}^{n} k2^k = 2 + (n - 1)2^{n+1}$$

for every positive integer n.

9. Set

$$u(k) = 2(3^{k-1}), \qquad U(k) = 3^k, \qquad k = 0, 1, 2, \ldots,$$

and use Theorem 3.1 to verify that

$$\sum_{k=1}^{n} 2(3^{k-1}) = 3^n - 1$$

for every positive integer n. Establish this formula also by a second method.

10. Set

$$u(k) = k(k!), \qquad U(k) = (k + 1)!, \qquad k = 0, 1, 2, \ldots,$$

and use Theorem 3.1 to verify that

$$\sum_{k=1}^{n} k(k!) = (n + 1)! - 1$$

for every positive integer n.

11. Show that for every positive integer n,

$$\sum_{k=1}^{n} \cos k\theta = \frac{\sin (n + \frac{1}{2})\theta - \sin (\theta/2)}{2 \sin (\theta/2)}, \qquad \sin (\theta/2) \neq 0.$$

[*Hint:* Set

$$u(k) = \cos k\theta, \qquad U(k) = \frac{\sin (k + \frac{1}{2})\theta}{2 \sin (\theta/2)}$$

and use Theorem 3.1.]

3.7 FACTORIAL FUNCTIONS

The *rising factorial function* $k^{(r)}$ is defined by the following equations:

$$\begin{aligned}
k^{(0)} &= 1, \\
k^{(r)} &= k(k + 1)(k + 2) \cdots (k + r - 1), \qquad r = 1, 2, \ldots
\end{aligned} \tag{1}$$

For the sake of brevity in this section, the rising factorial function will be called the factorial function. In this section we shall derive some important relations between the factorial function $k^{(r)}$ and the power function k^r, and we shall use these relations and Theorem 3.1 in Section 3.6 to obtain a general method for evaluating sums of the form

$$\sum_{k=1}^{n} k^r,$$

where r is a positive integer.

From the definition of $k^{(r)}$ in equations (1) we find

$$k^{(1)} = k, \qquad k^{(r+1)} = k^{(r)}(k + r) = kk^{(r)} + rk^{(r)}. \tag{2}$$

Equation (2) can be used as a recurrence relation to compute $k^{(1)}, k^{(2)}, k^{(3)}, \ldots$ successively in terms of the power functions $k, k^2, k^3, \ldots$ The values of $k^{(1)}, k^{(2)}, \ldots, k^{(8)}$ are given in the table in Fig. 3.15; the recurrence relation in Eq. (2) can be used to extend the table indefinitely.

$$\begin{aligned}
k^{(1)} &= k \\
k^{(2)} &= k + k^2 \\
k^{(3)} &= 2k + 3k^2 + k^3 \\
k^{(4)} &= 6k + 11k^2 + 6k^3 + k^4 \\
k^{(5)} &= 24k + 50k^2 + 35k^3 + 10k^4 + k^5 \\
k^{(6)} &= 120k + 274k^2 + 225k^3 + 85k^4 + 15k^5 + k^6 \\
k^{(7)} &= 720k + 1764k^2 + 1624k^3 + 735k^4 + 175k^5 + 21k^6 + k^7 \\
k^{(8)} &= 5040k + 13{,}068k^2 + 13{,}132k^3 + 6769k^4 + 1960k^5 + 322k^6 + 28k^7 + k^8
\end{aligned}$$

Fig. 3.15. The factorial function $k^{(r)}$ expressed as a linear combination of the power functions $k, k^2, k^3, \ldots, k^r$ for $r = 1, 2, 3, \ldots, 8$.

There is a simple relation between the coefficients in two successive equations in the table in Fig. 3.15. Observe first that all the signs in this table are plus. If

$$k^{(r)} \quad = \cdots + a_{s-1}k^{(s-1)} + a_s k^{(s)} + \cdots,$$
$$k^{(r+1)} = \cdots \qquad\qquad + b_s k^{(s)} + \cdots,$$

then

$$b_s = ra_s + a_{s-1}. \tag{3}$$

The entire table in Fig. 3.15 can be written out quickly with the aid of the relation in Eq. (3). Furthermore, by using Eq. (3), we can easily extend the table to give the values of $k^{(9)}, k^{(10)}, \ldots$

It is possible to consider the equations in the table in Fig. 3.15 as linear equations in $k, k^2, k^3, \ldots$ From the first equation we find that $k = k^{(1)}$. If this value of k is substituted for k in the second equation, we obtain $k^2 = k^{(2)} - k^{(1)}$. Continuing in this fashion, we obtain the results given in the table in Fig. 3.16.

There is a simple relation between the coefficients in two successive equations in the table in Fig. 3.16. Observe first that the signs are alternately plus and minus. If

$$k^r \quad = \cdots \pm c_{s-1}k^{(s-1)} \mp c_s k^{(s)} \pm \cdots,$$
$$k^{r+1} = \cdots \qquad\qquad \pm d_s k^{(s)} \mp \cdots,$$

then

$$d_s = sc_s + c_{s-1}. \tag{4}$$

The entire table in Fig. 3.16 can be written out quickly with the aid of the relation in Eq. (4). Furthermore, by using Eq. (4), we can easily extend the table to give the values of $k^9, k^{10}, \ldots$

Theorem 3.3. There exist constants $a_{r1}, a_{r2}, \ldots, a_{rr}$ and $b_{r1}, b_{r2}, \ldots, b_{rr}$ such that

$$k^{(r)} = a_{r1}k + a_{r2}k^2 + \cdots + a_{rr}k^r, \tag{5}$$

$$k^r = b_{r1}k^{(1)} + b_{r2}k^{(2)} + \cdots + b_{rr}k^{(r)}, \tag{6}$$

for $r = 1, 2, 3, \ldots$

Proof. The proof in each case is by mathematical induction. Equation (5) has been proved already for $r = 1, 2, \ldots, 8$ (see the table in Fig. 3.15). The proof of Eq. (5) can be completed by mathematical induction by using the recurrence relation in Eq. (2).

Equation (6) has been proved already for $r = 1, 2, \ldots, 8$ (see the table in Fig. 3.16). The following identity can be verified easily by using the definition of the factorial function in equations (1):

$$k \cdot k^{(r)} = k^{(r+1)} - r \cdot k^{(r)}, \qquad r = 0, 1, 2, \ldots \tag{7}$$

$$k = k^{(1)}$$
$$k^2 = -k^{(1)} + k^{(2)}$$
$$k^3 = k^{(1)} - 3k^{(2)} + k^{(3)}$$
$$k^4 = -k^{(1)} + 7k^{(2)} - 6k^{(3)} + k^{(4)}$$
$$k^5 = k^{(1)} - 15k^{(2)} + 25k^{(3)} - 10k^{(4)} + k^{(5)}$$
$$k^6 = -k^{(1)} + 31k^{(2)} - 90k^{(3)} + 65k^{(4)} - 15k^{(5)} + k^{(6)}$$
$$k^7 = k^{(1)} - 63k^{(2)} + 301k^{(3)} - 350k^{(4)} + 140k^{(5)} - 21k^{(6)} + k^{(7)}$$
$$k^8 = -k^{(1)} + 127k^{(2)} - 966k^{(3)} + 1701k^{(4)} - 1050k^{(5)} + 266k^{(6)} - 28k^{(7)} + k^{(8)}$$

Fig. 3.16. The power function k^r expressed as a linear combination of the factorial functions $k^{(1)}, k^{(2)}, k^{(3)}, \ldots, k^{(r)}$ for $r = 1, 2, \ldots, 8$.

Assume that Eq. (6) is true for some value of r. Then, for this value of r,

$$k^{r+1} = k \cdot k^r = k[b_{r1}k^{(1)} + b_{r2}k^{(2)} + \cdots + b_{rr}k^{(r)}]$$
$$= b_{r1}k \cdot k^{(1)} + b_{r2}k \cdot k^{(2)} + \cdots + b_{rr}k \cdot k^{(r)}.$$

Replace the terms $k \cdot k^{(1)}, k \cdot k^{(2)}, \ldots, k \cdot k^{(r)}$ in the last equation by their values as given by Eq. (7) and simplify. The resulting equation expresses k^{r+1} as a linear combination of $k^{(1)}, k^{(2)}, \ldots, k^{(r)}, k^{(r+1)}$. Then by a complete induction, Eq. (6) is true for $r = 1, 2, 3, \ldots$ ▲

Theorem 3.4. If n is a positive integer, then

$$\sum_{k=1}^{n} k^{(r)} = \frac{n^{(r+1)}}{r+1}, \qquad r = 0, 1, 2, \ldots \tag{8}$$

Proof. Set

$$U(k) = \frac{k^{(r+1)}}{r+1}.$$

Then

$$U(k) - U(k-1) = \frac{k^{(r+1)} - (k-1)^{(r+1)}}{r+1} = \frac{k^{(r)}[(k+r) - (k-1)]}{r+1} = k^{(r)}.$$

By Theorem 3.1,

$$\sum_{k=1}^{n} k^{(r)} = U(n) - U(0) = \frac{n^{(r+1)}}{r+1} - 0 = \frac{n^{(r+1)}}{r+1}. \quad ▲$$

Theorem 3.5. If n is a positive integer, then for $r = 0, 1, 2, \ldots$ the sum

$$\sum_{k=1}^{n} k^r$$

can be expressed as a polynomial in n of degree $r + 1$.

Proof. If $r = 0$, then

$$\sum_{k=1}^{n} k^r = n$$

and the theorem is true in this case. Assume next that $r \geq 1$. By Eqs. (6) and (8)

$$\sum_{k=1}^{n} k^r = \sum_{k=1}^{n} [b_{r1}k^{(1)} + b_{r2}k^{(2)} + \cdots + b_{rr}k^{(r)}]$$

$$= b_{r1} \sum_{k=1}^{n} k^{(1)} + b_{r2} \sum_{k=1}^{n} k^{(2)} + \cdots + b_{rr} \sum_{k=1}^{n} k^{(r)}$$

$$= b_{r1} \frac{n^{(2)}}{2} + b_{r2} \frac{n^{(3)}}{3} + \cdots + b_{rr} \frac{n^{(r+1)}}{r+1}.$$

By Eq. (5), the terms $n^{(2)}$, $n^{(3)}$, $\ldots$, $n^{(r+1)}$ are polynomials in n of degrees $2, 3, \ldots, r + 1$, respectively. Thus the last expression above for

$$\sum_{k=1}^{n} k^{(r)}$$

is a polynomial in n of degree $r + 1$.▲

EXAMPLE 1. Express

$$\sum_{k=1}^{n} k^4$$

as a polynomial in n.

By the table in Fig. 3.16 and Eq. (8) we have

$$\sum_{k=1}^{n} k^4 = \sum_{k=1}^{n} [-k^{(1)} + 7k^{(2)} - 6k^{(3)} + k^{(4)}]$$

$$= -\sum_{k=1}^{n} k^{(1)} + 7 \sum_{k=1}^{n} k^{(2)} - 6 \sum_{k=1}^{n} k^{(3)} + \sum_{k=1}^{n} k^{(4)}$$

$$= -\frac{n^{(2)}}{2} + \frac{7n^{(3)}}{3} - \frac{6n^{(4)}}{4} + \frac{n^{(5)}}{5}.$$

By using the values given for $n^{(2)}$, $n^{(3)}$, $\ldots$, $n^{(5)}$ in the table in Fig. 3.15, the last expression can be simplified to

$$\frac{n(n + 1)(2n + 1)(3n^2 + 3n - 1)}{30},$$

which is the value given for

$$\sum_{k=1}^{n} k^4$$

in Exercise 3 in Section 3.6.

EXERCISES

1. Use the methods and results of this section to establish the following formulas.

   (a) $1 + 2 + 3 + \cdots + n = \dfrac{n(n + 1)}{2}$

   (b) $1^2 + 2^2 + 3^2 + \cdots + n^2 = \dfrac{n(n + 1)(2n + 1)}{6}$

   (c) $1^3 + 2^3 + 3^3 + \cdots + n^3 = \dfrac{n^2(n + 1)^2}{4}$

2. Find the value of
   $$1^5 + 2^5 + 3^5 + \cdots + n^5.$$

3. Consider the coefficients in the equations in the table in Fig. 3.15. Verify the following statements: (The symbol $n!$ used below is defined in Definition 4.2 of Chapter 4.)

   $1 = 1 = 1!$
   $1 + 1 = 2 = 2!$
   $2 + 3 + 1 = 6 = 3!$
   $6 + 11 + 6 + 1 = 24 = 4!$
   $24 + 50 + 35 + 10 + 1 = 120 = 5!$
   $120 + 274 + 225 + 85 + 15 + 1 = 720 = 6!$
   $720 + 1764 + 1624 + 735 + 175 + 21 + 1 = 5040 = 7!$
   $5040 + 13{,}068 + 13{,}132 + 6769 + 1960 + 322 + 28 + 1 = 40{,}320 = 8!$

4. Consider the sum of the coefficients in Eq. (5). Use mathematical induction and the recurrence relation in Eq. (3) to prove that

   $$a_{r1} + a_{r2} + \cdots + a_{rr} = r!, \qquad r = 1, 2, 3, \ldots$$

5. The following identity is a special case of the more general identity given in Exercise 4(d) in Section 6.5:

   $$\sum_{i=0}^{r} \binom{r}{i} n^{(r-i)} m^{(i)} = (n + m)^{(r)}. \tag{9}$$

   The binomial coefficients $\binom{r}{0}$, $\binom{r}{1}$, ..., $\binom{r}{r}$ and the binomial theorem are treated in Section 4.4. Use the formula in Eq. (9) to prove the following identity [see Eq. (7)]:

   $$kk^{(r)} = k^{(r+1)} - rk^{(r)}, \qquad r = 0, 1, 2, \ldots \tag{10}$$

   [*Hint:* The equation in (10) is true for $r = 0$ by equations (1). Assume next that $r \geq 1$. In Eq. (9) replace n by $k + 1$ and m by -1; then Eq. (9) becomes

   $$(k + 1)^{(r)} - r(k + 1)^{(r-1)} = k^{(r)}. \tag{11}$$

   Multiply this equation by k:

   $$k(k + 1)^{(r)} - rk(k + 1)^{(r-1)} = kk^{(r)}. \tag{12}$$

   Use the definition of the factorial function in equations (1) to reduce Eq. (12) to Eq. (10).]

CHAPTER 4

Counting Methods

4.1 INTRODUCTION; ARRANGEMENTS AND SEQUENTIAL COUNTING

Counting the number of elements in a small set is a familiar operation and is usually considered to be a simple problem. The basic rule for counting the number of elements in a set is to count each element in the set once and only once. There are no difficulties so long as the number of elements in the set is small, permitting each element to be exhibited individually. However, many quite simple problems in mathematics involve sets which contain millions and billions of elements. Problems arise immediately when we attempt to count the number of elements in such sets because we cannot exhibit the elements one by one. Procedures based on descriptions of these sets and on properties of their members must be developed to enable us to count the number of elements in these sets. These counting problems are one part of a branch of mathematics known as *combinatorial analysis*.

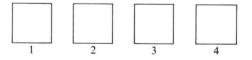

Fig. 4.1. Four cells to be used in forming an arrangement of the elements of the set $\{a, b, c, d\}$.

Let us consider the following problem. The set $\{a, b, c, d\}$ of four distinct elements is given, and the four cells shown in Fig. 4.1 are given also. The four cells are ordered so that we have a first cell, a second cell, a third cell, and a fourth cell. Usually the cells are pictured as arranged in a horizontal row, with the first cell at the left and the fourth (or last) cell at the right as in the figure. The elements of the set $\{a, b, c, d\}$ are to be placed in the four cells so that each element of the set is in one of the cells and so that each of the four cells contains one element of the set. The problem is to find the total number of ways in which the elements of the set can be placed in the cells under the restrictions described.

One way to solve this problem is to list all the ways in which the elements of the set can be placed in the four cells; the list is given in Fig. 4.2. Each way of putting the elements of $\{a, b, c, d\}$ in the four cells so that each element is in one cell and each cell contains exactly one element of the set is called an *arrangement* of the elements of the set. For example, *a b c d* represents one arrangement, and *c d a b* is another. Sometimes we are interested in the arrangements themselves, but more frequently we need to know only the total number of such arrangements. By counting the list of arrangements in Fig. 4.2, we find that there are 24 arrangements of the elements of the set $\{a, b, c, d\}$ in the four cells in Fig. 4.1.

a b c d	*b a c d*	*c a b d*	*d a b c*
a b d c	*b a d c*	*c a d b*	*d a c b*
a c b d	*b c a d*	*c b a d*	*d b a c*
a c d b	*b c d a*	*c b d a*	*d b c a*
a d b c	*b d a c*	*c d a b*	*d c a b*
a d c b	*b d c a*	*c d b a*	*d c b a*

Fig. 4.2. List of all of the ways in which the elements of the set $\{a, b, c, d\}$ can be arranged in the four cells in Fig. 4.1.

Although we have solved the special problem of finding the number of ways of arranging four elements in four cells, the solution has not provided us with much information which will help in solving other similar problems. We need an algorithm for solving the following class of problems. Find the number of ways in which the n distinct elements of the set $\{a_1, a_2, \ldots, a_n\}$ can be placed in n ordered cells so that each element of the set is in one cell, and so that each cell contains one element of the set.

Definition 4.1. Given a set $S = \{a_1, a_2, \ldots, a_n\}$ with n distinct elements and given n ordered cells, an arrangement of the elements of S is formed by placing the elements of S in the cells so that (1) each element of S is in a cell, and (2) each cell contains exactly one element of S. Two arrangements A_1 and A_2 of the elements of S are equal if and only if, for each i ($1 \leq i \leq n$), the element of S in the ith cell of A_1 is the same as the element of S in the ith cell of A_2.

Before we undertake to determine the number of arrangements of n elements in n cells, let us analyze the special case of arranging four elements in four cells. The first step in forming an arrangement is to select one of the four elements to

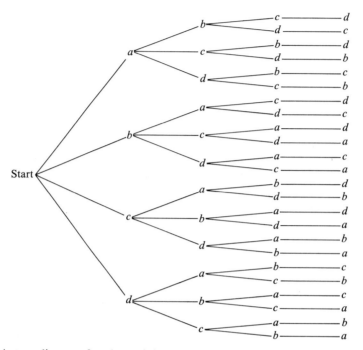

Fig. 4.3. A tree diagram for determining the arrangements of the elements of the set $\{a, b, c, d\}$ in four cells.

place in the first cell. The diagram in Fig. 4.3 shows that either a, b, c, or d can be chosen as the element to be placed in the first cell. The diagram shows that either b, c, or d can be placed in the second cell if a was placed in the first; three branches, with ends marked b, c, d proceed from the branch whose end is marked a. Other branches of the diagram show the elements which can be placed in the second cell corresponding to the choices b, c, and d for the first cell. Continuing in this fashion, we complete the diagram in Fig. 4.3 which contains a complete analysis of the ways in which arrangements can be made of the elements of $\{a, b, c, d\}$ by placing these elements in the four cells.

A diagram such as the one in Fig. 4.3 is called a *tree diagram* because it resembles a tree and its branches. A succession of branches forming a broken line which joins the word "start" at the left with the end of a branch at the right is called a *path*. There is a one-to-one correspondence between the paths in the diagram and the arrangements of the elements of the set $\{a, b, c, d\}$. It is easy to count the paths in Fig. 4.3 by counting their terminals at the right, and thus determine that there are 24 arrangements of the four elements of the set. This example suggests the following general principle.

Principle of Sequential Counting. If a first act can be performed in m ways and if, after the first act has been performed, a second act can be performed in n ways, then these two acts can be performed in this order in mn ways. More generally, if a first act can be performed in n_1 ways, a second in n_2 ways, . . . , and an rth act in n_r ways, then these r acts can be performed in this order in $n_1 n_2 \ldots n_r$ different ways.

Consider the case in which there are two acts to be performed; a tree diagram will be constructed to indicate the correctness of the principle. The word "start" is followed by m branches corresponding to the m ways of performing the first act. Each of these branches is followed by n branches corresponding to the n ways of performing the second act. The tree diagram thus contains mn paths from "start" to a terminal, and there are mn ways of performing the two acts.

The case in which there are r acts, $r > 2$, can be treated either by drawing the corresponding tree diagram or by applying induction to the case already treated. There are $n_1 n_2$ ways to perform the first two acts (now considered a single operation), and n_3 ways to perform the third; thus there are $(n_1 n_2)n_3$ ways to perform the three acts. It is clear how the proof is to be completed by induction.

It will be convenient to define a new function before we state and prove a theorem which completes the problem of finding the number of arrangements of the elements of a set of n objects.

Definition 4.2. The function F defined on the nonnegative integers by the values

$$F(0) = 1,$$
$$F(n) = n(n - 1)(n - 2) \cdots 3 \cdot 2 \cdot 1, \qquad n \geq 1,$$

is called the *factorial function*. The values of this function are usually denoted by $n!$ (read, n factorial). Thus by definition,

$$0! = 1,$$
$$n! = n(n - 1)(n - 2) \cdots 3 \cdot 2 \cdot 1, \qquad n \geq 1,$$

and the factorial function is $\{(n, n!) \mid n \in \omega_0\}$, where ω_0 is the set of non-negative integers.

From the definition of $n!$ we see that $n! = n[(n - 1)!]$ for $n \geq 1$. This relation enables us to compute the first few values of $n!$ without difficulty and we find that

$0! = 1,$	$6! = 720,$
$1! = 1,$	$7! = 5,040,$
$2! = 2,$	$8! = 40,320,$
$3! = 6,$	$9! = 362,880,$
$4! = 24,$	$10! = 3,628,800,$
$5! = 120,$	$11! = 39,916,800.$

The values of the factorial function increase very rapidly as n increases. However, these values can be computed with relative ease with a modern automatic digital computing machine.

Theorem 4.1. The number of arrangements of the n distinct elements of the set $\{a_1, a_2, \ldots, a_n\}$ is $n!$.

Proof. The proof of this theorem uses the principle of sequential counting. Any one of the n elements of the set can be placed in the first cell. After each of the choices for the first cell, $(n - 1)$ elements remain in the set and any one of them can be placed in the second cell. Continuing in this manner, we see that one element remains after the first $(n - 1)$ cells have been filled; thus there is one way to fill the last cell. Hence the total number of ways to form an arrangement of the n elements of the set is $n(n - 1)(n - 2) \cdots 3 \cdot 2 \cdot 1$, or $n!$.▲

There is a generalization of the problem of arranging n distinct elements in n cells. It frequently happens that the number of cells is r, where $0 \leq r \leq n$. An *arrangement of n distinct elements taken r at a time* is formed as follows: exactly one element of the set $\{a_1, a_2, \ldots, a_n\}$ is placed in each of the r cells. If $r = 0$, then there is exactly one way in which the arrangement can be formed. If $1 \leq r \leq n$, the first cell can be filled in n ways, the second in $(n - 1)$ ways, $\ldots$, and the rth can be filled in $(n - r + 1)$ ways. It follows from the principle of sequential counting that the total number of arrangements in this case is $n(n - 1) \cdots (n - r + 1)$.

The symbol $P_n(r)$ is frequently used to denote the number of arrangements of n distinct objects taken r at a time. We have shown that

$$P_n(0) = 1;$$

$$P_n(r) = n(n - 1) \cdots (n - r + 1) = \frac{n!}{(n - r)!}, \qquad 1 \leq r \leq n.$$

If r is set equal to zero in the second expression here for $P_n(r)$, it gives the correct value, 1, for $P_n(0)$. We have thus proved the following theorem.

Theorem 4.2. If $P_n(r)$ denotes the number of arrangements of n distinct elements taken r at a time, then

$$P_n(r) = \frac{n!}{(n - r)!}, \qquad 0 \leq n, \quad 0 \leq r \leq n. \tag{1}$$

EXAMPLE 1. How many distinct "words" of four letters each can be made by using the four letters in the word "MATH" once in each "word"?

Here the term "word" means an arrangement of the four letters in "MATH" without regard to sense. Thus each arrangement of the letters A, H, M, T forms a "word," and conversely, each "word" formed from these letters gives an arrangement of the letters. Therefore the number of "words" is the number of arrangements of the set of four distinct objects, and the number of "words" is 4!, or 24, by Theorem 4.1.

EXAMPLE 2. Find the number of ways in which r elements, $0 \leq r \leq n$, can be selected *successively without replacement* from a set $S = \{a_1, a_2, \ldots, a_n\}$ of n distinct elements. More precisely, the problem is the following. Select an element from S and remove it from the set; without replacing the first element selected, choose a second element and remove it. Continue in this fashion until r elements have been selected successively without replacement.

The selection of r elements from S under the conditions described is clearly equivalent to the formation of an arrangement of the n elements of S taken r at a time. Thus, by Theorem 4.2, the number of ways in which r elements can be selected successively without replacement from a set of n elements is $P_n(r)$, where $P_n(r)$ has the value stated in (1).

EXAMPLE 3. How many "words" of three letters each can be formed from the six letters of the word "MATRIX"?

In this example, each arrangement of three letters selected from the six letters is a "word," and each "word" of three letters is an arrangement of the six letters taken three at a time. Thus, by Theorem 4.2, the number of "words" is $P_6(3)$, or 120.

EXAMPLE 4. How many "words" of either two letters or three letters can be formed from the six letters of the word "MATRIX"?

By Example 3 above, 120 "words" of three letters each can be formed from the six letters of "MATRIX." Similarly, there are $P_6(2)$, or 30, "words" with two letters each. Thus the total number of ways to form "words" with either two or three letters is $120 + 30 = 150$.

The reader might be tempted to try to apply the principle of sequential counting by analyzing the problem as follows. First, select the number of letters to be used in making words (there are two choices: either two or three). Second, form "words" with the chosen number of letters. There are two acts to be performed in succession, but the number of ways in which the second act can be performed depends on which of the two possible choices was made for the first act. The principle of sequential counting can be applied only if the number of ways in which the second act can be performed is the same for each of the possible ways of performing the first act. The solution of this example requires an application of the principle of disjunctive counting which will be treated later in this section.

Although the principle of sequential counting cannot be applied, this example can be analyzed with the aid of a tree diagram. The first step in solving the problem is to choose the number of letters to be used in making "words." Corresponding to the two ways in which this decision can be made are two branches which proceed to the right from the word "start" in Fig. 4.4. The second step is to form "words" with the appropriate number of letters. A branch is added to the tree diagram for each "word." One branch at the first stage is followed by 30 branches at the second stage, but the other branch at the first stage is followed by 120 branches at the second stage. The total number of ways to form "words" of two or three letters is the total number of paths through the tree diagram. This number is easily seen to be 150.

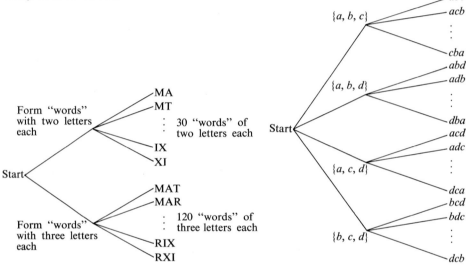

Fig. 4.4. Tree diagram for Example 4.   **Fig. 4.5.** Tree diagram for Example 5.

EXAMPLE 5. Let S be a set with four distinct elements, $S = \{a, b, c, d\}$. Compute by a second method the number $P_4(3)$ of arrangements of the four elements of S taken three at a time.

This problem will be analyzed with the aid of a tree diagram. Arrangements of the four elements of S taken three at a time can be made in the following way: first, select three of the elements; second, make all possible arrangements from these three elements. There are clearly four different ways to select three elements, for each of the four elements can be omitted in turn. Corresponding to the four ways of selecting three elements from $\{a, b, c, d\}$, there are four branches in Fig. 4.5 which lead from "start" to the following four sets: $\{a, b, c\}$, $\{a, b, d\}$, $\{a, c, d\}$, and $\{b, c, d\}$. By Theorem 4.1, three elements can be arranged in 3!, or 6, different ways. Thus each of the first four branches in the tree diagram in Fig. 4.5 is followed by six branches, one for each of the arrangements of the three letters in the set at the end of the first branch. The principle of sequential counting applies, and there are $4 \cdot 6$, or 24, arrangements of the four elements taken three at a time. This result agrees with the one given by Theorem 4.2, for

$$P_4(3) = \frac{4!}{1!} = 24.$$

In Section 4.3 an important result will be obtained from the two ways of counting the number of arrangements of n distinct objects taken r at a time. The two ways of counting must give the same result. Let $C_n(r)$ denote the number of sets of r objects that can be selected from a set of n objects. In this example we have shown that

$$P_4(3) = C_4(3) \cdot 3!.$$

Thus

$$C_4(3) = \frac{P_4(3)}{3!} = \frac{4!}{3!1!} = 4.$$

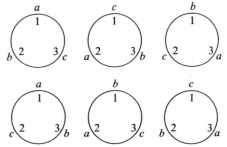

In the present example the value of $C_4(3)$ was known to be 4, and nothing new has been obtained. The method used here, however, will be employed in Section 4.3 to show that

$$C_n(r) = \frac{n!}{r!(n - r)!}.$$

Fig. 4.6. Arrangements of three persons around a circular table.

EXAMPLE 6. In how many ways can n persons be seated around a circular table?

A special case of this problem will be solved, and the general case will be left as an exercise (see Exercises 5 and 6). We shall consider the problem of arranging three persons around a circular table.

Let the three persons be a, b, c, and let the three positions at the table be denoted by 1, 2, 3. There are three ways to select a person for the first position, two ways to select a person for the second position once the first has been filled, and one way to select a person for the third position after the first two have been filled. By the principle of sequential counting, there are 3!, or 6, different ways to seat the three persons in the three positions at the table. These six arrangements are shown in Fig. 4.6.

The answer to the problem is clearly six if we are concerned only with the positions occupied by the three persons. But there is another problem which has a different answer. In the three arrangements in the top row of Fig. 4.6 we observe that b sits to the right of a and to the left of c, that c sits to the right of b and to the left of a, and that a sits to the right of c and to the left of b. These three arrangements will be defined to be the same; similarly, the three arrangements in the bottom row are defined to be the same. Thus in terms of the seating order around the table, there are only two arrangements.

There is a third problem which has still a third answer. In each of the arrangements in Fig. 4.6, we observe that the neighbors of a (the set consisting of the
person who sits on the right of a and the person who sits on the left of a) are
$\{b, c\}$, the neighbors of b are $\{a, c\}$, and the neighbors of c are $\{a, b\}$. The six
arrangements in Fig. 4.6 are defined to be the same in terms of sets of neighbors.
Thus in terms of neighbors, there is only one arrangement of the three persons
around a circular table.

EXERCISES

1. Find the value of each of the following expressions.

   (a) $13!$ (b) $\dfrac{8!}{6!2!}$ (c) $\dfrac{10!}{8!}$

   (d) $\dfrac{52!}{50!2!}$ (e) $\dfrac{101!}{99!}$ (f) $\dfrac{12!}{9!}$

2. How many "words" (meaningless or not) can be formed from the letters of the
   word "HERMAN"? The set to be counted consists of "words" of one letter, two
   letters, three letters, four letters, five letters, and six letters.

3. Make a tree diagram to show all the arrangements of the elements of the set $\{a, b, c\}$
   where a, b, and c are assumed to be distinct objects.

4. How many different ways are there to seat seven people at a counter which has
   seven seats? At a counter which has ten seats?

5. In how many ways can four persons be seated around a circular conference table?
   Draw a figure to show all the arrangements when positions at the table are taken
   into consideration. How many arrangements are there if two arrangements are
   considered to be different if and only if they involve a different seating order? Indicate in your figure which of the original arrangements involve the same seating
   order and can be considered the same in the second part of the problem. Finally,
   how many arrangements are there if two arrangements are considered to be different if and only if at least one of the four persons has different sets of neighbors
   in the two arrangements? Indicate in your figure which of the original arrangements
   provide the same sets of neighbors for each of the four persons.

6. In how many different ways can n people be seated around a circular conference
   table?

7. A certain club has four members. In how many ways can the club elect a president,
   a secretary, and a treasurer? Solve the problem in two ways.

8. Compute $P_5(4)$ in two ways. First, apply the principle of sequential counting to the
   successive selection of elements to fill the four cells in the arrangement. Second,
   apply the same principle to the selection of four of the elements from the five given
   and the formation of arrangements from them. Show that the two methods of
   counting give the same result.

9. A club with 100 members wishes to elect a set of officers consisting of a president, a
   vice-president, a secretary, and a treasurer. How many different sets of officers can
   the club elect?

10. A first urn contains one white ball and one black ball, and a second urn contains one red ball, one green ball, and one yellow ball. An experiment is performed as follows. One ball is drawn at random from the first urn and placed in the second urn; two balls are then drawn successively without replacement from the second urn. Draw a tree diagram to analyze all possible outcomes of this experiment. Count the number of outcomes by counting the number of paths in the tree diagram. In addition, count the number of outcomes by using the principle of sequential counting.

11. Consider again the experiment in Exercise 10; a different experiment is performed as follows. If the white ball is drawn from the first urn, it is placed in the second urn and two balls are drawn successively without replacement from the second urn. If the black ball is drawn from the first urn, it is placed in the second urn and three balls are drawn successively without replacement from the second urn. Draw a tree diagram to analyze and count the set of outcomes of this experiment. It is not possible to use the principle of sequential counting to count the set of outcomes in this case. Why?

12. Show that the following relations hold for every nonnegative integer n.
    (a) $n! + (n + 1)! = (n + 2)(n!)$ (b) $(n + 1)! - n! = n(n!)$

13. Use the fact that $n! = n[(n - 1)!]$ for $n \geq 1$ to explain how one could successively compute the values of $n!$.

14. If $k^{(r)}$ denotes the values of the rising factorial function of Section 3.7, show that $1^{(n)} = n!$.

15. Consider Example 6 again. There are six arrangements of the three persons at the circular table if arrangements are counted in terms of positions at the table. Let S denote this set of six arrangements. Define a relation $\simeq$ on S as follows. If A and B are two elements of S, then $A \simeq B$ if and only if the seating order in the arrangements A and B are the same. Show that $\simeq$ is an equivalence relation on the set S. Define a second relation, $\approx$, on S as follows. If A and B are two elements of S, then $A \approx B$ if and only if each person has the same set of neighbors in A and in B. Show that $\approx$ is an equivalence relation on S.

16. The arrangements of four persons around a circular table were considered in Exercise 5. Define the relations $\simeq$ and $\approx$ on the set S of these arrangements as in Exercise 15 and investigate the properties of these relations.

17. The arrangements of n persons around a circular table were considered in Exercise 6. Define the relations $\simeq$ and $\approx$ on the set S of these arrangements as in Exercise 15 and investigate the properties of these relations.

4.2 MORE SEQUENTIAL COUNTING AND DISJUNCTIVE COUNTING

The following examples illustrate further counting problems.

EXAMPLE 1. In Example 1 of Section 4.1 we showed that 24 "words" of four letters can be formed from the letters of the word "MATH" if each letter is used exactly once. Consider a new problem in which "words" of four letters each are to be formed, but in which any one of the four letters in "MATH" can be used for each of the four letters in the "word." The first letter can now be selected in four ways, the second in four ways, the third in four ways, and the fourth in four ways. By the principle of sequential counting, a total of $4 \cdot 4 \cdot 4 \cdot 4$, or 256, "words" can be formed.

EXAMPLE 2. A set S with n distinct elements is given. An element is drawn from the set, noted, and replaced in the set. A total of r elements are drawn *successively with replacement.* How many different outcomes are there to the r drawings? Since each element is replaced after it is drawn, any one of the n elements in the set can be drawn on each of the r drawings. By the principle of sequential counting, there are $n \cdot n \cdot \ldots \cdot n$ (r factors n), or n^r, different ways in which the r elements can be drawn.

EXAMPLE 3. A set S with n distinct elements is given. Find the number of subsets of S.

A subset of S is formed in the following manner. Each element of S is considered, and a decision is made to accept it for the subset or to reject it. The decision to accept or reject can be made for each of the n elements in S. These decisions can be made in $2 \cdot 2 \cdot \ldots \cdot 2$, or 2^n, different ways; therefore, the set S has 2^n subsets. One of these 2^n subsets of S is S itself (every element of S is accepted), and one of the subsets is the empty set $\emptyset$ (every element of S is rejected).

Each of the Examples 1, 2, and 3 required special cases of a certain general theorem for its solution. This theorem provides a simple method for counting the number of elements in a Cartesian product. It is stated in Theorem 4.3.

To give a concise statement of Theorem 4.3 we need some notation for the number of elements in a finite set. The process of counting the number of elements in a finite set associates a nonnegative integer with the set. Counting is thus a process of finding a value of a certain function. This function is defined as follows.

Definition 4.3. The function $\{(S, N(S)) \mid S$ is a finite set, $N(S)$ is the number of elements in $S\}$ is called the *counting function.* The domain of the counting function is the set of all finite sets; the range of the counting function is the set of nonnegative integers. The values of the counting function are denoted by $N(S)$.

Having defined the counting function, we are ready to state Theorem 4.3.

Theorem 4.3. If $S, S_1, S_2, \ldots, S_r$ are finite sets, then

$$N(S_1 \times S_2 \times \cdots \times S_r) = N(S_1) \cdot N(S_2) \cdot \ldots \cdot N(S_r),$$
$$N(S \times S \times \cdots \times S) = [N(S)]^r.$$

Here the second formula is the special case of the first in which

$$S_1 = S_2 = \cdots = S_r = S.$$

Proof. Recall that $S_1 \times S_2 \times \cdots \times S_r$ is the set of r-tuples in which the first element of each r-tuple is chosen from S_1, the second from $S_2, \ldots,$ and the rth from S_r. Since the set S_i contains $N(S_i)$ elements, $i = 1, 2, \ldots, r$, there are $N(S_i)$ ways to make the ith choice. By the principle of sequential counting, there are $N(S_1) \cdot N(S_2) \cdot \ldots \cdot N(S_r)$ ways to make the r successive choices. The second statement in the theorem is a corollary of the first .▲

If S has n elements, there are n^r ways of making r successive selections, with replacement, from S; and there are $P_n(r) = n!/(n - r)!$ ways of making r successive selections, without replacement, from S. It is clear that $n^r > P_n(r)$ for $r \geq 2$ and $n \geq 2$.

There is a final counting principle which is employed in determining the number of elements in the union of two finite sets. This principle is so intuitively obvious that it has been used throughout the book without special mention. It is the following.

The Principle of Disjunctive Counting. If A and B are finite sets, and if $A \cap B = \emptyset$, then

$$N(A \cup B) = N(A) + N(B). \tag{1}$$

There are many generalizations of the principle of disjunctive counting, and many theorems which result from it. Among the most useful of these results are the following:

If $A \subset B$, then $N(B - A) = N(B) - N(A)$. \hfill (2)

If $A \subset B$, then $N(A) \leq N(B)$. \hfill (3)

If A and B are any finite sets, then $N(A \cup B) = N(A) + N(B) - N(A \cap B)$. \hfill (4)

EXAMPLE 4. Consider the 5-by-5 matrices each of whose elements is a member of the set $\{1, 2, 3, 4, 5\}$. How many such matrices are there?

Theorem 4.3 shows that a 5-by-5 matrix has 5^2 elements. Since each of the integers in the set $\{1, 2, 3, 4, 5\}$ can be chosen as each of the 5^2 elements in the matrix, there are $5^{(5^2)}$ matrices of the kind described.

EXAMPLE 5. Let S be the set of n-by-n matrices each of whose elements is a member of a set T of r distinct real numbers. Theorem 4.3 shows that there are $r^{(n^2)}$ matrices of the kind described.

EXAMPLE 6. Let M be an n-by-n matrix, let A be the set of its elements on the principal diagonal, let B be the set of its elements above the principal diagonal, and let C be the set of its elements below the principal diagonal. If D is the set of all elements of the matrix M, then $D = A \cup B \cup C$, and A, B, and C are disjoint. It follows from the principle of disjunctive counting that

$$N(D) = N(A \cup B \cup C) = N(A) + N(B) + N(C).$$

By Theorem 4.3, $N(D) = n^2$; obviously $N(A) = n$; and clearly $N(B) = N(C)$. Then

$$n^2 = n + N(B) + N(B) \quad \text{or} \quad N(B) = \frac{n(n-1)}{2}.$$

Consider the matrices whose elements are members of a set T with r distinct members. There are r^n diagonal matrices whose elements are members of T. There are $r^{n(n+1)/2}$ lower triangular matrices with elements in T. There are $r^{n(n-1)/2}$ strictly lower triangular matrices with elements in T.

EXAMPLE 7. Let S be a set which contains four different elements. In how many ways is it possible to select from S two elements successively without replacement, three elements successively with replacement, or four elements successively without replacement?

Let A be the set of ordered pairs of elements obtained by selecting two elements from S successively without replacement; then

$$N(A) = P_4(2) = \frac{4!}{2!} = 12.$$

Let B be the set of ordered triples obtained by selecting from S three elements successively with replacement; then

$$N(B) = 4^3 = 64.$$

Let C be the set of ordered 4-tuples obtained by selecting from S four elements successively without replacement; then

$$N(C) = 4! = 24.$$

The problem asks us to find $N(A \cup B \cup C)$. Since A, B, and C are disjoint, it follows from the principle of disjunctive counting that

$$N(A \cup B \cup C) = N(A) + N(B) + N(C) = 12 + 64 + 24 = 100.$$

EXERCISES

1. How many "words" of six letters each can be formed from the letters in "MATRIX" if any one of the six letters can be used for each of the letters of the "word"?

2. How many "words" of three letters each, four letters each, five letters each, or six letters each can be formed from the letters of the word "MATRIX" if any one of the six letters can be used for each of the letters in the various "words"?

3. How many different "words" of six or fewer letters can be formed from the letters of the word "HERMAN" if each of its letters can be used in each of the positions in each of the "words" formed? Compare this exercise with Exercise 2 of Section 4.1.

4. How many seven-digit telephone numbers can be formed from the digits 0, 1, 2, ..., 9?

5. How many different numbers of four digits each can be formed from the digits 0, 1, . . . , 9 if each of the digits can be used in any one of the four positions in the number?

6. How many different numbers of one digit each, two digits each, three digits each, or four digits each can be formed from the digits 0, 1, 2, . . . , 9 if each of the digits can be used in any one of the positions in the numbers? The answer is the same as the answer to Exercise 5. How do you explain the apparent contradiction?

7. How many ordered pairs with first and second elements different can be formed from the elements of a set which has n different elements?

8. A sergeant has eleven men in his squad.
   (a) In how many ways can he select one or more men for a patrol?
   (b) Two or more men for a patrol?

9. State University Press has published ten new books during the past twelve months.
   (a) In how many ways can the press select one or more of its new books for an exhibit?
   (b) In how many ways could the press prepare an exhibit consisting of two or more of its new books?
   (c) Can you solve the problem if the exhibit is to contain five or more of the new books?

10. The set $\{a, b, c\}$ with three distinct elements is given. Three successive drawings with replacement are made from the set. Construct a tree diagram to show the set of all possible outcomes for the three drawings. Compare this tree diagram with the one you drew in Exercise 3 of Section 4.1. Recall that the arrangements of the elements of $\{a, b, c\}$ are exactly the ways in which three elements can be drawn successively without replacement from $\{a, b, c\}$.

11. A set S with n distinct elements is given. The number of ways in which n elements can be drawn successively from S without replacement is $n!$; the number of ways in which n elements can be drawn from S successively with replacement is n^n. Intuitively, is $n!$ or n^n the larger number? Investigate the relative sizes of the two numbers. Exercise 10 provides information about a special case of this problem.

12. If $S = \emptyset$, what is $N(S)$? Show that your answer can be obtained directly from Eq. (2).

13. Let A and B be finite sets. Prove each of the following statements.
   (a) If $A \subset B$, then $N(B - A) = N(B) - N(A)$.
   (b) If $A \subset B$, then $N(A) \leq N(B)$.
   (c) $N(A \cup B) = N(A) + N(B) - N(A \cap B)$.

14. A penny is tossed four times. Make a list showing all possible outcomes for this experiment. Show that this experiment is equivalent to four successive drawings with replacement from a set which contains the two distinct elements H and T.

15. An experiment is performed by tossing a penny n times. Describe the set S of outcomes for this experiment. In Chapter 5 the set S will be called a *sample space* for the experiment. Find the number of elements in S.

16. An experiment is performed by throwing two dice (or by throwing one die twice). Make a table showing all possible outcomes for this experiment. How many possible outcomes are there?

17. An experiment is performed by throwing an ordinary die n times. Show that the set of all possible outcomes for this experiment can be described as the set of all n-tuples that can be formed from the integers 1, 2, 3, 4, 5, 6. How many such n-tuples are there?

4.3 DICHOTOMIES AND COMBINATIONS

A rug manufacturer has 1000 rugs in his warehouse which he would like to sell. Upon investigation, he finds that they differ in quality. He decides to classify them into three quality grades, 1, 2, and 3, and to offer them for sale. Each rug is inspected, and a tag is attached bearing one of the numbers 1, 2, or 3. Let us look more closely to see what has happened from a mathematical point of view, and what has been accomplished.

Let S denote the set of 1000 rugs. By attaching a tag bearing one of the numbers 1, 2, or 3 to each of the rugs, the manufacturer has defined a function F whose domain is S and whose range is in the set $\{1, 2, 3\}$. This function defines the following three sets:

$$A_1 = \{a \mid a \in S,\ F(a) = 1\},$$
$$A_2 = \{a \mid a \in S,\ F(a) = 2\},$$
$$A_3 = \{a \mid a \in S,\ F(a) = 3\}.$$

The three sets A_1, A_2, A_3 have the following properties:

$$A_1 \cup A_2 \cup A_3 = S;$$
$$A_i \cap A_j = \emptyset, \qquad i \neq j,\quad i = 1, 2, 3,\quad j = 1, 2, 3.$$

The set S has been subdivided into the ordered triple (A_1, A_2, A_3) of subsets. The ordered triple is a *classification* of the set S of rugs into the three quality grades. More precisely, (A_1, A_2, A_3) is a *three-part classification* of S. Section 4.5 will treat *k-part classifications*, and this section will treat the special case of *two-part classifications*. The two-part classifications are also known as dichotomies, as explained in the next definition.

Definition 4.4. An ordered couple (A_1, A_2) of sets A_1 and A_2 is a dichotomy of a set S if and only if A_1 and A_2 have the following properties:

$$A_1 \subset S,\ A_2 \subset S, \tag{1}$$

$$A_1 \cap A_2 = \emptyset, \tag{2}$$

$$A_1 \cup A_2 = S. \tag{3}$$

A dichotomy of S can be established by defining a function F whose domain is S and whose range is in $\{1, 2\}$. The dichotomy of S is then the ordered couple $(\{a \mid a \in S, F(a) = 1\}, \{a \mid a \in S, F(a) = 2\})$. Furthermore, if a dichotomy (A_1, A_2) is given, there exists a corresponding function F whose domain is S and whose range is in $\{1, 2\}$; this function F is defined as follows:

$$F(a) = 1, \quad a \in A_1,$$
$$F(a) = 2, \quad a \in A_2. \tag{4}$$

In considering a dichotomy (A_1, A_2) of a set S, it often happens that A_1 is the accepted set and that A_2 is the rejected set. If S has n elements and A_1 has r elements, A_1 is described as a *combination of n things taken r at a time*. Observe that A_1 is a set and recall that the concept of set does not include any notion of order. It is necessary to distinguish carefully between an arrangement of n things taken r at a time and a combination of n things taken r at a time.

As might be expected in this chapter, one of the problems to be considered is that of finding the number of dichotomies of a set of n elements and, correspondingly, the number of combinations of n things taken r at a time. Appropriate notation will assist us in treating these counting problems. The following two symbols denote the number of combinations of r elements that can be selected from a set of n elements:

$$\binom{n}{r}, \quad C_n(r). \tag{5}$$

Each of these symbols also denotes the number of dichotomies (A_1, A_2) of a set S of n elements in which A_1 contains r elements and A_2 contains $(n - r)$ elements.

Each of the notations in (5) has its special uses. The first symbol is frequently preferred because it has an obvious generalization to denote the number of k-part classifications of a set S of n elements; this symbol will be employed in Section 4.5. The objection to using the first symbol in (5) is that it is difficult to print. The second symbol in (5) has two advantages and one disadvantage. The advantages are that it is easy to print, and it is analogous to the symbol $P_n(r)$ used to denote the number of arrangements of n things taken r at a time. There is a certain disadvantage connected with the symbol $C_n(r)$ because there is no similar symbol in common use to indicate the number of k-part classifications of a set of n elements.

The symbols in (5) have many interesting properties; two of them are stated in the following theorem.

Theorem 4.4. If n is any nonnegative integer, and if r is an integer, then

$$\binom{n}{r} = \binom{n}{n - r}, \quad 0 \leq r \leq n; \tag{6}$$

$$\binom{n}{0} = \binom{n}{n} = 1. \tag{7}$$

Proof. The statement in Eq. (7) follows from the definition of the symbols. Consider Eq. (6). The symbol on the left denotes the number of dichotomies (A_1, A_2) in which the first set A_1 contains r elements; the symbol on the right in (6) is the number of dichotomies in which the first set contains $(n - r)$ elements. But there is a one-to-one correspondence between these two sets of dichotomies, for, if (A_1, A_2) is a dichotomy in which the first set contains r elements, then (A_2, A_1) is a dichotomy in which the first set contains $(n - r)$ elements, and conversely. Equation (6) follows from these considerations.▲

Theorem 4.5. If n is any nonnegative integer and if r is an integer, then

$$\binom{n}{r} = C_n(r) = \frac{n!}{r!(n - r)!}, \qquad 0 \le r \le n. \tag{8}$$

In preparation for the proof of this theorem, the reader should reread Example 5 and Exercise 8 in Section 4.1. The problem can be analyzed with the aid of a tree diagram as in Fig. 4.5.

Proof. Let the $C_n(r)$ dichotomies of the set S with n elements, in which the first set contains r elements, be denoted by

$$(A_{1j}, A_{2j}), \qquad j = 1, 2, \ldots, C_n(r). \tag{9}$$

We shall now analyze the problem of counting the number of ways of making an arrangement of r elements selected from the n elements of S. We know from Theorem 4.2 that the number of ways to make such arrangements is

$$P_n(r) = \frac{n!}{(n - r)!}. \tag{10}$$

We know, however, that these arrangements can be obtained by taking each of the sets $A_{11}, A_{12}, \ldots, A_{1,C_n(r)}$ and arranging the elements in each of them in all possible ways. The set A_{1j} can be selected in $C_n(r)$ ways, and the elements in each of these sets can be arranged in $r!$ ways by Theorem 4.1. Then by the principle of sequential counting (see Section 4.1), the number of distinct arrangements $P_n(r)$ of r elements selected from the n elements of S is $C_n(r) \cdot r!$, or

$$C_n(r) \cdot r! = P_n(r). \tag{11}$$

If we insert the value of $P_n(r)$ from (10), the result is

$$C_n(r) \cdot r! = \frac{n!}{(n - r)!}. \tag{12}$$

Equation (8) follows from Eq. (12).▲

n	r								
	0	1	2	3	4	5	6	7	. . .
0	1	0	0	0	0	0	0	0	. . .
1	1	1	0	0	0	0	0	0	. . .
2	1	2	1	0	0	0	0	0	. . .
3	1	3	3	1	0	0	0	0	. . .
4	1	4	6	4	1	0	0	0	. . .
5	1	5	10	10	5	1	0	0	. . .
6	1	6	15	20	15	6	1	0	. . .
7	1	7	21	35	35	21	7	1	. . .
:	:	:	:	:	:	:	:	:	

Fig. 4.7. Table of some of the values of $\binom{n}{r}$.

In preparation for the next theorem, we shall construct a table which shows some of the values of $C_n(r)$. Since $C_n(r)$ depends on two parameters, a two-way table is required.

Figure 4.7 shows some of the values of $C_n(r)$; the entries which are not zero in this table can be computed from the formula in Eq. (8). The nonzero entries in the table in Fig. 4.7 are known as *Pascal's Triangle*. For $r > n$, the two symbols in (5) are arbitrarily defined to be zero. The definition is appropriate since it is not possible to select a combination of more than n elements from a set which contains n elements. Thus a zero is entered in each position above the principal diagonal in Fig. 4.7.

The calculation of the entries in the table in Fig. 4.7 from the formula in Eq. (8) would clearly become laborious for large values of n and r, and a better method of computing the entries in the table is needed. The next theorem contains a type of formula known as a *recurrence relation*, which provides an easy means of computing the entries $C_n(r)$ in the table for all values of n and r.

Theorem 4.6. If n and r are integers such that $1 \leq n$ and $1 \leq r$, then

$$\binom{n}{r} = \binom{n-1}{r-1} + \binom{n-1}{r}. \tag{13}$$

Proof. If $r = n$, Eq. (13) is true because the number on the left is one [see Eq. (7)], the first number on the right is one [see Eq. (7)], and the second number on the right is zero as explained above. For $r > n$, each of the symbols in Eq. (13) has the value zero, and the equation is true. We shall now show that Eq. (13) is true in the remaining cases, namely, in the cases such that $1 \leq r \leq n - 1$. By replacing the symbols with their values from Eq. (8), it is easy to verify that Eq. (13) is true in these cases.

It will be instructive, however, to give a second proof of Eq. (13) in those cases for which $1 \leq r \leq n - 1$. Equation (13) will be proved by showing that each side of the equation represents the number of ways of forming a dichotomy (A_1, A_2) of a set of n elements in which the first set, A_1, contains r elements. This statement is true for the left-hand member of Eq. (13) by the definition of the symbol which appears there. We shall now consider the right-hand member of Eq. (13).

Remove one element from the set of n elements. Form a dichotomy of the remaining $(n - 1)$ elements in which the accepted set contains $(r - 1)$ elements. Add the element that was removed to the accepted set, and we have a dichotomy of the set of n elements in which the accepted set contains r elements. The number of these dichotomies that can be formed in this manner is given by the first term on the right in Eq. (13). But dichotomies in which the accepted set contains r elements can be formed in a second way. As before, remove the element from the set of n elements to form a set of $(n - 1)$ elements. Form a dichotomy of this set in which the accepted set contains r elements; place the element that was removed in the rejected set. The number of these dichotomies is given by the second term on the right of Eq. (13). It is easy to see that the dichotomies formed in the two ways are distinct (those formed in the first way contain the element

n	r			
	$\cdots$	$r-1$	r	$\cdots$
0				
1				
$\vdots$				
$n-1$		$\binom{n-1}{r-1}$	$\binom{n-1}{r}$	
n			$\binom{n}{r}$	
$\vdots$				

Fig. 4.8. Relationship in Pascal's Triangle of the three terms which appear in Eq. (13).

Dichotomies	Combinations	Arrangements	
$(\{a, b\}, \{c, d\})$	$\{a, b\}$	(a, b)	(b, a)
$(\{a, c\}, \{b, d\})$	$\{a, c\}$	(a, c)	(c, a)
$(\{a, d\}, \{b, c\})$	$\{a, d\}$	(a, d)	(d, a)
$(\{b, c\}, \{a, d\})$	$\{b, c\}$	(b, c)	(c, b)
$(\{b, d\}, \{a, c\})$	$\{b, d\}$	(b, d)	(d, b)
$(\{c, d\}, \{a, b\})$	$\{c, d\}$	(c, d)	(d, c)

Fig. 4.9. Dichotomies in which the first set contains two elements, combinations of two elements, and arrangements of two elements formed from the set $\{a, b, c, d\}$ with four distinct elements.

that was removed, but those formed in the second way do not). Further, every dichotomy of the set of n elements in which the accepted set contains r elements can be formed in one of the two ways. The proof that the right-hand member of Eq. (13) is also the number of ways in which dichotomies can be formed with r elements in the accepted set is thus complete.

Equation (13) has thus been established for $1 \leq r \leq n - 1$, and the proof of the entire theorem is complete.▲

Equation (13) asserts that any entry in the table in Fig. 4.7 for which $n \geq 1$ and $r \geq 1$ is the sum of two entries in the preceding row. The relationship of these three terms in Pascal's Triangle is shown in Fig. 4.8. Each element in Pascal's Triangle is the sum of the element above it plus the element above and one column to the left of it.

Equation (8) shows that every entry in the first column of the table in Fig. 4.7 is a one; further, all other entries in the first row are zero. With this beginning it is now easy to use Eq. (13) to compute all other entries in the table. The reader should verify Eq. (13) for a number of entries in the table of Fig. 4.7.

EXAMPLE 1. Let $\{a, b, c, d\}$ be a set with four distinct elements. Figure 4.9 shows the following three sets: (1) the set of dichotomies of the set of four elements in which the first set in each dichotomy contains two elements, (2) the set of combinations of the four elements taken two at a time, and (3) the set of arrangements of the four elements taken two at a time.

EXAMPLE 2. Let S be a set with n distinct elements. A *k-part partition* of the set S is a set $\{A_1, A_2, \ldots, A_k\}$ of k sets $A_1, A_2, \ldots, A_k$ with the following properties:

$$A_i \subset S, \quad i = 1, 2, \ldots, k, \tag{14}$$

$$A_i \cap A_j = \emptyset, \quad i \neq j, \quad i, j = 1, 2, \ldots, k, \tag{15}$$

$$A_1 \cup A_2 \cup \cdots \cup A_k = S. \tag{16}$$

It is important to compare classifications and partitions of a set S, but since classifications have not yet been defined in the general case, this comparison must be postponed until Section 4.5. A two-part classification (or dichotomy), however, is an ordered couple of subsets of S, whereas a two-part partition is only a set of two subsets of S.

Consider the special case of dichotomies and two-part partitions. The dichotomies of the set $\{a, b, c, d\}$ (see Example 1) in which each set contains two elements are shown in Fig. 4.9. The set $\{a, b, c, d\}$ also has two-part partitions in which each set has two elements. These partitions and the corresponding dichotomies are shown in Fig. 4.10.

Partitions	Dichotomies
$\{\{a, b\}, \{c, d\}\}$	$(\{a, b\}, \{c, d\})$
	$(\{c, d\}, \{a, b\})$
$\{\{a, c\}, \{b, d\}\}$	$(\{a, c\}, \{b, d\})$
	$(\{b, d\}, \{a, c\})$
$\{\{a, d\}, \{b, c\}\}$	$(\{a, d\}, \{b, c\})$
	$(\{b, c\}, \{a, d\})$

Fig. 4.10. Two-part partitions and dichotomies of the set $\{a, b, c, d\}$ in which each of the subsets contains two elements.

EXAMPLE 3. We shall now prove the following important formula:

$$\binom{n}{0} + \binom{n}{1} + \binom{n}{2} + \cdots + \binom{n}{n} = 2^n, \qquad n \in \omega_0. \tag{17}$$

Recall the meaning of the symbols on the left in Eq. (17). Let S be a set with n distinct elements. Then the successive terms on the left in Eq. (17) represent the number of dichotomies of S with zero elements in the first set, one element in the first set, two elements in the first set, . . . , n elements in the first set. Thus the left-hand member of Eq. (17) is the total number of dichotomies of S. We shall show that the total number of dichotomies of S is the same as the number of sets in the power set $\Pi(S)$. This statement is true because there is a one-to-one correspondence between the dichotomies of S and the sets in $\Pi(S)$. For, if $A \in \Pi(S)$, then $(A, S - A)$ is a corresponding dichotomy of S; and if (A, B) is any dichotomy of S, then A is a corresponding set in $\Pi(S)$. Thus we have shown that the left-hand member of Eq. (17) is equal to the number of sets in $\Pi(S)$, that is, to the number of subsets of S. It was shown in Example 3 of Section 4.2, however, that S has 2^n subsets. The proof of Eq. (17) is complete.

EXAMPLE 4. We shall now find the number of two-part partitions of a set S with n distinct elements. There are two dichotomies which correspond to each partition in Fig. 4.10. Furthermore, if $\{A_1, A_2\}$ is any two-part partition of S,

Partitions	Dichotomies	Combinations
$\{\emptyset, \{a, b, c\}\}$	$(\emptyset, \{a, b, c\})$ $(\{a, b, c\}, \emptyset)$	$\emptyset$ $\{a, b, c\}$
$\{\{a\}, \{b, c\}\}$	$(\{a\}, \{b, c\})$ $(\{b, c\}, \{a\})$	$\{a\}$ $\{b, c\}$
$\{\{b\}, \{a, c\}\}$	$(\{b\}, \{a, c\})$ $(\{a, c\}, \{b\})$	$\{b\}$ $\{a, c\}$
$\{\{c\}, \{a, b\}\}$	$(\{c\}, \{a, b\})$ $(\{a, b\}, \{c\})$	$\{c\}$ $\{a, b\}$

Fig. 4.11. Partitions and the corresponding dichotomies and combinations of the set $\{a, b, c\}$ of three distinct elements.

then (A_1, A_2) and (A_2, A_1) are two corresponding dichotomies of S. Thus the number of two-part partitions of S is one-half the number of dichotomies of S. Since there are 2^n dichotomies of S by Example 3, there are 2^{n-1} two-part partitions of a set with n distinct elements.

EXAMPLE 5. Let $S = \{a, b, c\}$ be a set with three distinct elements. The first column of Fig. 4.11 shows all the two-part partitions of S; there are 2^2, or four, of them as required by Example 4. The second column in the figure shows the dichotomies of S which correspond to the partitions in the first column; there are two dichotomies for each partition. Finally, the third column shows the combinations (the accepted sets) which correspond to the dichotomies in the second column; there is one combination for each dichotomy. The column of combinations contains all the sets in the power set $\Pi(S)$ of S. Since S has three elements, $\Pi(S)$ has 2^3 sets, and there are 2^3 dichotomies of S. These facts agree with the results established above. Figure 4.12 shows the arrangements that can be made from each of the combinations in the third column of Fig. 4.11. A count shows that there are 16 of these arrangements.

EXAMPLE 6. In how many ways can a sample of three light bulbs be selected from a lot which contains 30 light bulbs?

A sample is a set. The problem asks for the number of combinations of 30 things taken three at a time. By Theorem 4.5 the answer is

$$\binom{30}{3} = \frac{30!}{3!27!} = 4060.$$

EXAMPLE 7. A lot of 100 light bulbs contains eight which are defective. In how many ways can a sample of ten bulbs be selected which contains six good bulbs and four defective ones?

Combinations	Arrangements	n	P_n
$\emptyset$	(__) (the 0-tuple)	0	1
$\{a, b, c\}$	(a, b, c) (a, c, b) (b, c, a) (b, a, c) (c, a, b) (c, b, a)	1	2
		2	5
$\{a\}$	(a) (the 1-tuple)	3	16
		4	65
$\{b, c\}$	(b, c) (c, b)	5	326
$\{b\}$	(b)	6	1,957
$\{a, c\}$	(a, c) (c, a)	7	13,700
		8	109,601
$\{c\}$	(c)	9	986,410
$\{a, b\}$	(a, b) (b, a)	10	9,864,101

Fig. 4.12. Table showing the arrangements that can be formed from each of the combinations in Fig. 4.11.

Fig. 4.13. Table of values of P_n.

The selection of the sample specified can be performed as a first act followed by a second one. The first act is the selection of six good bulbs from the 92 in the lot and can be performed in $C_{92}(6)$ different ways. The second act is the selection of four defective bulbs from the eight in the lot and can be performed in $C_8(4)$ different ways. By the principle of sequential counting, the total number of ways to select a sample of six good bulbs and four defective ones is

$$C_{92}(6) \cdot C_8(4) = \frac{92!}{6!86!} \cdot \frac{8!}{4!4!} = 49{,}914{,}784{,}920.$$

EXAMPLE 8. Consider again the lot of 100 light bulbs in Example 7. In how many ways can a sample of ten bulbs be selected so that either the sample contains six good and four defective bulbs, or the sample contains five good and five defective bulbs?

It was shown in Example 7 that $C_{92}(6) \cdot C_8(4)$ different samples of ten bulbs can be drawn which contain six good bulbs and four defective bulbs. In the same way it can be shown that $C_{92}(5) \cdot C_8(5)$ different samples of ten bulbs can be drawn which contain five good bulbs and five defective ones. The two sets of samples are disjoint. By the principle of disjunctive counting (see Section 4.2) the total number of ways to draw a sample of the kinds described is

$$C_{92}(6) \cdot C_8(4) + C_{92}(5) \cdot C_8(5).$$

EXERCISES

1. Evaluate each of the following expressions.

(a) $\dbinom{7}{5}$

(b) $\dbinom{8}{6}$

(c) $\dbinom{101}{99}$

2. A box of 500 light bulbs contains 10 defective bulbs. In how many ways can a sample of 20 bulbs be selected so that the 20 bulbs are good? In how many ways can a sample of 20 bulbs be selected so that exactly one is defective?

3. How many dichotomies are there of a set of nine elements? In how many of these dichotomies does each subset contain at least three elements?

4. The United States Senate contains 100 members, two being elected from each of the 50 states. Consider the dichotomies of the Senate into a set of "yes" votes and a set of "no" votes of equal size (50 members each). In how many of these dichotomies is the State of Kansas not represented in the set of "yes" votes?

5. A club has six members; three are men and three are women. A committee with three members is to be selected. In how many ways can the committee be selected so that it contains at least one woman? Give two solutions.

6. Use the recurrence relation in Eq. (13) to extend the table in Fig. 4.7 to $n = 15$.

7. Let $S = \{a, b, c, d\}$ be a set with four distinct elements. Construct a table with four columns which shows in the first column all the two-part partitions of S. In the other three columns show the corresponding dichotomies, combinations, and arrangements (see Figs. 4.11 and 4.12). Parts of the required table are shown in Figs. 4.9 and 4.10. Verify that there are 2^3 two-part partitions, 2^4 dichotomies, 2^4 combinations, and 65 arrangements.

8. There are 16 arrangements in the table in Fig. 4.11, and there are 65 arrangements in the corresponding table constructed in Exercise 7. Determine the number of these arrangements for a set of n distinct elements for $n = 1, 2, \ldots, 12$. Can you find the general formula? [*Hint:* Let P_n denote the number of arrangements for a set of n distinct elements. Then

$$P_n = 0! \binom{n}{0} + 1! \binom{n}{1} + \cdots + r! \binom{n}{r} + \cdots + n! \binom{n}{n},$$

for each of the $\binom{n}{r}$ combinations of n elements taken r at a time can be arranged in $r!$ different ways. We compute the first few values of P_n from this formula as follows:

$$P_0 = 1, \qquad P_1 = 2, \qquad P_2 = 5, \qquad P_3 = 16, \qquad P_4 = 65.$$

If we insert the values of the symbols in the formula from Eq. (8) and simplify, we find that

$$P_n = 1 + n + n(n - 1) + \cdots + n!$$
$$= 1 + n[1 + (n - 1) + (n - 1)(n - 2) + \cdots + (n - 1)!] = 1 + nP_{n-1}.$$

Thus we have shown that the numbers P_n satisfy the following recurrence relation, or difference equation:

$$P_n = 1 + nP_{n-1}.$$

If we start with $P_0 = 1$, this recurrence relation can be used to compute all of the values of P_n in succession. The values of $P_0, P_1, \ldots, P_{10}$ are shown in the table in Fig. 4.13.

9. An urn contains three red balls and three green balls. Each ball is numbered so that it can be identified; the red balls are numbered 1, 2, 3, and the green balls are numbered 1, 2, 3.

   (a) How many samples consisting of two red balls can be selected from the urn?
   (b) How many samples consisting of one red ball and one green ball can be selected from the urn?
   (c) How many samples consisting of one red ball and two green balls can be selected from the urn? Identify each of these samples by specifying the balls contained in it.
   (d) How many samples consisting of either two red balls, two green balls, or one red ball and one green ball can be selected from the urn?
   (e) Write the set of all samples (combinations) of two balls that can be selected from the urn. Verify the answers to parts (a), (b), and (d) of this exercise by counting the number of samples of the kinds described.

10. Construct a flow chart for computing

$$\binom{n}{r}, \quad 0 \le r \le n,$$

   by using the formula

$$\binom{n}{r} = \frac{n!}{r!(n-r)!}.$$

11. Construct a flow chart for computing $\binom{n}{r}$, $0 \le r \le n$, by using the formula

$$\binom{n}{r} = \binom{n-1}{r-1} + \binom{n-1}{r}, \quad 1 \le r \le n-1.$$

4.4 BINOMIAL COEFFICIENTS AND THE BINOMIAL THEOREM

In Section 4.3 the symbols

$$\binom{n}{r}, \quad C_n(r)$$

were introduced to denote the number of combinations of n things taken r at a time or the number of dichotomies of a set of n elements in which the first set contains r elements. These numbers have many interesting properties, and they have many important applications throughout mathematics. This section treats one of the most important of these applications.

The reader will recall the following familiar formulas from algebra:

$$(x + y)^2 = x^2 + 2xy + y^2, \tag{1}$$

$$(x + y)^3 = x^3 + 3x^2y + 3xy^2 + y^3, \tag{2}$$

$$(x + y)^4 = x^4 + 4x^3y + 6x^2y^2 + 4xy^3 + y^4. \tag{3}$$

In these formulas x and y are any real numbers.

We wish to find a formula for $(x + y)^n$ for every positive integer n. Formulas (1), (2), and (3) indicate clearly the nature of the terms to be expected in $(x + y)^n$; the only problem is to find the coefficients of the successive terms. Let us examine the coefficients in (1), (2), and (3) which are listed below.

$$
\begin{array}{ccccc}
1 & 2 & 1 & & \\
1 & 3 & 3 & 1 & \\
1 & 4 & 6 & 4 & 1
\end{array}
\tag{4}
$$

The reader will undoubtedly recall that this array of numbers occurs as a part of Pascal's Triangle in Fig. 4.7. Investigation of Pascal's Triangle shows that $(x + y)^n$ can be written in the following form for $n = 0, 1, 2, 3$, and 4:

$$(x + y)^0 = \binom{0}{0},$$

$$(x + y)^1 = \binom{1}{0} x + \binom{1}{1} y,$$

$$(x + y)^2 = \binom{2}{0} x^2 + \binom{2}{1} xy + \binom{2}{2} y^2,$$

$$(x + y)^3 = \binom{3}{0} x^3 + \binom{3}{1} x^2 y + \binom{3}{2} xy^2 + \binom{3}{3} y^3,$$

$$(x + y)^4 = \binom{4}{0} x^4 + \binom{4}{1} x^3 y + \binom{4}{2} x^2 y^2 + \binom{4}{3} xy^3 + \binom{4}{4} y^4.$$

This discovery leads us to conjecture that the following theorem is true.

Theorem 4.7 (*The Binomial Theorem*). If n is any nonnegative integer, and if x and y are any real numbers, then

$$(x + y)^n = \binom{n}{0} x^n + \binom{n}{1} x^{n-1} y + \cdots + \binom{n}{r} x^{n-r} y^r + \cdots + \binom{n}{n} y^n, \tag{5}$$

or, in summation notation,

$$(x + y)^n = \sum_{r=0}^{n} \binom{n}{r} x^{n-r} y^r. \tag{6}$$

Sir Isaac Newton (1642–1727) was the first to give a proof of the binomial theorem, and several proofs are now known. We shall give a proof which employs the methods and results which were developed in Section 4.3.

Proof. By definition, for $n \geq 1$, $(x + y)^n$ is the product of n factors each of which is $(x + y)$. To form a term in the expansion of $(x + y)^n$, either the x or the y is chosen from each of the factors $(x + y)$, and the n letters so chosen are multiplied together. If the x is chosen from $(x + y)$, we shall say that the factor $(x + y)$ is selected for a first set. If the y is chosen from $(x + y)$, we shall say that $(x + y)$ is selected for a second set. Proceeding in this manner, for each factor $(x + y)$, we establish a dichotomy of the set of n factors $(x + y)$. If the first set of this dichotomy contains $(n - r)$ factors, the second set contains r factors, and the corresponding term in the expansion of $(x + y)^n$ is $x^{n-r}y^r$. The term $x^{n-r}y^r$ is obtained once for each dichotomy of the n factors $(x + y)$ in which the first set contains $(n - r)$ factors; the number of these dichotomies is $\binom{n}{n-r}$, and this number, by Theorem 4.4, is equal to $\binom{n}{r}$. Thus the term $x^{n-r}y^r$ occurs $\binom{n}{r}$ times in the expansion of $(x + y)^n$. These terms can be collected, combined into a single term, and written more briefly in the form $\binom{n}{r}x^{n-r}y^r$. The expansion of $(x + y)^n$ is the sum of all the terms which can be formed in the manner described. Thus we have shown that the expansion of $(x + y)^n$ is given by the expression in Eq. (5) or Eq. (6).▲

Because the numbers $\binom{n}{r}$ occur as the coefficients in the binomial theorem, they are frequently called *binomial coefficients*.

EXERCISES

1. Use the binomial theorem to obtain the expansion of each of the following.
   (a) $(x + y)^5$
   (b) $(x - y)^5$
   (c) $(a + b)^6$
   (d) $(x + y)^{10}$
   (e) $(1 + x)^8$
   (f) $(1 - x)^6$
   (g) $(x + 2y)^4$
   (h) $(2x - 3y)^4$
   (g) $(1 - 2x)^7$

2. Find the coefficient of x^6y^2 in the expansion of $(2x + y)^8$.

3. Give a detailed treatment of the expansion of $(x + y)^3$. Justify each step you take by quoting an appropriate algebraic property of the real numbers.

4. Verify, by the method used in proving Theorem 4.7, that the expansion of $(x + y)^n$ contains only one term x^n, only one term y^n, only n terms $x^{n-1}y$, and exactly $\binom{n}{2}$ terms $x^{n-2}y^2$ and x^2y^{n-2}.

5. Is there a binomial theorem for $(x + y)^n$ if x and y are complex numbers? If there is, what is it?

The next three exercises require a knowledge of algebraic structures.

6. Is there a binomial theorem for $(x + y)^n$ if x and y are elements of an arbitrary field? Use the algebraic properties of a field to give a detailed proof of the binomial theorem for $(x + y)^n$ for $n = 2$ and $n = 3$. Show that the formulas you obtain are included in Eqs. (5) and (6). Prove that Eqs. (5) and (6) are valid for $n \geq 0$ if x and y are elements of an arbitrary field in which the field operations are called addition and multiplication.

7. Let x and y be elements of a commutative ring in which the ring operations are called addition and multiplication. Use the algebraic properties (associativity, commutativity, and distributivity) of the ring operations to obtain expansions for $(x + y)^2$ and $(x + y)^3$. Can the results be put in the form shown in formula (5)? Show that there is a binomial formula for $(x + y)^n$, $n \geq 1$, and that it is given by formula (5).

8. Let x and y be elements of a noncommutative ring in which the ring operations are called addition and multiplication. Use the algebraic properties of the ring to obtain expansions for $(x + y)^2$ and $(x + y)^3$. Can the results be put in the form shown in formula (5)? Can you find a formula for $(x + y)^n$ for $n \geq 1$?

9. The binomial theorem can be proved by induction. Formula (5) is known to be true for small values of n. Assume that (5) is true for exponent $n - 1$ and show that it is then true for exponent n by using the fact that

$$(x + y)^n = (x + y)(x + y)^{n-1}.$$

In carrying out the details of this proof it is necessary to use the algebraic properties of addition and multiplication in the system of real numbers (or in a commutative ring) and the recurrence relations (13) in Section 4.3 for the binomial coefficients. Give the details of this proof of the binomial theorem by induction.

10. Give a second proof of the following formula (see Example 3 of Section 4.3):

$$\binom{n}{0} + \binom{n}{1} + \binom{n}{2} + \cdots + \binom{n}{n} = 2^n, \qquad n \in \omega_0.$$

[*Hint:* Set $x = 1$ and $y = 1$ in formula (5).]

4.5 CLASSIFICATIONS AND MULTINOMIAL COEFFICIENTS

Section 4.3 treated two-part classifications (also called dichotomies), but the opening paragraph of that section described a three-part classification of a lot of 1000 rugs into three quality grades. That example serves as an introduction to the general problem of k-part classifications of a set S of n distinct elements.

Definition 4.5. An ordered k-tuple of sets $(A_1, A_2, \ldots, A_k)$ is a *k-part classification* of S if and only if the sets A_i, $i = 1, 2, \ldots, k$, have the following properties:

$$A_i \subset S, \qquad i = 1, 2, \ldots, k; \tag{1}$$

$$A_i \cap A_j = \emptyset, \qquad i \neq j, \qquad i, j = 1, 2, \ldots, k; \tag{2}$$

$$A_1 \cup A_2 \cup \cdots \cup A_k = S. \tag{3}$$

A k-part classification of a set S can be established by defining a function F whose domain is S and whose range is in $\{1, 2, \ldots, k\}$. The classification of S is the ordered k-tuple $(A_1, A_2, \ldots, A_k)$, where

$$A_i = \{a \mid a \in S, F(a) = i\}, \qquad i = 1, 2, \ldots, k. \tag{4}$$

Further, if a k-part classification $(A_1, A_2, \ldots, A_k)$ is given, there exists a corresponding function F whose domain is S and whose range is in $\{1, 2, \ldots, k\}$. This function F is defined by

$$F(a) = i, \qquad a \in A_i, \qquad i = 1, 2, \ldots, k. \tag{5}$$

The reader should review at this time the definition of a k-part partition of the set S which was given in Example 2 of Section 4.3. It is important to emphasize that a k-part classification is a k-tuple $(A_1, A_2, \ldots, A_k)$ and thus consists of an ordered set of k subsets of S. A k-part partition is a set $\{A_1, A_2, \ldots, A_k\}$ and therefore consists of an unordered set of k subsets of S.

In keeping with the subject of this chapter, the problem to be considered in this section is that of counting the number of k-part classifications and the number of k-part partitions of a set S of n distinct elements. First, let us introduce some notation.

The symbol

$$\binom{n}{r_1, r_2, \ldots, r_k} \tag{6}$$

denotes the number of k-part classifications $(A_1, A_2, \ldots, A_k)$ of a set S of n distinct elements in which

$$A_i \text{ contains } r_i \text{ elements,} \qquad i = 1, 2, \ldots, k. \tag{7}$$

The number in (6) is called a *multinomial coefficient* because it occurs as a coefficient in the multinomial theorem.

Theorem 4.8. If $r_1, r_2, \ldots, r_k$ are any nonnegative integers such that $r_1 + r_2 + \cdots + r_k = n$, then

$$\binom{n}{r_1, r_2, \ldots, r_k} = \frac{n!}{r_1! r_2! \ldots r_k!}. \tag{8}$$

Proof. This theorem can be proved by using the value for $\binom{n}{r}$ given in Theorem 4.5. The left-hand member of (8) is the number of k-part classifications $(A_1, A_2, \ldots, A_k)$ of S. To form this k-part classification, it is first necessary to select r_1 elements from S to form the set A_1. By Theorem 4.5, the set A_1 can be selected in

$$\binom{n}{r_1} = \frac{n!}{r_1!(n - r_1)!} \tag{9}$$

different ways. After r_1 elements have been selected to form the set A_1, there remain $n - r_1$ elements in S. From them, r_2 elements can be selected in

$$\binom{n - r_1}{r_2} = \frac{(n - r_1)!}{r_2!(n - r_1 - r_2)!} \tag{10}$$

different ways to form the set A_2. Continuing in this manner, we see that finally r_k elements can be selected to form the set A_k in

$$\binom{n - r_1 - r_2 - \cdots - r_{k-1}}{r_k} = \frac{(n - r_1 - r_2 - \cdots - r_{k-1})!}{r_k!(n - r_1 - \cdots - r_k)!} \tag{11}$$

different ways (since $r_1 + r_2 + \cdots + r_k = n$, the number in Eq. (11) is clearly 1). By the principle of sequential counting, the number of ways to select $A_1, A_2, \ldots, A_k$ in succession is

$$\frac{n!}{r_1!(n - r_1)!} \cdot \frac{(n - r_1)!}{r_2!(n - r_1 - r_2)!} \cdots \frac{(n - r_1 - r_2 - \cdots - r_{k-1})!}{r_k!0!}.$$

This number simplifies to the number given on the right in Eq. (8).▲

The reader is undoubtedly familiar with a few special cases of the trinomial theorem. For example,

$$(x + y + z)^2 = x^2 + y^2 + z^2 + 2xy + 2xz + 2yz, \tag{12}$$

$$(x + y + z)^3 = x^3 + 3x^2y + 3x^2z + 6xyz + 3xy^2 + 3xz^2 + y^3 \tag{13}$$
$$+ 3y^2z + 3yz^2 + z^3.$$

From Eq. (8) we see that the expansion in Eq. (13) can be written in the following form:

$$(x + y + z)^3 = \binom{3}{3,0,0} x^3 + \binom{3}{2,1,0} x^2y + \binom{3}{2,0,1} x^2z$$
$$+ \binom{3}{1,1,1} xyz + \binom{3}{1,2,0} xy^2 + \binom{3}{1,0,2} xz^2$$
$$+ \binom{3}{0,3,0} y^3 + \binom{3}{0,2,1} y^2z + \binom{3}{0,1,2} yz^2$$
$$+ \binom{3}{0,0,3} z^3. \tag{14}$$

These expansions are special cases of the following general theorem.

Theorem 4.9 (*The Multinomial Theorem*). Let n be any nonnegative integer, and let $x_1, x_2, \ldots, x_k$ be any real numbers. Then

$$(x_1 + x_2 + \cdots + x_k)^n = \sum \binom{n}{r_1, r_2, \ldots, r_k} x_1^{r_1} x_2^{r_2} \ldots x_k^{r_k}, \tag{15}$$

where the summation is extended over all ordered k-tuples $(r_1, r_2, \ldots, r_k)$ of nonnegative integers $r_1, r_2, \ldots, r_k$ such that $r_1 + r_2 + \cdots + r_k = n$.

The proof of this theorem is similar to the proof of Theorem 4.7; the details of this proof are left as an exercise for the reader.

EXAMPLE 1. In how many different ways can the 52 cards in a deck be dealt into four hands for a bridge game?

The question is really this: how many classifications (A_1, A_2, A_3, A_4) are there of a set of 52 distinct elements in which A_1, A_2, A_3, and A_4 contain 13 elements? By (6) and Theorem 4.8, the answer is

$$\binom{52}{13,\ 13,\ 13,\ 13} = \frac{52!}{13!\,13!\,13!\,13!}.\tag{16}$$

The number of different ways in which the 52 cards can be dealt is clearly a very large number.

EXAMPLE 2. Both the binomial coefficients (see Theorem 4.6) and the multinomial coefficients satisfy recurrence relations. For example, the trinomial coefficients satisfy the following recurrence relation:

$$\binom{n}{r_1, r_2, r_3} = \binom{n-1}{r_1-1, r_2, r_3} + \binom{n-1}{r_1, r_2-1, r_3} + \binom{n-1}{r_1, r_2, r_3-1}.\tag{17}$$

The truth of formula (17) can be verified by replacing the multinomial coefficients by their values as given in formula (8). It is also possible to give a proof of Eq. (17) which is similar to the second proof of Theorem 4.6. The details are left as an exercise for the reader.

Three-part partitions	Three-part classifications	Number of three-part classifications
$\{\{a, b, c\},\ \emptyset,\ \emptyset\}$	$(\{a, b, c\},\ \emptyset,\ \emptyset)$ $(\emptyset,\ \{a, b, c\},\ \emptyset)$ $(\emptyset,\ \emptyset,\ \{a, b, c\})$	3
$\{\{a, b\},\ \{c\},\ \emptyset\}$		6
$\{\{a, c\},\ \{b\},\ \emptyset\}$		6
$\{\{b, c\},\ \{a\},\ \emptyset\}$		6
$\{\{a\},\ \{b\},\ \{c\}\}$		6
	Total	27

Fig. 4.14. Three-part partitions, three-part classifications, and the number of three-part classifications of a set $\{a, b, c\}$ with three distinct elements.

EXAMPLE 3. Let $S = \{a, b, c\}$ be a set with three distinct elements. The first column in the table in Fig. 4.14 contains all of the three-part partitions of $\{a, b, c\}$. The second column contains some of the three-part classifications which correspond to the three-part partitions listed in the first column. Because the set S is small, it is easy to give an explicit listing of all of the three-part partitions of S; there are five of them as shown in the first column. Because two of the sets in the first partition are the empty set, there are only three corresponding classifications, and this number is shown in the third column. The results in Section 4.1 show that there are $3! = 6$ classifications corresponding to each of the other four partitions.   Thus the set $S = \{a, b, c\}$, with three distinct elements, has 5 three-part partitions and 27 three-part classifications.

EXAMPLE 4.   It has been shown in Example 3 of Section 4.3 and in Exercise 10 of Section 4.4 that

$$\sum_{r=0}^{n} \binom{n}{r} = 2^n. \tag{18}$$

The two proofs given for this formula can be generalized to show that

$$\sum \binom{n}{r_1, r_2, \ldots, r_k} = k^n, \tag{19}$$

where the summation is extended over all ordered k-tuples $(r_1, r_2, \ldots, r_k)$ of nonnegative integers $r_1, r_2, \ldots, r_k$ such that $r_1 + r_2 + \cdots + r_k = n$.

Consider the first proof.   Let S be a set $\{a_1, a_2, \ldots, a_n\}$ which contains n distinct elements.   To form a k-part classification of S, it must be decided for each element a_i whether it is to be placed in A_1, in A_2, \ldots, or in A_k.   There are n elements, and the decision about where each element is placed can be made in k ways.   By the principle of sequential counting, the decisions can be made in k^n different ways.   Each different way of making the set of decisions gives a classification of S, and each classification of S corresponds to exactly one way of making the n decisions.   These facts establish formula (19).   The reader will find it instructive to reread Example 3 of Section 4.2.

A second proof of formula (19) is obtained by setting $x_1 = x_2 = \cdots = x_k$ in formula (15).

EXAMPLE 5.   Find the number of three-part partitions of a set S with n distinct elements.

The number of three-part classifications of S is known by the result established in Example 4.   The number of three-part partitions will be found by establishing a relation between the number of partitions and the number of classifications.

Let $P_n(3)$ denote the number of three-part partitions of S.   One of these partitions is $\{S, \emptyset, \emptyset\}$, and from this partition we obtain the following three classifications: $(S, \emptyset, \emptyset)$, $(\emptyset, S, \emptyset)$, and $(\emptyset, \emptyset, S)$.   From each of the other $P_n(3) - 1$ partitions it is possible to form 3! classifications (see Fig. 4.14).   Since the total number of three-part classifications of S is 3^n by Eq. (19), we have

$$3!(P_n(3) - 1) + 3 = 3^n.$$

Solving this equation for P_n, we obtain

$$P_n(3) = \frac{3^{n-1} + 1}{2}. \tag{20}$$

This formula gives $P_3(3) = 5$, a result which agrees with that shown in Fig. 4.14.

EXERCISES

1. Expand each of the following expressions by using the multinomial theorem.
   (a) $(x + y + z)^4$ (b) $(x + y + z + w)^3$
   (c) $(1 - x - y)^4$ (d) $(1 + 2x - 2y)^4$
   (e) $(ax + by + cz)^n$ (f) $(x + y + z + w)^5$

2. In the expansion of $(x + y + z + w)^{10}$, compute the coefficients of the following terms.
   (a) x^{10} (b) y^5z^5 (c) $x^4y^2zw^3$

3. Find the number of terms in each of the following expansions.
   (a) $(x + y + z)^4$ (b) $(x + y + z)^5$ (c) $(x + y + z + w)^3$
   (d) $(x + y + z + w)^4$ (e) $(x_1 + x_2 + \cdots + x_k)^n$

4. How many ways are there to distribute a penny, a nickel, a dime, a quarter, a half-dollar, and a silver dollar among three boys so that the first receives three coins, the second two coins, and the third one coin? If the third boy is to receive the half-dollar or the silver dollar, then how many ways are there?

5. State University has a small residence hall which contains four single rooms, six double rooms, and three rooms for three students each. In how many ways can 25 men be assigned to the 13 rooms?

6. Complete the second column in Fig. 4.14 and verify that there are 3^3, or 27, three-part classifications of the set $\{a, b, c\}$ of three distinct elements.

7. A set $S = \{a, b, c, d\}$ with four distinct elements is given. Construct a table for the set $\{a, b, c, d\}$ which corresponds to the table in Fig. 4.14 for the set $\{a, b, c\}$. Show that there are 14 three-part partitions of S [see Example 5 and formula (20)] and 3^4, or 81, three-part classifications of S.

8. Give a proof of the multinomial theorem.

9. Write the second proof of formula (17).

10. A set S contains n distinct elements. How many n-part classifications $(A_1, A_2, \ldots, A_n)$ of S are there in which each set $A_1, A_2, \ldots, A_n$ contains exactly one element? Explain your answer.

11. Compute the number of four-part partitions of a set S which contains four distinct elements.

12. A recurrence relation for the multinomial coefficient

$$\binom{n}{r_1, r_2, r_3}$$

is given in Eq. (17). State and prove a similar recurrence relation for the multinomial coefficient

$$\binom{n}{r_1, r_2, \ldots, r_k}.$$

4.6 INDISTINGUISHABLE ELEMENTS

In Section 4.1 we developed methods for counting the number of arrangements of a set of n elements, but it was assumed that the n elements were distinct. Other counting problems have been treated in this chapter, but the assumption has always been the same: that all the elements are distinct. In some counting problems, however, we either cannot distinguish among some of the elements of a set, or we do not care to do so. The following examples will illustrate these types of problems.

EXAMPLE 1. How many different "words" of four letters each can be made by using all the letters of the word "MOON" exactly once in each word? As before, a "word" is any sequence of the four letters in "MOON" without regard to sense.

The number of letters in the word "MOON" is small, and the problem can be solved by listing all the words and counting them. The list is shown below.

M O O N	O O M N	N M O O
M O N O	O O N M	N O O M
M N O O	O M O N	N O M O
	O M N O	
	O N M O	
	O N O M	

By counting the words in the list, we find that there are 12 distinguishable arrangements of the four letters in the word "MOON." The method used here, however, is not practical if the number of elements to be arranged is large.

EXAMPLE 2. Consider again the problem in Example 1. The construction of a tree diagram provides a systematic method of forming all the arrangements of the letters of the word "MOON." Figure 4.15 shows a tree diagram for this problem. The "words" listed in Example 1 are shown on this tree diagram. The reader should compare Fig. 4.15 with Fig. 4.3. The latter contains a tree diagram for finding the arrangements of the elements of the set $\{a, b, c, d\}$. The reader should compare the two figures carefully to see why there are 24 arrange-

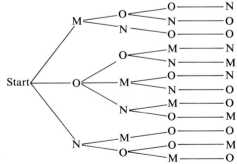

Fig. 4.15. Tree diagram for finding the distinguishable arrangements of the letters of the word "MOON."

ments of the elements of the set $\{a, b, c, d\}$, but only 12 distinguishable arrangements of the letters of the word "MOON."

EXAMPLE 3. We shall give a third solution for the problem in Example 1. Consider the cells in Fig. 4.16; each cell is identified by its number. Arrangements of the letters in "MOON" are formed by putting one letter in each cell. We can obtain all possible distinguishable "words" in the following way. Form all classifications (A_1, A_2, A_3) of the elements of the set $\{1, 2, 3, 4\}$ in which A_1 contains two elements and A_2 and A_3 contain one element each. The letter "O" is placed in the two cells corresponding to the integers in the set A_1, the letter "M" is placed in the cell designated by the integer in A_2, and the letter "N" is placed in the cell designated by A_3. By Section 4.5 [see Eq. (6) and Theorem 4.8], there are

$$\binom{4}{2, 1, 1} = \frac{4!}{2!1!1!} = 12$$

different classifications of the kind described. The reader should write out the 12 classifications, place the four letters in the cells designated, and verify that the distinguishable arrangements of the letters of the word "MOON" are those listed in Example 1.

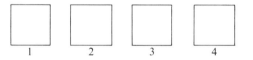

Fig. 4.16. Ordered cells to be used in forming distinguishable arrangements of the letters in the word "MOON."

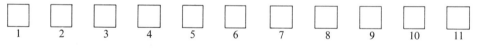

Fig. 4.17. Cells for the arrangements in Example 4.

EXAMPLE 4. Find the number of distinguishable arrangements of the letters in the word "MISSISSIPPI."

The number of letters to be arranged in this case is large, and it would be difficult (essentially impossible!) to list all of them (see Example 1). If the arrangements themselves are desired, however, the construction of a tree diagram (see Example 2) provides a systematic method of forming these arrangements. If only the number of distinguishable arrangements is required, it can be found easily by the method used in Example 3. The eleven letters of the word "MISSISSIPPI" are to be placed in the cells shown in Fig. 4.17. The letter "M" occurs once, the letter "I" occurs four times, the letter "S" occurs four times, and the letter "P" occurs twice. Form classifications (A_1, A_2, A_3, A_4) of the set $S = \{1, 2, 3, \ldots, 11\}$ in which A_1 contains a single integer in S, A_2 contains four integers in the set S, A_3 contains four integers in S, and A_4 contains two integers in S. There are

$$\binom{11}{1, 4, 4, 2} = \frac{11!}{1!4!4!2!} = 34,650$$

such classifications. An arrangement of the letters in the word "MISSISSIPPI" is formed by putting the letter "M" in the cells designated by the integers in A_1, the letter "I" in the cells designated by the integers in A_2, the letter "S" in the cells designated by the integers in A_3, and the letter "P" in the cells designated by the integers in A_4. All distinguishable arrangements are obtained in this manner; there are 34,650 of them.

EXAMPLE 5. In how many ways can eight customers be seated at a lunch counter which contains twelve seats?

We shall solve the problem first on the assumption that the eight customers are distinguishable. Number the twelve seats at the counter with the integers in the set $\{1, 2, \ldots, 12\}$. Form all possible classifications $(A_1, A_2, \ldots, A_8, A_9)$ of $\{1, 2, \ldots, 12\}$ in which $A_1, A_2, \ldots, A_8$ contain one integer each, and A_9 contains four integers. There are

$$\binom{12}{1, 1, \ldots, 1, 4} = \frac{12!}{1! \ldots 1!4!} = 19,958,400$$

different classifications of the kind described. Customer C_1 is placed in the seat designated by the integer in A_1, customer C_2 in the seat designated by the integer in $A_2, \ldots$, and customer C_8 in the seat designated by the integer in A_8. The seats designated by the integers in A_9 are left empty. All possible arrangements of the eight customers occupying the twelve seats at the counter are formed in this manner.

A second interpretation of the problem can result in a very different answer. We can assume that the customers are indistinguishable. In this case our only concern is whether the seats are filled or empty. To solve the problem, we form classifications (A_1, A_2) of the set $1, 2, \ldots, 12$ in which A_1 contains eight integers (designating seats for the customers) and A_2 contains four integers (designating seats to be left empty). There are

$$\binom{12}{8, 4} = \frac{12!}{8!4!} = 495$$

such classifications. There are thus 495 ways to arrange the eight customers in the twelve seats at the lunch counter, if the customers are indistinguishable and we are concerned only with whether seats are filled or empty.

Two-part classifications of the set $\{a, b, c\}$		Distinguishable arrangements of $\{a, a, a\}$ in TWO cells	
a, b, c		a, a, a	
a, b	c		
a, c	b	a, a	a
b, c	a		
a	b, c		
b	a, c	a	a, a
c	a, b		
	a, b, c		a, a, a

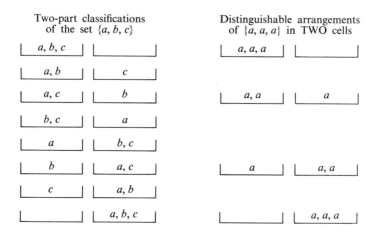

Fig. 4.18. Two-part classifications of the set $\{a, b, c\}$ and distinguishable arrangements of the set $\{a, a, a\}$ in two cells.

EXAMPLE 6. There are many problems in which we are asked to distribute a set of n indistinguishable objects in k cells. The column on the right in Fig. 4.18 shows all arrangements of the three indistinguishable elements a, a, a in two cells. The column on the left in the same figure shows the eight two-part classifications of the set $\{a, b, c\}$ of three distinct elements. The second, third, and fourth classifications of distinct elements correspond to a single arrangement in the two cells of the three indistinguishable elements; similarly, the fifth, sixth, and seventh classifications of the three distinct elements correspond to one arrangement of the indistinguishable elements. The arrangements of the indistinguishable elements can be indicated as follows:

$$|\,a\,a\,a\,|\;\;|, \qquad |\,a\,a\,|\,a\,|, \qquad |\,a\,|\,a\,a\,|, \qquad |\;\;|\,a\,a\,a\,|.$$

The spaces between the vertical bars are the cells. There must be a vertical bar at each end, but between these vertical bars we have the distinguishable arrangements of four elements, three of which are of one kind (the elements) and one of which is of another kind (the vertical bar). As shown above the number of distinguishable arrangements of these elements is

$$\binom{4}{3,\,1} = \frac{4!}{3!\,1!} = 4.$$

If there are n indistinguishable elements and k cells, then the problem is solved (see Fig. 4.19) by finding the number of distinguishable arrangements of $(k - 1) + n$,

Fig. 4.19. Analysis of the problem of distributing n indistinguishable elements in k cells.

$$\Big|\;\;|\;\;|\;\;|\;.\,.\,.\;|\;a\;a\;a\;.\,.\,.\;a\;\;\Big|$$

or $n + k - 1$, elements, of which n are of one kind and $k - 1$ are of another kind. Thus, as shown above, the number of ways to put the n elements in the k cells is

$$\binom{n + k - 1}{n} = \frac{(n + k - 1)!}{n!(k - 1)!}.$$

EXAMPLE 7. Find the number of different terms in the expansion of $(x_1 + x_2 + \cdots + x_k)^n$ by the multinomial theorem.

In preparation for the solution of this problem, the reader should reread the proof of Theorem 4.7. To form a term in the multinomial expansion, each of the n indistinguishable factors $(x_1 + x_2 + \cdots + x_k)$ must be placed in one of k cells. In forming terms in the expansion, x_1 is selected from each factor in the first cell, x_2 from each factor in the second cell, . . . , and x_k is selected from each factor in the kth cell. Each different way of placing the n factors in the k cells gives a different term in the expansion. Since there are

$$\binom{n + k - 1}{n} = \frac{(n + k - 1)!}{n!(k - 1)!}$$

different ways to place the n factors in k cells, there are also this many different terms in the expansion of

$$(x_1 + x_2 + \cdots + x_k)^n.$$

According to the formula just derived, the expansions of $(x + y + z)^2$ and $(x + y + z)^3$ contain six and ten terms respectively. These results can be verified by counting the terms in these expansions in Eqs. (12) and (13) of Section 4.5.

In the course of solving the problems in the above examples, two theorems have essentially been proved. Formal statements of these theorems will be given now so that reference to them will be easy in the future.

Theorem 4.10. The number of distinguishable arrangements of n elements, r_1 of which are (indistinguishable) of one kind, r_2 of which are (indistinguishable) of a second kind, . . . , and r_k of which are (indistinguishable) of a kth kind is

$$\binom{n}{r_1, r_2, \ldots, r_k} = \frac{n!}{r_1! r_2! \ldots r_k!}.$$

A formal proof of this theorem can be given by the methods employed in Examples 3 and 4 above.

Theorem 4.11. The number of ways in which n indistinguishable elements can be placed in k cells, any number of elements being permitted in each cell, is

$$\binom{n + k - 1}{n} = \frac{(n + k - 1)!}{n!(k - 1)!}.$$

EXERCISES

1. How many different arrangements can be made from five quarters, six dimes, four nickels, and seven pennies?

2. Draw the first two sets of branches of a tree diagram for solving the problem in Example 4.

3. How many arrangements can be made from the president, the four vice-presidents, and the ten deans of State University?

4. One hundred votes are cast for three candidates for the same office in a certain club. How many different ways can these votes be cast?

5. An elevator which serves 13 floors has nine passengers.
   (a) In how many ways can the passengers be discharged if we do not distinguish among passengers?
   (b) In how many of these ways do no two get off at the same floor?

6. How many different "words" of four letters or less can be formed by using each letter of the word "MOON" at most once?

7. A state legislature has 25 units of money which it can appropriate for five special projects. In how many different ways can the 25 units of money be allocated among the five projects?

8. Find the number of terms in the expansion of $(x + y + z)^{10}$; in the expansion of $(x + y + z + w)^6$; in the expansion of $(x + y)^n$.

9. One hundred persons cast votes for three candidates for the same office in a certain club. In how many ways can the 100 persons, considered as distinguishable, cast their votes for the three candidates?

10. How many four-part partitions are there of the set $S = \{a, b, c, d\}$ of four distinct elements? [*Hint:* It is known that the set S has 4^4, or 256, four-part classifications (see Example 4 of Section 4.5). The problem will be solved by establishing the connection between the number of four-part partitions and the number of four-part classifications. The reader should reread Example 5 of Section 4.5.

    Let $P_4(4)$ denote the number of four-part partitions of S. These partitions are of three types: (a) the partition $\{S, \emptyset, \emptyset, \emptyset\}$, (b) partitions of the form $\{A_1, A_2, \emptyset, \emptyset\}$, where $A_1 \cup A_2 = S$, $A_1 \cap A_2 = \emptyset$, and A_1 and A_2 are not empty, and (c) all the others. Since there are 2^{n-1} two-part partitions of a set of n distinct elements (see Example 4 of Section 4.5), there are seven partitions of type (b) [the partition in (a) is one of the eight two-part partitions]. Four classifications can be made by rearranging the sets in the partition in (a). Since A_1 and A_2 are distinct, it is possible to make

$$\binom{4}{1, 1, 2} = \frac{4!}{1!1!2!} = 12$$

different classifications by rearranging the sets in the partitions in (b). A total of $4!$ different classifications can be made from each of the $P_4(4) - 8$ partitions in (c).

These facts yield the equation

$$4 + 7 \cdot 12 + 4!(P_4(4) - 8) = 256.$$

By solving this equation we find $P_4(4)$.]

11. How many four-part partitions are there of the set $S = \{a_1, a_2, \ldots, a_n\}$ of n distinct elements? [*Hint:* The solution is similar to that of Exercise 10. There is one partition of type (a) from which four classifications can be made. There are $2^{n-1} - 1$ partitions of type (b) and $4!/2!$ classifications can be made from each of them. If $P_n(4)$ is the total number of partitions, then there are $P_n(4) - 2^{n-1}$ partitions of type (c) and $4!$ classifications can be made from each of them. The total number of four-part classifications of a set of n distinct elements is 4^n (see Example 4 of Section 4.5). These facts lead to the following equation:

$$4 + \frac{4!}{2!}(2^{n-1} - 1) + 4!(P_n(4) - 2^{n-1}) = 4^n.$$

Solve this equation for $P_n(4)$.]

12. How many five-part partitions are there of a set $S = \{a_1, a_2, \ldots, a_n\}$ of n distinct elements?

CHAPTER 5

Probability Spaces

5.1 INTRODUCTION

Undergraduate courses in mathematics have long been dominated by calculus, differential equations, advanced calculus, and other subjects which are now described as "deterministic, few-variable" mathematics. The success of Sir Isaac Newton (1642–1727) in solving the problem of determining the motions of the solar system undoubtedly helped to establish the study of calculus and differential equations in a central position. In recent years, however, the theory of probability has become increasingly important not only as a subject in theoretical mathematics, but also as a tool for use in the biological, management, and social sciences, as well as in the physical sciences and engineering.

The theory of probability treats phenomena in which chance events occur. Probability theory, as we know it today, has developed from the investigations of games of chance initiated by Blaise Pascal (1623–1662). It has been discovered recently, however, that Girolamo Cardano (1501–1576) also made extensive studies of the theory of probability in connection with games of chance and gambling. A major advance in the development of the subject occurred early in the nineteenth century when Pierre-Simon de Laplace (1749–1827) showed that probability theory can be applied to many other problems of both a scientific and practical nature.

We have said that probability theory can be approached both as a subject in theoretical mathematics and as a tool for the study of certain problems in applied mathematics. As a subject in pure mathematics, probability theory, in its most general form, is an advanced and sophisticated area of mathematics which requires a knowledge of modern measure theory and integration theory; it is well beyond the scope of this book. However, there are elementary but nonetheless important parts of the subject for which mathematically correct and complete treatments can be given; these are the parts of the subject which are included in this book.

As a tool for the study of certain problems in applied mathematics, probability theory appears as a mathematical model. A mathematical model is an abstraction which usually ignores many elements and relationships in the real world problem it is designed to interpret. This is also true for probability theory considered as a mathematical model for the study of chance phenomena. The mathematical model which can be constructed with the aid of the elementary parts of the theory of probability is adequate for the study of many applied problems of the highest importance and significance.

The mathematical model which will be constructed in this chapter is called a *probability model* or a *probability space*. The treatment will separate the mathematical construction and development of the model from its applications in the study of real world problems. This separation is made so that the mathematical character of a probability space is not obscured by the details of the situations in which probability spaces are applied; it is important that the general and essential features of a probability space are clear no matter what the applications may be. After the mathematical treatment of probability spaces has been presented, we will work many examples in an effort to show the nature of the applications of probability theory. Finally, we will provide many exercises designed to illustrate the basic ideas and general principles as well as to give practice in applying the theory.

5.2 THE SAMPLE SPACE

In Chapter 1 the concept of a set was introduced. In the present chapter a set is given a new name; a set S is called a *sample space*. If S has only a finite number of elements, then S is called a *finite sample space*. In the present chapter all sets have only a finite number of elements; thus this chapter is restricted to a study of finite sample spaces. A singleton subset $\{a\}$ of a sample space S is called an *elementary event*. A subset A of S is called an *event;* in particular, an elementary event is an event. Furthermore, since $\emptyset \subset S$ and $S \subset S$, $\emptyset$ and S are events. The null set $\emptyset$ is called the *impossible event*, and the entire sample space S is called the *certain* or *sure event*. If A and B are any events, then the event A *or* B is the event $A \cup B$, and the event A *and* B is the event $A \cap B$.

EXAMPLE 1. Let S be the set $\{1, 2, 3, 4\}$. Then S is a finite sample space, and the elementary events are

$$\{1\}, \quad \{2\}, \quad \{3\}, \quad \{4\}.$$

There are $2^4 = 16$ events; they are the subsets of S listed below:

$\{1\}$,	$\{2\}$,	$\{3\}$,	$\{4\}$,
$\{1, 2\}$,	$\{1, 3\}$,	$\{1, 4\}$,	
$\{2, 3\}$,	$\{2, 4\}$,	$\{3, 4\}$,	
$\{1, 2, 3\}$,	$\{1, 2, 4\}$,	$\{1, 3, 4\}$,	$\{2, 3, 4\}$,
S,	$\emptyset$.		

EXAMPLE 2.   Consider the sample space S in Example 1 again.   The events "*A* or *B*" and "*A* and *B*," for a number of events A and B, are given in the table in Fig. 5.1.

A	B	A or B	A and B
$\{1, 2\}$	$\{2, 4\}$	$\{1, 2, 4\}$	$\{2\}$
$\{1, 2\}$	$\{3, 4\}$	S	$\emptyset$
$\{1, 3, 4\}$	$\{1, 2, 4\}$	S	$\{1, 4\}$
S	$\emptyset$	S	$\emptyset$
$\{1, 2, 3, 4\}$	$\{2, 4\}$	$\{1, 2, 3, 4\}$	$\{2, 4\}$
$\{2, 3, 4\}$	$\{3, 4\}$	$\{2, 3, 4\}$	$\{3, 4\}$
$\{1, 3, 4\}$	$\{2\}$	S	$\emptyset$

Fig. 5.1. Table of events "*A* or *B*" and "*A* and *B*" for the given events A and B.

EXAMPLE 3.   Let S be the sample space $\{H, T\}$.   Then S is a finite sample space, and the four possible events are $\emptyset$, $\{H\}$, $\{T\}$, and S. The elementary events are $\{H\}$ and $\{T\}$.   The event $\{H\}$ or $\{T\}$ is S; the event $\{H\}$ and $\{T\}$ is $\emptyset$.

EXAMPLE 4.   Let $S = \{(i, j) \mid i$ and j are integers, $1 \leq i \leq 6,\ 1 \leq j \leq 6\}$. Then S is a finite sample space which has 36 elementary events.   The number of events is equal to the number of sets in the power set of S; hence, there are 2^{36} events.   If $A = \{(i, j) \mid i, j$ are positive integers, $i + j = 7\}$, $B = \{(1, 6), (3, 4), (5, 2)\}$, then A or B is the event A, and A and B is the event B.

EXERCISES

1. Let $S = \{a, b, c\}$. Show that S is a finite sample space, and that there are three elementary events and eight events. List all possible events for the sample space S.

2. A five-place arrangement is made from the letters H and T; the set S consists of all of these arrangements. Show that S is a finite sample space, and that there are $2^5 = 32$ elementary events. List all of the elementary events. Show that there are

2^{32} events for this sample space. If $A = \{(H, H, T, T, T), (H, H, H, T, T)\}$ and $B = \{(H, H, T, T, T), (T, T, H, H, H)\}$, find the event A or B and the event A and B.

3. An urn contains three red balls (numbered 1, 2, 3 so that they can be distinguished) and two green balls (numbered 1, 2). The set S consists of all combinations (samples) of the five balls taken three at a time that can be selected from the urn. Show that S is a finite sample space. List all elementary events for the sample space S. Let A be the following event: each element of A is a sample of three balls which contains at least one red ball. Let B be the following event: each element of B is a sample of three balls which contains at least one green ball. List the elements in the event A and in the event B. List the elements in the event A or B and also in the event A and B.

4. Consider again the urn and the balls in Exercise 3. Let S be the set of arrangements of the five balls taken three at a time; equivalently, S is the set of ordered samples that can be formed by three successive drawings, without replacement, from the urn. Show that S is a finite sample space, and that there are 60 elementary events. List all elementary events. Compare the sample spaces in Exercises 3 and 4.

5. A sample consisting of two unordered cards is drawn from a deck of 52 cards. A sample space S consists of all unordered samples of two cards that can be drawn in this manner. Describe this sample space. How many elementary events does it contain?
   (a) Let A be the event which consists of all samples in which both cards are aces. How many elementary events are there in A?
   (b) Let B be the event which consists of all samples in which both cards are diamonds. How many elementary events are there in B?
   (c) Let C be the event which consists of all samples in which each card in the sample is either an ace or a king. How many elementary events are there in C?
   (d) Describe the event A and B. How many elementary events are there in A and B?
   (e) Describe the event A or B. How many elementary events are there in A or B?
   (f) Describe each of the following events: A and C, B and C, A and B and C. How many elementary events are there in each of these events?
   (g) Describe each of the following events: A or C, B or C, A or B or C. How many elementary events are there in each of these events?

6. A student takes a multiple choice examination which contains 25 questions. For each question the student can check an answer numbered 1, 2, 3, 4, or 5. A complete answer for the examination is an ordered set of integers $(i_1, i_2, \ldots, i_k, \ldots, i_{25})$, where i_k is 1, 2, 3, 4, or 5 for each integer k such that $1 \leq k \leq 25$. Let S be the set of all complete answers to the examination. Describe the sample space S. How many elementary events are there in S?

7. A lot of 100 transistor radios contains five defective radios. Let S consist of all samples of ten radios selected from the lot. How many elementary events are there in S?
   (a) Let A_i, $i = 0, 1, 2, 3, 4, 5$, be the event which consists of all samples which contain exactly i defective radios. How many elementary events are there in A_i?
   (b) Show that $A_i \cap A_j = \emptyset$ if $i \neq j$.

5.3 PROBABILITY SPACES

Let S be a finite sample space, and let $\Pi(S)$ be the power set of S, that is, the set of all events for the sample space S.

Definition 5.1. The function $P = \{(A, P(A)) \mid A \in \Pi(S), P(A)$ is a real number$\}$ is called a *probability function* if and only if it has the following properties:

$P(A) \geq 0$ for every event A in $\Pi(S)$;   (1)

$P(S) = 1$;   (2)

for every two events A and B such that $A \cap B = \emptyset$,

$$P(A \cup B) = P(A) + P(B).\tag{3}$$

The function P is called a *set function* because its domain is a family $\Pi(S)$ of sets; furthermore, P is called an *additive* set function because it has property (3). The number $P(A)$ is called the *probability of the event A*. A *finite probability space* is a finite sample space S together with a probability function P which is defined on the family $\Pi(S)$ of events; a finite probability space is denoted by (S, P).

Since all sample spaces to be considered in this and later chapters are finite, a finite probability space henceforth will be called a probability space.

EXAMPLE 1. Let $S = \{H, T\}$; then $\Pi(S)$ consists of the events $\emptyset$, $\{H\}$, $\{T\}$, S. Definite a function P on $\Pi(S)$ as follows:

$$P(\emptyset) = 0, \quad P(\{H\}) = \tfrac{1}{2}, \quad P(\{T\}) = \tfrac{1}{2}, \quad P(S) = 1.$$

Then S and P form a probability space (S, P).

EXAMPLE 2. Let $S = \{1, 2, 3, 4, 5, 6\}$, and let $\Pi(S)$ be the family of all subsets of S. Define a function $P = \{(A, P(A)) \mid A \in \Pi(S), P(A)$ is a real number$\}$ as follows:

$$P(A) = \frac{N(A)}{N(S)} = \frac{N(A)}{6}.\tag{4}$$

Here $N(A)$ and $N(S)$ denote the number of elements in the sets A and S respectively (see Definition 4.3). Then P is a probability function, and (S, P) is a probability space.

To prove that (S, P) is a probability space, we must show that P has properties (1), (2), and (3) listed in Definition 5.1. Since the number of elements in any set A is nonnegative, it is clear that $P(A) \geq 0$. Next, the number of elements in S is six; hence, $P(S) = \tfrac{6}{6} = 1$. Finally, let A and B be events which contain i and j elements respectively, and assume that $A \cap B = \emptyset$. Then $A \cup B$ contains $i + j$

elements and

$$P(A \cup B) = \frac{i + j}{6} = \frac{i}{6} + \frac{j}{6} = P(A) + P(B).$$

It follows that P is a probability function, and that (S, P) is a probability space.

If (S, P) is a probability space, the function P is defined for every event in $\Pi(S)$. Because of the property stated in Eq. (3), however, all values of P are determined if its values are specified for the elementary events in S. Thus if $S = \{a_1, a_2, \ldots, a_n\}$, $P(A)$ is determined for every event A in $\Pi(S)$ if the values

$$P(\{a_1\}), \ P(\{a_2\}), \ \ldots, \ P(\{a_n\}) \tag{5}$$

are specified. For if $A = \{a_{i_1}, a_{i_2}, \ldots, a_{i_k}\}$, then

$$P(A) = P(\{a_{i_1}\}) + P(\{a_{i_2}\}) + \cdots + P(\{a_{i_k}\}) \tag{6}$$

by the property stated in Eq. (3).

The problem of defining a probability function P is thus reduced to that of defining P for the elementary events in S [see (5) and Eq. (6)]. In defining P so that (S, P) is a probability space, we must take into account both mathematical and practical considerations. The only restrictions placed on the definition of P by the mathematical considerations are that the numbers in (5) can be chosen arbitrarily so long as

$$0 \leq P(\{a_i\}) \leq 1, \qquad i = 1, 2, \ldots, n, \tag{7}$$

$$\sum_{i=1}^{n} P(\{a_i\}) = 1. \tag{8}$$

The practical considerations require that P be defined in such a way that the probability space (S, P) is useful in the study of an experiment, or more generally, the chance phenomena under consideration. The practical considerations will be discussed in the next section.

EXERCISES

1. Which of the following definitely could not be probability functions regardless of what probabilities the function P assigns to the other possible events? Give reasons for your answers.
   (a) $P(\{a, b\}) = \frac{1}{2}$, $P(\{a\}) = \frac{2}{3}$.   (b) $P(\{a, b\}) = \frac{1}{4}$, $P(\{c, d\}) = \frac{1}{2}$.
   (c) $P(\{a, b\}) = \frac{1}{2}$, $P(\{c\}) = \frac{1}{2}$.   (d) $P(\{a, b, c\}) = 0$.
   (e) $P(\{a, b\}) = \frac{1}{2}$, $P(\{b, c, d\}) = \frac{1}{2}$, $P(\{a\}) = \frac{1}{4}$.
   (f) $P(\{a, b, c\}) = P(\{a, b, d\}) = P(\{a, c, d\}) = P(\{b, c, d\}) = \frac{1}{6}$.
   (g) $P(\{b\}) = P(\{c\}) = P(\{d\}) = \frac{1}{3}$.
   (h) $P(\{a, b, c\}) = \frac{2}{3}$, $P(\{a, b\}) = P(\{b, c\}) = \frac{1}{4}$.

2. Let S be the set $\{1, 2, \ldots, n\}$. How is the probability function P defined if the probability of each elementary event $\{1\}, \{2\}, \ldots, \{n\}$ is the same?

3. If $S = \{a_1, a_2, \ldots, a_n\}$ and if $P(\{a_i\}) = 1/n$ for each elementary event, show that

$$P(A) = \frac{N(A)}{n}$$

for each event A.

4. Let $S = \{a, b, c\}$ and define a function P so that $P(\{a\}) = \frac{1}{2}$, $P(\{b\}) = \frac{1}{2}$, and $P(\{c\}) = 0$. Use Eq. (6) to define P for other events in S. Verify that P is a probability function and that (S, P) is a probability space.

5. Consider Exercise 2 in Section 5.2. If $\{a_1\}, \{a_2\}, \ldots, \{a_{32}\}$ are the elementary events in S, define P so that $P(\{a_i\}) = \frac{1}{32}$ for $i = 1, 2, \ldots, 32$. Use Eq. (6) to define P for other events in S. Verify that P is a probability function. If C is any event in S, find a formula for $P(C)$. Find $P(A \cup B)$ and $P(A \cap B)$.

6. The sample space S in Exercise 3 in Section 5.2 contains 10 elementary events. Define P so that the probability of each of these elementary events is $\frac{1}{10}$ and define P for all other events in S by Eq. (6). Verify that P is a probability function. Find $P(A \cup B)$ and $P(A \cap B)$.

7. Consider the sample space S in Exercise 4 in Section 5.2. Define a probability function P on $\Pi(S)$ so that the probabilities of all elementary events are equal. Define A to be the event consisting of all arrangements of three balls (see Exercises 3 and 4 of Section 5.2) which contain at least one red ball. Let B be the event consisting of all arrangements of three balls which contain at least one green ball. List the elements in the event A and in the event B. Find $P(A \cup B)$ and $P(A \cap B)$ and compare these values with those found in Exercise 6.

8. Consider the sample space S in Exercise 5 in Section 5.2. Define a probability function P on $\Pi(S)$ so that the probabilities of all elementary events are equal. Find the value of each of the following.
   (a) $P(A)$, $P(B)$, $P(C)$
   (b) $P(A \cup B)$, $P(A \cup C)$, $P(B \cup C)$, $P(A \cup B \cup C)$
   (c) $P(A \cap B)$, $P(A \cap C)$, $P(B \cap C)$, $P(A \cap B \cap C)$

9. Consider the sample space S in Exercise 7 in Section 5.2. Define a probability function P on $\Pi(S)$ so that the probabilities of all elementary events are equal.
   (a) Show that

$$P(A_i) = \frac{\binom{5}{i}\binom{95}{10-i}}{\binom{100}{10}}, \qquad i = 0, 1, 2, \ldots, 5.$$

   (b) Let S' be the sample space $\{0, 1, 2, \ldots, 10\}$. Define P' on $\Pi(S')$ so that

$$P'(\{i\}) = \frac{\binom{5}{i}\binom{95}{10-i}}{\binom{100}{10}}, \qquad i = 0, 1, 2, \ldots, 10,$$

   and complete the definition of P' by Eq. (6). Show that (S', P') is a probability space. Find $P'(\{i\})$ for $i = 6, 7, \ldots, 10$.

5.4 CONSTRUCTION OF PROBABILITY SPACES

We shall now describe how a probability space can be associated with certain chance phenomena in the real world. One of the typical applications of probability theory is concerned with a study of the set of all possible outcomes of an experiment. The tossing of an ordinary six-sided die is an example of an experiment. In one analysis of this experiment, the outcome of each trial is a number —the number of dots on the upturned face of the die. Then the set of all possible outcomes of the experiment is the set $\{1, 2, 3, 4, 5, 6\}$, and the outcome of each performance of the experiment is exactly one of the integers in this set. In this analysis of the experiment, the set $\{1, 2, 3, 4, 5, 6\}$ is chosen as the sample space S. The object of the experiment, however, might be to study the appearance of an even or an odd number of dots on the die. Then it would be appropriate to choose $\{$even, odd$\}$ as the sample space S. Here again, each performance of the experiment results in one and only one of the outcomes in the sample space.

Thus in the analysis of any experiment (many are far more complicated than tossing a die!) by probability theory, the first step is the construction of a sample space. The sample space constructed has two properties: (1) it contains all possible outcomes of the experiment (in some appropriate form of analysis), and (2) each performance of the experiment results in exactly one of the possible outcomes in the sample space. Each possible outcome of the experiment corresponds to an elementary event in the sample space. As examples, observe that the sample space in Example 3 of Section 5.2 adequately describes the experiment of flipping a coin, and that the sample space in Example 4 of Section 5.2 describes the experiment of tossing a single die twice (or tossing a pair of distinguishable dice once).

The second step in the analysis of an experiment by probability theory is the assignment of probabilities to the elementary events—the definition of P for the elementary events in the sample space S. From the mathematical point of view, the definition of P on the elementary events has only the restrictions stated in Eqs. (7) and (8) of Section 5.3. From a practical point of view, however, Eqs. (7) and (8) are not very helpful. If $S = \{a_1, a_2, \ldots, a_n\}$, then in many cases we set $P(\{a_i\}) = 1/n$ for $i = 1, 2, \ldots, n$. The probabilities of the elementary events are defined to be equal when the person constructing the probability space (S, P) feels that one elementary event is just as likely to occur as any other elementary event. If $P(\{a_i\}) = 1/n$ for $i = 1, 2, \ldots, n$, we say that the elementary events are *equally likely* and that the resulting probability space (S, P) is an *equiprobable* probability space. Observe that, in an equiprobable probability space,

$$P(A) = \frac{N(A)}{N(S)}, \tag{1}$$

where N is the counting function, since each of the $N(A)$ elementary events in the event A has the same probability $1/N(S)$ (see Exercise 3 in Section 5.3).

The experimenter may doubt that the elementary events are equally likely. For this and other reasons he may wish to investigate the outcome of many repetitions of the experiment. Each repetition, or performance, of the experiment is called a *trial* of the experiment. The *relative frequency* of the elementary event $\{a_i\}$ in m trials of the experiment is defined as

$$\text{relative frequency of } \{a_i\} \text{ in } m \text{ trials} = \frac{\text{number of occurrences of } a_i \text{ in } m \text{ trials}}{m}. \quad (2)$$

There are intuitive reasons for hoping that an appropriate probability space (S, P) for the study of the experiment can be obtained by defining $P(\{a_i\})$ to be the relative frequency of the outcome a_i in m trials. Moreover, if $P(\{a_i\})$ is defined in this manner, it can be shown that P is a probability function (see Exercise 11). Unfortunately, the relative frequency of $\{a_i\}$ in m trials [see Eq. (2)] is a function of m, and two different values of m may give quite different values for the relative frequency of $\{a_i\}$. Since we have no reason to prefer one value of m to another, relative frequency does not provide the answer to the crucial question of how $P(\{a_i\})$ is to be defined.

It might be possible to overcome these objections to the use of relative frequency by defining $P(\{a_i\})$ as

$$P(\{a_i\}) = \lim_{m \to \infty} \frac{\text{number of occurrences of } a_i \text{ in } m \text{ trials}}{m}. \quad (3)$$

But in the attempt to define $P(\{a_i\})$ by Eq. (3) we encounter at least two obvious difficulties: (a) the limit in Eq. (3) cannot be determined even if we are assured that it exists, (b) it may not be possible to employ the definition in Eq. (3) because the experiment cannot be repeated. Thus efforts to base the definition of probabilities either on relative frequencies or on the limits of relative frequencies encounter insurmountable difficulties.

We shall adopt the following position, supported by many modern probabilists, as the most reasonable solution to the problem of defining probabilities. We adopt the position that probabilities will be assigned in a subjective but coherent manner, based on our beliefs regarding equally likely situations (symmetry) and influenced by relative frequency considerations. Thus we assert that the probability function P for the probability space (S, P) designed to assist in the analysis of an experiment should be defined by the person analyzing the experiment. The definition should be based on the experimenter's beliefs concerning the performance of the experiment. For example, consider the tossing of a die. If the experimenter believes that the die is unbiased (fair), he would undoubtedly assign equal probabilities to each of the six elementary events in the sample space. If the experimenter believes that the die is biased, however, he might compute the relative frequencies of the elementary events $\{a_i\}$ in m trials [see Eq. (2)] and use this information as a guide in defining probabilities. Even after the probability function P for the probability space (S, P) has been defined, the experimenter might toss the die several times (m times!) to test whether the experiment agrees satisfactorily with the predictions based on his definition of probabilities. This further testing leads to the theory of *testing of statistical hypotheses* in statistics.

For a more detailed discussion of the assignment of probabilities, the interested reader is referred to an article by de Finetti [1], from which the following statement is quoted:

> [This subjective method of assigning probabilities] calls on personal responsibility, and mathematical developments based on the coherence conditions show how and why the usual prescriptions—above all, those based on symmetry and frequency—ought to be applied, not as rigid artificial rules, but as patterns open to intelligence and discernment for proper interpretation in each case.

The above description of the construction of an appropriate probability space (S, P) for the analysis of an experiment can be summarized as follows.

(a) Select a sample space S which has the following two properties: (1) it contains all possible outcomes of the experiment (in some appropriate form of analysis), and (2) each performance of the experiment results in exactly one of the possible outcomes in the sample space.

(b) Define the probability function P for each elementary event in S in a reasonable (coherent) manner, making use of any help that can be obtained from a knowledge of symmetries involved in the experiment and of relative frequencies obtained from previous trials of the experiment.

The following example illustrates the two steps in the construction of a probability space to be used in the analysis of an experiment.

EXAMPLE 1.   Consider again the experiment of tossing an ordinary die. Choose the sample space S to be the set $\{1, 2, 3, 4, 5, 6\}$. If the die has been accurately made so that it is symmetric and so that there is reason to believe the center of gravity is at the center of the die, then it is reasonable to assign equal probabilities to the elementary events $\{1\}, \ldots, \{6\}$ in S. Thus the probability function P is defined by setting

$$P(\{i\}) = \tfrac{1}{6}, \qquad i = 1, 2, \ldots, 6. \tag{4}$$

The probability space (S, P) thus defined is a perfectly proper one, and it is not subject to any checks or verifications of any kind. However, if the probability space (S, P) is considered as a mathematical model to assist in the study of the experiment which consists of tossing a die, it is subject to an empirical verification of its appropriateness. If the mathematical model explains the observed phenomena and gives good predictions, it is considered a good model. If the predictions of the model do not agree reasonably well with the observed facts, the model may be rejected as inappropriate for the experiment. Consider, for example, the experiment of tossing a cheap die. A cheap die bought at a dime store is usually symmetric, but there are strong reasons for believing that its center of gravity is not located in the center of the die. The spots are made by drilling holes in the faces; one face has one hole, but the opposite face has six holes. An empirical test shows rather quickly that the probability space (S, P), where P is defined by Eq. (4), is not a satisfactory mathematical model for the experiment which consists of tossing a cheap die.

Finally, it should be stated that probability models are used in many situations which do not have all (and may not have any) of the characteristics of the experiment described above. A good understanding of how the probability model is constructed and applied in the canonical experiment, however, will assist the reader in applying probability theory in other situations. In spite of the many obvious logical and philosophical difficulties, the theory of probability has proved to be an important and powerful branch of applied mathematics.

EXAMPLE 2. An urn contains a red ball, a green ball, a blue ball, and a yellow ball. The balls are indistinguishable in every way except for color. A random sample of three balls is drawn from the urn. Construct a probability space (S, P) for the study of this experiment.

A "sample of three balls" is usually interpreted to mean a "combination of the four balls taken three at a time." The problem is thus concerned with unordered sets of three balls rather than with (ordered) arrangements of three balls. A *random sample* is one drawn under conditions which make each of the possible samples equally likely. Then the probability model (S, P) for the experiment described is defined by the following:

$$S = \{\{R, G, B\}, \{R, G, Y\}, \{R, B, Y\}, \{G, B, Y\}\};$$
$$P(\{R, G, B\}) = P(\{R, G, Y\}) = P(\{R, B, Y\}) = P(\{G, B, Y\}). \tag{5}$$

Because the example specifies that the experiment consists of drawing random samples, (S, P) is an equiprobable probability space.

EXAMPLE 3. It is possible to give a completely different analysis of the experiment in Example 2. The random samples of three balls can be obtained by (random) drawing of three balls successively from the urn without replacement. The sample space S can now be taken as the 24 arrangements of the four balls taken three at a time. Thus S consists of the following set of 24 arrangements of the four balls taken three at a time.

(R, G, B)	(R, G, Y)	(R, B, Y)	(G, B, Y)
(R, B, G)	(R, Y, G)	(R, Y, B)	(G, Y, B)
(G, R, B)	(G, R, Y)	(B, R, Y)	(B, G, Y)
(G, B, R)	(G, Y, R)	(B, Y, R)	(B, Y, G)
(B, R, G)	(Y, R, G)	(Y, R, B)	(Y, G, B)
(B, G, R)	(Y, G, R)	(Y, B, R)	(Y, B, G)

$$\tag{6}$$

Since the samples are random samples, each elementary event is equally likely; (S, P) is thus the equiprobable probability space obtained by assigning the probability $\frac{1}{24}$ to each of the elementary events.

There is a close connection between the probability spaces (S, P) defined in Examples 2 and 3. The sample space (6) is described as a *finer analysis* of the outcomes of the experiment than the one given in (5). The sample space (6) can be used to answer questions about Example 2. For example, (5) shows that the probability of a sample consisting of a red ball, a green ball, and a blue ball is $\frac{1}{4}$. In Example 3 let A be the following event: the sample contains a red ball, a green ball, and a blue ball. Then A contains the elements shown in the first column of (6). Thus

$$A = \{(R, G, B)\} \cup \{(R, B, G)\} \cup \{(G, R, B)\} \cup \{(G, B, R)\}$$
$$\cup \{(B, R, G)\} \cup \{(B, G, R)\}. \tag{7}$$

Each elementary event on the right in (7) has probability $\frac{1}{24}$. Then by Eq. (6) of Section 5.3,

$$P(A) = \tfrac{1}{24} + \tfrac{1}{24} + \tfrac{1}{24} + \tfrac{1}{24} + \tfrac{1}{24} + \tfrac{1}{24} = \tfrac{1}{4},$$

and we find once more that the probability of a sample which contains a red ball, a green ball, and a blue ball is $\frac{1}{4}$.

EXAMPLE 4. A jewelry store offers a certain type of wristwatch for sale on a day when it has six of these wristwatches in inventory. Construct an appropriate probability space for the study of the experiment which consists of offering the six watches for sale.

This experiment lacks the repeatable character described in the instructions given above for the construction of a probability model. Furthermore, there is nothing in the experiment which enables us to assign probabilities on *a priori* grounds. Probabilities can be assigned only in terms of the previous experience of the jewelry store. Finally, the example describes two possible experiments; one of them is concerned with the demand for the wristwatches, and the other is concerned with their sale. The probability spaces for the two experiments are shown in the table in Fig. 5.2 at the top of the next page. The first column under Experiment 1: Demand in the table lists one set of possible elementary events in a sample space for this experiment; the other column lists the probabilities. The probabilities are obtained from the records of the jewelry store; each probability is the relative frequency of the corresponding demand during the past history of the store. The first column under Experiment 2: Sales lists one set of possible elementary events in a sample space for this experiment, and the other column lists the probabilities. Once more, the probabilities are relative frequencies of the corresponding sales during the past history of the jewelry store.

EXAMPLE 5. A meteorologist predicts one of the following four conditions for the weather on the following day: clear, partly cloudy, rain, snow. Clear, partly cloudy, and rain are equally likely, but rain is twice as likely as snow. Describe an appropriate sample space S and probability function P.

Experiment 1: Demand		Experiment 2: Sales	
Number of watches demanded	Probability	Number of watches sold	Probability
0	0.05	0	0.05
1	0.10	1	0.10
2	0.10	2	0.10
3	0.20	3	0.20
4	0.25	4	0.25
5	0.15	5	0.15
6	0.10	6	0.15
≥ 7	0.05		

Fig. 5.2. The two probability spaces for Example 4.

The weather is not a repeatable experiment, and past history cannot be considered a reliable guide in predicting tomorrow's weather. Nevertheless, probability theory is applied also in such situations. The meteorologist's predictions suggest that the set {clear, partly cloudy, rain, snow} should be taken as the sample space S. Since

$$P(\{\text{clear}\}) = P(\{\text{partly cloudy}\}) = P(\{\text{rain}\}) = 2\,P(\{\text{snow}\}),$$

we see that

$$P(\{\text{clear}\}) = P(\{\text{partly cloudy}\}) = P(\{\text{rain}\}) = \tfrac{2}{7} \quad \text{and} \quad P(\{\text{snow}\}) = \tfrac{1}{7}.$$

The probabilities assigned in this case are to be interpreted as a measure of the confidence of the meteorologist that each of the conditions he has predicted will occur. In arriving at these "measures of confidence" concerning tomorrow's weather, the meteorologist studies today's weather map, past records of weather movements with similar weather maps, and past records of the weather for the given day of the year. Although the "experiment" in this case is very different from the repeatable experiments described above, nevertheless probability theory has its applications here also.

EXERCISES

1. A balanced (unbiased) die is thrown twice.
   (a) Describe a probability space (S, P) for this experiment.
   (b) Describe the following event in terms of the sample space S in (a): the sum of the two numbers which turn up on the two throws of the die is seven.
   (c) Find the probability of the event described in (b).

2. An experiment consists of throwing a die once. The die is biased (loaded) in such a way that the probability of each face is proportional to the number of dots on that face. Describe an appropriate sample space S and define the probability function P. What is the probability that the number which turns up on one throw will be odd?

3. In a certain election the probability that Jones will win is three times the probability that Black will win, and the probability that Smith will win is twice the probability that Black will win.
(a) Describe an appropriate sample space S.
(b) What is the probability function P for the sample space in (a)?
(c) What is the probability of each of the eight events in S?
(d) Find two different events which have the same probability.

4. Three airplane manufacturers X, Y, and Z are seeking the contract to build a supersonic airliner. The sales manager of X estimates that the probability that his company will secure the contract is equal to the probability that Y will obtain the contract, but that the probability that X (and hence also Y) wins the contract is twice the probability that Z wins it.
(a) What is the sample space?
(b) Define P for the sample space in (a). Observe that P in this case cannot be defined on *a priori* grounds nor in terms of relative frequencies from past experience. The probabilities here are measures of the confidence on the part of X's sales manager that certain events will occur; the sales managers of Y and Z might assess these probabilities quite differently. The exercise illustrates one of the important ways in which the theory of probability is applied.
(c) What is the probability that X or Y will obtain the contract?
(d) What is the probability that X or Z will secure the contract?

5. The probability of more than five mistakes on a page of a first draft of a book is $\frac{1}{8}$; the probability of no mistakes on a page is also $\frac{1}{8}$. The probability of exactly n mistakes ($n = 1, 2, 3, 4, 5$) is inversely proportional to n. Describe an appropriate sample space. Find the probability of each of the following events:
(a) either one or two mistakes on a page,
(b) more than three mistakes on a page,
(c) less than two mistakes on a page,
(d) more than seven mistakes.

6. A bag contains five white and four black balls. The nine balls are removed from the bag one at a time by random drawings. What is the probability that the first ball removed is white, the second black, and so on alternately?

7. An experiment consists of taking two photographs, developing and printing them, and rating them as either satisfactorily exposed, underexposed, or overexposed. Let these three conditions be denoted respectively by s, u, and o. Describe the sample space. It is given that the probabilities of each of the outcomes in S are the following:

$$P(\{(s, s)\}) = P(\{(u, u)\}) = P(\{(o, o)\}) = 0.12,$$
$$P(\{(u, s)\}) = P(\{(s, u)\}) = 0.20,$$
$$P(\{(s, o)\}) = P(\{(o, s)\}) = P(\{(o, u)\}) = P(\{(u, o)\}) = 0.06.$$

Find the probabilities of the following events.
(a) One or more satisfactory prints are obtained.
(b) Two satisfactory prints are obtained.
(c) Exactly one overexposed print is obtained.

8. The numbers 0, 1, 2, . . . , 9 are equally spaced about the circumference of a circle with a spinner. The needle is spun. Describe a sample space for this experiment. Find the probability that the needle stops between one and two.

9. What is wrong with the following argument? "If two coins are tossed, there are three possibilities: two heads, one head and one tail, and two tails. Hence, the probability of one head and one tail is $\frac{1}{3}$."

10. A lot of 100 transistor radios contains three defective radios. A random sample of five radios is selected from the lot.
(a) Find the probability that the sample contains one defective radio.
(b) Find the probability that the sample contains two defective radios.
(c) Find the probability that the sample contains either zero, one, or two defective radios.

11. Let the sample space S corresponding to a certain experiment be the set $\{a_1, a_2,$ . . . , $a_n\}$. The relative frequency f_i of the elementary event $\{a_i\}$ in m trials of the experiment is defined as in Eq. (2):

$$f_i = \frac{\text{number of occurrences of } a_i \text{ in } m \text{ trials}}{m}.$$

If P is defined so that

$$P(\{a_i\}) = f_i,$$

show that P is a probability function.

12. A counterfeiter has two counterfeit quarters and one genuine quarter in his pocket. He makes a purchase in a store, selects two quarters at random from his pocket, and gives them to the clerk in payment for his purchase. The clerk places the two quarters received in the cash drawer with three genuine quarters. The clerk selects at random a quarter from the five in the cash drawer and gives it as change to the next customer. What is the probability that this customer receives a counterfeit coin? Show that a sample space S can be constructed which consists of ordered pairs of the form $(\{a, b\}, c)$, where $\{a, b\}$ represents an unordered sample of two quarters selected from the three in the counterfeiter's pocket, and c represents a quarter selected from the five in the cash drawer. List all of the elements in the sample space. Are the various outcomes in S equally likely?

5.5 PROPERTIES OF PROBABILITY SPACES

A probability space (S, P) was defined in Section 5.3. The present section contains two theorems which state a number of properties common to all probability spaces. Only finite probability spaces were defined in Section 5.3, but both the theorems and the proofs of the theorems given in this section are valid for all probability spaces.

Theorem 5.1. Let (S, P) be an arbitrary probability space, and let A and B be events in S. Then P has the following properties:

$$P(A^c) = 1 - P(A), \text{ where } A^c = S - A; \tag{1}$$
$$0 \leq P(A) \leq 1; \tag{2}$$
$$P(\emptyset) = 0; \tag{3}$$
$$\text{if } A \subset B, \text{ then } P(B - A) = P(B) - P(A); \tag{4}$$
$$\text{if } A \subset B, \text{ then } P(A) \leq P(B); \tag{5}$$
$$P(A \cup B) = P(A) + P(B) - P(A \cap B). \tag{6}$$

Proof of (1). From the definition of the event A^c it follows that $A \cup A^c = S$ and that $A \cap A^c = \emptyset$. From properties (2) and (3) of a probability function P (see Definition 5.1) it follows that

$$1 = P(S) = P(A \cup A^c) = P(A) + P(A^c).$$

Subtracting $P(A)$ from the right and left sides of this equation, we obtain,

$$P(A^c) = 1 - P(A). \blacktriangle$$

Proof of (2). By part (1) of the theorem, $P(A^c) = 1 - P(A)$. Since the probability of any event is nonnegative by property (1) of a probability function (see Definition 5.1), it follows that

$$P(A^c) = 1 - P(A) \geq 0.$$

This statement and property (1) of a probability function imply part (2) of the theorem. $\blacktriangle$

Proof of (3). Since $A \cup \emptyset = A$ and $A \cap \emptyset = \emptyset$, it follows from property (3) of P in Definition 5.1 that

$$P(A) = P(A \cup \emptyset) = P(A) + P(\emptyset).$$

Subtracting $P(A)$ from the right-hand and left-hand sides of this equation, we obtain $P(\emptyset) = 0. \blacktriangle$

Equation (3) states that the probability of the impossible event is zero. In terms of the applications of probability theory to the real world, this result seems intuitively correct.

Proof of (4). If $A \subset B$, then B is composed of two parts, namely A and $B - A$, that part of B which is not in A (see Fig. 5.3). Thus $B = A \cup (B - A)$.

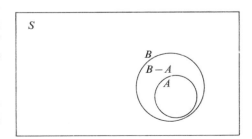

Fig. 5.3. Figure for part (4) of Theorem 5.1.

Also, $A \cap (B - A) = \emptyset$ since no element in A is in $B - A$. Therefore, by property (3) of P (see Definition 5.1),

$$P(B) = P(A \cup (B - A)) = P(A) + P(B - A).$$

Subtracting $P(A)$ from the right-hand and left-hand sides of this equation, we have

$$P(B) - P(A) = P(B - A).\blacktriangle$$

Proof of (5). Since $P(B - A) \geq 0$ and $A \subset B$, we see from part (4) of the theorem that

$$P(B) - P(A) \geq 0.$$

Then $P(A) \leq P(B).\blacktriangle$

Next let us consider the meaning of the statement in part (6) of the theorem. The elements in $A \cap B$ occur in both A and B and thus they affect both $P(A)$ and $P(B)$. The elements in $A \cap B$ have an effect on $P(A \cup B)$ only once. By subtracting $P(A \cap B)$ we compensate for the double effect of the elements in $A \cap B$ on the right-hand side of (6).

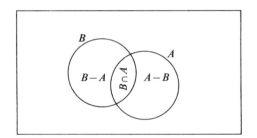

Fig. 5.4. Figure for part (6) of Theorem 5.1.

Proof of (6). It is easy to prove the following identities (see Fig. 5.4):

$$A = (A - B) \cup (A \cap B),$$
$$B = (B - A) \cup (A \cap B).$$

Furthermore,

$$(A - B) \cap (A \cap B) = \emptyset,$$
$$(B - A) \cap (A \cap B) = \emptyset.$$

Then since P is an additive set function (see Definition 5.1),

$$P(A) = P(A - B) + P(A \cap B),$$
$$P(B) = P(B - A) + P(A \cap B).$$

From these equations it follows that

$$P(A) + P(B) - P(A \cap B) = P(A - B) + P(B - A) + P(A \cap B). \tag{7}$$

Furthermore, it is easy to prove the following relations; they are suggested by the Venn diagram in Fig. 5.4:

$$A \cup B = (A - B) \cup (B - A) \cup (A \cap B),$$
$$(A - B) \cap (B - A) = \emptyset,$$
$$\{(A - B) \cup (B - A)\} \cap (A \cap B) = \emptyset.$$

Then by repeated application of the additive property of the probability function P, we find that

$$P(A \cup B) = P(\{(A - B) \cup (B - A)\} \cup (A \cap B)),$$
$$P(A \cup B) = P((A - B) \cup (B - A)) + P(A \cap B),$$
$$P(A \cup B) = P(A - B) + P(B - A) + P(A \cap B). \tag{8}$$

From Eqs. (7) and (8) it now follows that

$$P(A \cup B) = P(A) + P(B) - P(A \cap B). \blacktriangle$$

Some of the details in the proof of part (6) of Theorem 5.1 would have been shorter and simpler if we had proved first an extension of the additive property of the probability function P (see Definition 5.1). This extension of the additive property is given in the next theorem.

Theorem 5.2. Let (S, P) be an arbitrary probability space, and let $A_1, A_2, \ldots,$ A_n be any n events in S such that

$$A_i \cap A_j = \emptyset, \quad i \neq j, \quad i, j = 1, 2, \ldots, n. \tag{9}$$

Then

$$P\left(\bigcup_{i=1}^{n} A_i\right) = \sum_{i=1}^{n} P(A_i). \tag{10}$$

Property (3) of P in Definition 5.1 is the special case of this theorem in which $n = 2$. The proof of the theorem will now be given by mathematical induction.

The theorem is true for $n = 1$ and $n = 2$. Assume that the theorem is true for any k events $A_1, A_2, \ldots, A_k$ such that

$$A_i \cap A_j = \emptyset, \quad i \neq j, \quad 1 \leq i \leq k, \quad 1 \leq j \leq k.$$

Then

$$P\left(\bigcup_{i=1}^{k} A_i\right) = \sum_{i=1}^{k} P(A_i). \tag{11}$$

Next assume that

$$A_i \cap A_j = \emptyset, \quad i \neq j, \quad 1 \leq i \leq k + 1, \quad 1 \leq j \leq k + 1. \tag{12}$$

Then

$$\left(\bigcup_{i=1}^{k} A_i\right) \cap A_{k+1} = \bigcup_{i=1}^{k} (A_i \cap A_{k+1}) = \emptyset$$

by (12). Therefore by property (3) of P (see Definition 5.1),

$$P\left(\bigcup_{i=1}^{k+1} A_i\right) = P\left(\left(\bigcup_{i=1}^{k} A_i\right) \cup A_{k+1}\right) = P\left(\bigcup_{i=1}^{k} A_i\right) + P(A_{k+1}).$$

Now use the induction hypothesis (11) to find that

$$P\left(\bigcup_{i=1}^{k+1} A_i\right) = \sum_{i=1}^{k} P(A_i) + P(A_{k+1}) = \sum_{i=1}^{k+1} P(A_i).$$

This statement is Eq. (10) with $n = k + 1$. We have thus shown two things: (a) Eq. (10) is true for $n = 1$ and $n = 2$; (b) if Eq. (10) is true for any value of n, it is also true for the next greater value of n. Thus, by a complete induction, Eq. (10) is true for every value of n.▲

The following example illustrates an application of property (1) in Theorem 5.1. To compute $P(A)$, it is sometimes easier to compute $P(A^c)$ and then to obtain $P(A)$ from the formula $P(A) = 1 - P(A^c)$.

EXAMPLE 1. A ball is drawn from a bag containing thirty balls numbered one through thirty. The number of the ball drawn is noted, and the ball is replaced. A second ball is drawn, the number noted, and the ball replaced. A third ball is drawn, the number noted, and the ball replaced. What is the probability that at least two of the balls drawn had the same number?

To solve this problem, it is necessary to construct an appropriate probability space (S, P). Let $S_1 = \{i \mid i$ is an integer, $1 \leq i \leq 30\}$. Then an appropriate sample space S for the experiment is the Cartesian product $S_1 \times S_1 \times S_1$, that is, the set of all 3-tuples (i, j, k) where $1 \leq i \leq 30, 1 \leq j \leq 30, 1 \leq k \leq 30$. Thus S contains 30^3 elementary events, each one being an ordered 3-tuple. Since each elementary event $\{a\}$ of S is equally likely, we define the probability function P by setting

$$P(\{a\}) = \frac{1}{30^3}, \qquad a \in S.$$

Next, consider the event A whose probability we are trying to find. We observe that A is the set of 3-tuples in S which have at least two equal entries; thus

$$A = \{(i, j, k) \mid (i, j, k) \in S, \text{ and either } i = j, \text{ or } i = k, \text{ or } j = k, \text{ or } i = j = k\}.$$

The complement A^c of A is the set of all 3-tuples in S which have no entries the same; thus

$$A^c = \{(i, j, k) \mid (i, j, k) \in S, \text{ and } j \neq i, k \neq i, k \neq j\}.$$

There are, by the principle of sequential counting, $30 \cdot 29 \cdot 28$ elementary events in A^c. Thus

$$P(A^c) = \frac{30 \cdot 29 \cdot 28}{30^3} = \frac{29 \cdot 28}{30^2},$$

and

$$P(A) = 1 - \frac{29 \cdot 28}{30^2}$$

by property (1) in Theorem 5.1.

The applications treated in the next chapter illustrate many of the other properties of probability spaces.

EXERCISES

1. The 24 volumes of an encyclopedia are placed at random on a shelf. What is the probability that the 24 volumes appear in the correct order?

2. In Exercise 1 what is the probability that the first three volumes are placed on the shelf in the correct order?

3. A lot of 100 light bulbs contains ten defective bulbs. A random sample of five bulbs is drawn from the lot. Let X be the number of defective bulbs in the sample. Find the probability that $X \leq 3$ and also the probability that $4 \leq X \leq 5$.

4. A real estate dealer estimates that within the next month he will sell at least five houses with probability 0.8 but less than eight houses with probability 0.4. What is the probability that he will sell five, six, or seven houses?

5. A contractor estimates that the probability he can finish a certain job within the next x days is $x/10$ for $x = 1, 2, 3, \ldots, 10$.
   (a) Describe an appropriate probability space (S, P) for the study of the situation described.
   (b) What is the probability that it takes exactly five days to finish the job?
   (c) What is the probability that it takes more than seven days to finish the job?
   (d) What is the probability that it will take an odd number of days to finish the job?

6. What is the probability that at least two out of ten people have their birthdays on the same date? Two out of twenty? Two out of thirty? Two out of n?

7. A certain committee plans one meeting during each of the four quarters of the following year. Assume that each day of the week is equally likely for each of the meetings. Find the probabilities of the following events.
   (a) The four meetings will all be held on Saturday.
   (b) One meeting will be held on Monday, another on Wednesday, and another on Friday.
   (c) One meeting will be held on Monday.
   (d) Exactly one meeting will be held on Saturday.
   (e) Only one meeting will be held on a Monday or a Wednesday.
   (f) No meeting will be held on a Monday.

8. A certain manufacturing plant produces and classifies sweaters into five categories $C_1, C_2, \ldots, C_5$ depending upon quality characteristics. Assume that it is known that the following probabilities can be associated with the event that a sweater produced falls into a particular category: $P(\{C_1\}) = \frac{5}{16}$, $P(\{C_2\}) = \frac{1}{4}$, $P(\{C_3\}) = \frac{1}{4}$, $P(\{C_4\}) = \frac{1}{16}$, $P(\{C_5\}) = \frac{1}{8}$. Let A, B, D, E denote the following events.

   $A: \{C_1, C_2, C_3\}, \qquad B: \{C_1, C_2, C_4\}, \qquad D: \{C_3, C_4\}, \qquad E: \{C_2, C_5\}.$

   Compute each of the following probabilities.
   (a) $P(A), P(B), P(D), P(E)$ \qquad\qquad (b) $P(A \cup B), P(D \cup E)$
   (c) $P(A \cap B)$ \qquad\qquad\qquad\qquad\quad (d) $P(A \cap D)$
   (e) $P(A \cup B \cup D \cup E)$

9. A certain automatic screw machine produces ten slotless screws out of every lot of 1000. If each lot of 1000 screws is packaged in ten boxes of 100 screws each, what is the probability that a specified box will have exactly three slotless screws? Less than two slotless screws?

10. One card is drawn from each of two ordinary decks of 52 cards. Find the probability that at least one of the cards drawn is the ace of hearts.

11. A box of 500 light bulbs contains ten defective bulbs. If a customer buys twenty bulbs from the box, what is the probability that he will have one or more defective light bulbs?

12. Out of 100 applicants for a job, thirty have black hair, forty have brown hair, twenty are blond, and ten have red hair. If five are hired, find the probabilities of the following events.
   (a) Exactly two have black hair and three are blond.
   (b) The five have red hair.
   (c) There will be at least one of each of the four colors.
   (d) Three have brown hair.

13. Prove that the following relations hold for any two events A and B in a probability space:
$$P(A \cap B) \le P(A) \le P(A \cup B) \le P(A) + P(B).$$

14. The probability of an event A is the square of the probability that the event B does not happen. The probability that A does not happen is the square of twice the probability that B happens. Find the probability of A.

BIBLIOGRAPHY

1. B. DE FINETTI, "Probability: Philosophy and Interpretation," Preprint of an article to appear in the *International Encyclopedia of the Social Sciences*.

CHAPTER 6

Some Elementary Applications

6.1 INTRODUCTION

This chapter contains several elementary applications of the theory of probability. These applications concern problems from a wide range of disciplines—business, psychology, sociology, zoology, and medicine. Although most of the probability models involved in these applications are not very sophisticated, they nevertheless give an introductory account of some of the uses of probability theory. Most of the probability spaces which occur in these applications arise also as probability models constructed for the analysis and interpretation of certain experiments on random drawings of balls from urns. Furthermore, the urn models of chance events are especially simple and easy to understand. For this reason, we shall begin by investigating urn models and the associated probability spaces.

6.2 URN MODELS

In Examples 2 and 3 of Section 5.4 two different sample spaces were constructed for the experiment of drawing three balls from an urn containing four balls. Consider now the conceptually simpler situation of drawing one ball from an urn which contains n white balls and m black balls. The probability that one ball selected at random from the urn is white is $n/(n + m)$, and the probability that it is black is $m/(n + m)$. These statements are true because there are $n + m$ possible outcomes which can result from drawing one ball from the urn; n outcomes are a white ball and m outcomes are a black ball. This experiment which consists of drawing one ball from the urn is a very simple one. There are several ways to proceed if two or more balls are selected (drawn) from the urn, and the corresponding experiments are much more complicated. We shall investigate the urn models which arise from four different procedures for selecting the two or more balls. These procedures for selecting the balls are

(i) simultaneous selection (*unordered sampling*),
(ii) successive selection (*ordered sampling*) without replacement,
(iii) successive selection with replacement,
(iv) successive selection with some scheme for replacement depending on the color of the ball drawn.

In this section we shall analyze urn models which involve each of the first three procedures for selecting the balls. The fourth procedure leads to a large class of experiments, including an urn model known as *Polya's urn scheme*, which are investigated in Section 6.5.

In the study of urn models it is always assumed that the balls are distinguishable. Thus the n white balls can be identified as the first white ball, the second white ball, . . . , and the nth white ball, while the m black balls can be identified as the first black ball, the second black ball, . . . , and the mth black ball.

(i) *Simultaneous selection* (*unordered sampling*). In the urn model based on unordered sampling, two balls are selected from the n white balls and m black balls in the urn. An unordered sample in this case is a doubleton subset $\{a_1, a_2\}$ of the set of $n + m$ balls present in the urn. The sample space S consists of the $\binom{n+m}{2}$ combinations of $n + m$ things taken two at a time. Since the samples are selected at random, the $\binom{n+m}{2}$ elementary events in S are equally likely; hence, the probability of each elementary event is

$$\frac{1}{\binom{n+m}{2}}. \tag{1}$$

Thus the probability $P(A)$ of an event A is given by the following formula:

$$P(A) = \frac{N(A)}{\binom{n+m}{2}}, \tag{2}$$

where $N(A)$ denotes the number of outcomes in A.

EXAMPLE 1. An urn contains 10 white and 6 black balls. Two balls are selected at random (unordered sampling). What is the probability that exactly one is a black ball? What is the probability that at least one is a black ball?

To answer these questions, construct the sample space S of all combinations of 16 things taken 2 at a time and define P so that (S, P) is an equiprobable probability space. Let A be the event which consists of all samples of two balls which contain exactly one black ball, and let C be the event which consists of all samples which contain at least one black ball. Then

$$P(A) = \frac{N(A)}{\binom{16}{2}}, \qquad P(C) = \frac{N(C)}{\binom{16}{2}}.$$

Thus, to obtain the answers we must compute $N(A)$ and $N(C)$. An outcome of the experiment is in A if and only if the sample of two balls contains exactly one white ball and one black ball. The number of ways of drawing one white ball is $\binom{10}{1}$, and the number of ways of drawing one black ball is $\binom{6}{1}$. Then, by the principle of sequential counting,

$$N(A) = \binom{10}{1}\binom{6}{1} \qquad \text{and} \qquad P(A) = \frac{\binom{10}{1}\binom{6}{1}}{\binom{16}{2}} = \frac{1}{2}.$$

Let B be the event which consists of all samples of two balls which contain exactly two black balls. Then $C = A \cup B$ and $A \cap B = \emptyset$; hence, $N(C) = N(A) + N(B)$. Since B consists of combinations of the 6 black balls taken 2 at a time, $N(B) = \binom{6}{2}$. It has been shown already that $N(A) = \binom{10}{1}\binom{6}{1}$. Thus

$$P(C) = \frac{N(C)}{\binom{16}{2}} = \frac{N(A) + N(B)}{\binom{16}{2}} = \frac{\binom{10}{1}\binom{6}{1} + \binom{6}{2}}{\binom{16}{2}} = \frac{5}{8}.$$

There is a generalization of the problem we have considered in which samples of k balls ($k \leq n + m$) are drawn from the $n + m$ balls in the urn. For the case of simultaneous selection (unordered sampling), there are $\binom{n+m}{k}$ ways of selecting a sample of k balls from the $n + m$ balls in the urn. Then the sample space S contains $\binom{n+m}{k}$ elementary events, and (S, P) is an equiprobable probability space. Thus, for any event A,

$$P(A) = \frac{N(A)}{\binom{n + m}{k}}. \tag{3}$$

EXAMPLE 2.   A large grocery store receives 1000 quarts of milk on a certain day, but 100 of these quarts remain unsold at the end of the day. The next day the store receives 900 fresh quarts of milk, mixes them randomly with the 100 day-old quarts, and offers them for sale on the shelf. If a housewife selects at random five quarts of milk from the shelf, what is the probability that she obtains exactly one quart of day-old milk? At least one quart of day-old milk?

It is possible to interpret this problem as an experiment in drawing balls from an urn. Consider the 900 fresh quarts as 900 white balls in an urn, and consider the 100 day-old quarts as 100 black balls in the urn. Then the questions in the example become questions about the selection of white and black balls from an urn (the shelf in the store). Let A be the event which consists of samples of five quarts which contain exactly one quart of day-old milk. Then by the principle of sequential counting, $N(A) = \binom{100}{1}\binom{900}{4}$, and hence

$$P(A) = \frac{\binom{100}{1}\binom{900}{4}}{\binom{1000}{5}} = 0.346. \tag{4}$$

Let us now compute the probability that the five quarts of milk purchased by the housewife contain at least one day-old quart. Let B be the event which consists of all samples of five quarts which contain at least one day-old quart. Then B consists of samples which contain exactly one day-old quart, or exactly two day-old quarts, . . . , or exactly five day-old quarts. Then

$$N(B) = \binom{100}{1}\binom{900}{4} + \binom{100}{2}\binom{900}{3} + \binom{100}{3}\binom{900}{2}$$
$$+ \binom{100}{4}\binom{900}{1} + \binom{100}{5}\binom{900}{0},$$

and

$$P(B) = \frac{N(B)}{\binom{1000}{5}}.$$

But there is a much simpler way to compute $P(B)$. Since $B \cup B^c = S$ and $B \cap B^c = \emptyset$, $P(B) + P(B^c) = 1$ and $P(B) = 1 - P(B^c)$. Since B^c consists of samples of five quarts which do not contain a day-old quart, $N(B^c) = \binom{100}{0}\binom{900}{5}$ by the principle of sequential counting. Thus

$$P(B) = 1 - P(B^c) = 1 - \frac{\binom{100}{0}\binom{900}{5}}{\binom{1000}{5}} = 1 - 0.491 = 0.509. \tag{5}$$

Thus the probability that the housewife obtains one or more quarts of day-old milk when she buys five quarts is slightly greater than $\frac{1}{2}$.

There is a still further generalization of the problem we have been considering in which the urn contains balls of more than two colors. Assume that there are n_i balls of color i for $i = 1, 2, \ldots, r$. Set $l = n_1 + n_2 + \cdots + n_r$. Then there are $\binom{l}{k}$ different unordered random samples of k balls ($k \le l$) that can be selected from the urn. If A is any event in the sample space S, then

$$P(A) = \frac{N(A)}{\binom{l}{k}} . \tag{6}$$

If $r > 2$, there exist complicated events A for which $N(A)$ is difficult to compute. It is fortunate that many of the most important applications involve the case $r = 2$ in which there are only two types of objects—white and black, good and bad, new and old, or whatever they may be called—in the urn.

Several applications of unordered sampling are given in later sections (see Sections 6.3, 6.4, and 6.6).

(ii) *Successive selection (ordered sampling) without replacement.* Consider the urn model based on ordered sampling in the case in which two balls are drawn from an urn containing n white balls and m black balls. In ordered sampling a first ball is drawn at random from the urn, the identity of the ball is noted, and then (without returning the first ball to the urn) a second ball is drawn at random and its identity noted. The sampling in Example 3 of Section 5.4 is an example of ordered sampling. If ordered samples of two balls are drawn from an urn containing n white and m black balls, a suitable sample space S consists of all ordered pairs (a, b), where a is any one of the $n + m$ balls and b is any one of these balls which is distinct from a. It is clear that b is distinct from a, since a is not returned to the urn before b is drawn. By the principle of sequential counting, there are $(n + m)(n + m - 1)$ such ordered pairs (a, b). If the drawings are random drawings, then equal probabilities are assigned to the elementary events in the sample space S. Thus

$$P(\{(a, b)\}) = \frac{1}{(n + m)(n + m - 1)} ,$$

and

$$P(A) = \frac{N(A)}{(n + m)(n + m - 1)} , \tag{7}$$

where $N(A)$ is the number of ordered pairs (a, b) in the event A.

The sampling problem discussed in the last paragraph is a special case of the more general sampling problem in which k balls ($k \leq n + m$) are drawn successively from the urn without replacement. In this case the sample space S is the set of all possible ordered k-tuples without repetitions. Thus

$$S = \{(a_1, a_2, \ldots, a_k) \mid a_i \neq a_j \text{ for } i \neq j\}.$$

If we define the symbol $(l)_k$ by the statement

$$(l)_k = l(l - 1) \ldots (l - k + 1), \qquad k \leq l, \tag{8}$$

then

$$N(S) = (n + m)(n + m - 1) \ldots (n + m - k + 1) = (n + m)_k.$$

Finally, if A is an event in the sample space S for a sampling experiment in which k balls are drawn successively from the urn without replacement, then

$$P(A) = \frac{N(A)}{(n + m)_k}. \tag{9}$$

Formula (9) is correct also in cases in which k balls are drawn successively, without replacement, from an urn which contains balls of more than two colors.

EXAMPLE 3. An urn contains 10 white and 6 black balls. Two balls are selected successively at random (without replacement) from the urn. What is the probability that the first is white and the second black? What is the probability that exactly one of the balls is white?

To answer the first question, consider the equiprobable probability space (S, P) in which the sample space S consists of all ordered pairs of distinct balls drawn from the urn. This space S contains $16 \cdot 15 = 240$ ordered pairs. Let D be the event in S which consists of all ordered pairs for which the first ball is white and the second black. Then $N(D) = 10 \cdot 6$, and

$$P(D) = \frac{10 \cdot 6}{16 \cdot 15} = \frac{1}{4}.$$

The second question in the example can be answered by using the probability model in Example 1 since the question does not refer in any way to ordered samples. Thus, if A is the event which consists of all samples of two balls which contain exactly one white and one black ball, then $P(A) = \frac{1}{2}$ as shown in Example 1. However, the second question in Example 3 can also be answered by means of the probability model constructed in the preceding paragraph. Let E be the event in S which consists of all ordered pairs in which the first ball is black and the second is white. If A is the event in S which consists of all ordered samples which contain exactly one black ball, then $A = D \cup E$ and $D \cap E = \emptyset$. Then $P(A) = P(D) + P(E) = \frac{1}{4} + \frac{1}{4} = \frac{1}{2}$. Thus in both interpretations of the problem (simultaneous selection and successive selection without replacement), the probability of drawing a sample which contains exactly one white ball and one black ball is $\frac{1}{2}$.

EXAMPLE 4. On a certain day the grocery store in Example 2 offers 1000 quarts of milk for sale. The 1000 quarts consist of 900 fresh quarts and 100 day-old quarts which are randomly mixed. If a housewife buys one quart of milk, the probability that she receives a day-old quart is $\frac{1}{10}$. If, however, the housewife buys a quart after another customer has bought a quart of unknown type, what is the probability that she obtains a day-old quart?

In order to find the rather surprising answer to this problem, we employ an urn model which involves successive selection without replacement. The other customer's selection corresponds to the first drawing from the urn, and the housewife's selection corresponds to the second drawing. The sample space S consists of the $1000 \cdot 999$ ordered pairs that are the set of all possible outcomes of two successive selections without replacement. Let A denote the event which consists of all ordered pairs in which the second selection (the housewife's quart of milk) is a day-old quart. Then

$$P(A) = \frac{N(A)}{1000 \cdot 999},$$

and the problem can be completed by calculating $N(A)$.

Two simple methods can be employed to calculate $N(A)$. Consider the first method. The set A consists of all ordered pairs (a, b) in which b is a day-old quart and a is any quart distinct from b. There are 100 choices for b, and for each b there are 999 corresponding choices for a. Then by the principle of sequential counting, $N(A) = 100 \cdot 999$. The second method of calculating $N(A)$ is also simple and instructive. Let A_1 be the event in the sample space S which consists of all ordered pairs (a, b) in which both a and b are day-old quarts of milk, and let A_2 be the event which consists of all ordered pairs (a, b) in which a is a fresh quart and b is a day-old quart of milk. Since $A = A_1 \cup A_2$ and $A_1 \cap A_2 = \emptyset$, it follows that $N(A) = N(A_1) + N(A_2)$. By the principle of sequential counting, $N(A_1) = 100 \cdot 99$ and $N(A_2) = 900 \cdot 100$. Hence $N(A) = 100 \cdot 99 + 900 \cdot 100 = 100 \cdot 999$. Thus the two methods of computing $N(A)$ give the same result.

If the value of $N(A)$ is substituted in the formula above, we obtain

$$P(A) = \frac{100 \cdot 999}{1000 \cdot 999} = \frac{1}{10}.$$

If the housewife buys the first quart of milk from the 1000 quarts offered by the grocery store, the probability that she obtains a day-old quart is $\frac{1}{10}$. If the housewife buys the second quart, after another customer has bought a quart of unknown type, the probability that she obtains a day-old quart is still $\frac{1}{10}$. This result can be generalized. It can be shown that, if the housewife selects a quart after other customers have selected k quarts $(0 \leq k \leq 999)$ of unknown types, then the probability that she obtains a day-old quart is $\frac{1}{10}$ in all cases. This example will be discussed further in the next chapter in connection with conditional probability.

(iii) *Successive selection with replacement.* An experiment in which a ball is drawn at random from an urn, replaced, and a second ball is drawn at random is an example of successive selection with replacement. Let U denote the set of n balls in the urn. If k balls are selected from the urn by the method of successive selection with replacement, then an appropriate sample space S for the experiment consists of all ordered k-tuples $(a_1, a_2, \ldots, a_k)$ in which each entry is any element in the set U. Thus

$$S = \{(a_1, a_2, \ldots, a_k) \mid a_i \in U, \ 1 \leq i \leq k\}.$$

By the principle of sequential counting, $N(S) = n^k$ since there are n choices for each of the k entries in the ordered k-tuple $(a_1, a_2, \ldots, a_k)$. If the successive selections from the urn are made at random, then each of the elementary events in S is equally likely and has probability $1/n^k$. Thus, if A is any event in S,

$$P(A) = \frac{N(A)}{n^k}. \tag{10}$$

Equation (10) is independent of the composition of the set U of balls in the urn. However, the calculation of $N(A)$ must take account of the composition of the set U.

EXAMPLE 5. An urn contains 10 white and 6 black balls. Two balls are selected successively, at random, and with replacement. What is the probability that the first is white and the second is black? What is the probability that exactly one of the two balls is black?

Let F be the event in S which consists of ordered pairs (a_1, a_2) in which a_1 is white and a_2 is black. By the principle of sequential counting, $N(F) = 10 \cdot 6$. Then

$$P(F) = \frac{N(F)}{16^2} = \frac{10 \cdot 6}{16^2} = \frac{15}{64}.$$

Thus the probability that the first ball drawn is white and the second is black is $\frac{15}{64}$.

To answer the second question in Example 5, begin by letting G be the event in S which consists of all ordered pairs (a_1, a_2) in which exactly one of the elements a_1, a_2 is black. Let H be the set of ordered pairs (a_1, a_2) in which a_1 is black and a_2 is white, and let I be the set of ordered pairs (a_1, a_2) in which a_1 is white and a_2 is black. Then $G = H \cup I$ and $H \cap I = \emptyset$. It follows that

$$N(G) = N(H) + N(I) = 6 \cdot 10 + 10 \cdot 6 = 120.$$

Then

$$P(G) = \frac{N(G)}{16^2} = \frac{120}{256} = \frac{15}{32}.$$

The two questions in Examples 3 and 5 are the same, but their answers are different in the two examples—the probabilities are smaller in Example 5. The two balls in Example 3 are selected successively *without* replacement, and the two balls in Example 5 are selected successively *with* replacement. As a result, the sample space in Example 5 is larger (it has 16 additional elements) than the sample space in Example 3. The number of elements in corresponding events in the two examples is the same ($N(D) = N(F) = 60$ and $N(A) = N(G) = 120$).

EXAMPLE 6.   Consider again the situation described in Example 4.   The housewife selects at random a quart of milk after another customer has selected a quart of unknown type. We assume a new situation, however. As soon as the customer removes the first quart of milk from the shelf, the grocer replaces it by putting another quart of milk in the empty space on the shelf. The grocer might follow any one of several different policies in replacing the quart of milk purchased by the customer. Let us now consider the five alternative replacement policies in which the grocer replaces the quart of milk purchased by (a) a fresh quart, (b) a day-old quart, (c) a quart of the same type removed, (d) a quart of the type opposite to the one removed, and (e) a quart selected at random from a replacement supply which contains quarts of both types. The grocer would find it necessary, in employing replacement policies (c) and (d), to use a coding procedure so that he would know the type of each quart of milk purchased. In the remainder of this discussion we shall consider replacement policy (c). The replacement policies (c) and (d) are special cases of the general replacement scheme discussed in Section 6.5; policies (a) through (e) are all treated in Exercise 10 of Section 7.3. If the grocer follows replacement policy (c), the number of fresh quarts and the number of day-old quarts of milk on the shelf remain the same. Then the probability that a customer selects a day-old quart is always $\frac{1}{10}$. This result can be confirmed by a standard analysis of the experiment in terms of ordered pairs. The sample space S consists of the set of ordered pairs (a_1, a_2), where both a_1 and a_2 are any one of the 1000 quarts of milk. Then $N(S) = 1000^2$. Let J be the event in S which consists of ordered pairs (a_1, a_2) in which a_2 is a day-old quart. Then $N(J) = 1000 \cdot 100$ and

$$P(J) = \frac{N(J)}{1000^2} = \frac{1000 \cdot 100}{1000^2} = \frac{1}{10}.$$

EXAMPLE 7 (The Birthday Problem).   A certain class in probability theory contains 20 students. What is the probability that no two students in this class have the same birthday? We shall obtain the answer to this question with the aid of an urn model. First, however, it is necessary to make certain assumptions to simplify the problem. We assume that each year has 365 days (we ignore leap years), that each of the 365 days is a day on which a birthday can occur, and that each of the 365 days is equally likely to be the birthday of each student. Construct an urn model as follows. Label 365 identical balls with the numbers 1, 2, . . . , 365 and place them in an urn. Choose 20 balls from the urn by random successive selection with replacement. The sample space S for the experiment consists of the set of all ordered 20-tuples $(i_1, i_2, \ldots, i_k, \ldots, i_{20})$, where each i_k is one of the integers in the set $\{1, 2, \ldots, 365\}$. The sample space contains $(365)^{20}$ ordered 20-tuples. Let A be the event in S which consists of all those 20-tuples in which the 20 numbers are different. Each 20-tuple in A corresponds to a set of birthdays for the 20 members of the class in which no two students have the same birthday.

If $(i_1, i_2, \ldots, i_k, \ldots, i_{20})$ is in A, there are 365 choices for i_1, 364 choices for $i_2, \ldots$, and 346 choices for i_{20}. Then $N(A) = 365 \cdot 364 \cdot \ldots \cdot 346 = (365)_{20}$. [See the discussion of successive selection (ordered sampling) without replacement.] Then

$$P(A) = \frac{(365)_{20}}{(365)^{20}} = 0.589.$$

If the class contains 22 students a similar analysis shows that $P(A) = 0.524$; if the class contains 23 students, $P(A) = 0.493$; for 40 students, $P(A) = 0.109$; and for 60 students, $P(A) = 0.006$.

EXERCISES

1. An urn contains five white and three black balls. If three balls are drawn at random from the urn, what is the probability that they are black? That they are white? That at least one ball is white?

2. The milk shelf in a grocery store contains, randomly mixed, 90 fresh quarts of milk and 10 day-old quarts. A housewife buys five quarts of milk from the shelf. What is the probability that she selects exactly one day-old quart? At least one day-old quart? Compare your answers with those of Example 2.

3. What are the answers to the two questions in Exercise 2 if the housewife buys only three quarts of milk?

4. An urn contains three red balls, five white balls, and six black balls. If four balls are drawn at random from the urn, what is the probability that exactly two of them are red? What is the probability that two are red and two are black? What is the probability that at least one ball of each color is drawn?

5. Consider Example 4 again and assume that the housewife is the third customer to purchase a quart of milk. Show that the probability that she selects a day-old quart is $\frac{1}{10}$.

6. (The hat check problem.) Four men leave their hats with a hat check girl at a restaurant. Unfortunately, the girl loses the numbers that identify the hats. As a result, she returns the four hats to the four owners at random.
   (a) What is the probability that a specified man receives his own hat if he is the first to receive a hat?
   (b) What is the probability that a specified man receives his own hat if he is the second to receive a hat?
   (c) If three of the men have received hats and left the restaurant, what is the probability that the fourth man will receive his own hat?
   (d) What is the probability that each of the four men receives his own hat?
   (e) What is the probability that at least two of the four men receive their own hats?

7. Urn models can be used to study the tossing of an unbiased coin. From the point of view of probability theory, the tossing of an unbiased coin is the same as the random drawing of a ball from an urn which contains two balls, one of which is

labeled heads, and the other of which is labeled tails. Repeated tosses of the coin correspond to repeated drawings, with replacement, from the urn.

(a) If an unbiased coin is tossed 10 times, what is the probability that heads does not occur?

(b) What is the probability that heads occurs exactly once in 10 tosses of an unbiased coin?

(c) What is the probability that heads occurs exactly twice in 10 tosses of an unbiased coin?

8. An unbiased coin is tossed n times. What is the probability that heads occurs k times? (This problem will be treated again in connection with independent trials and binomial probabilities.)

9. An urn contains n white balls and m black balls. Two balls are drawn at random, successively, and without replacement. Show that the probability of drawing a black ball on the second drawing is $m/(n + m)$, which is the same as the probability of drawing a black ball on the first drawing. (This exercise generalizes the result established in Example 4.)

10. Consider the birthdays of the students in a class which contains exactly n members. Show that the probability that no two members of this class have the same birthday is

$$\frac{(365)_n}{(365)^n}, \qquad 1 \le n \le 365.$$

11. An urn contains n balls of which np are white and nq are black, where $p + q = 1$. A random sample of size m is taken with replacement. Show that the probability of exactly k white balls in the m drawn is

$$\binom{m}{k} p^k q^{m-k}.$$

12. A random sample of size m is drawn without replacement from an urn containing n objects. Show that the probability that N given elements will all be included in the sample is

$$\frac{\binom{n - N}{m - N}}{\binom{n}{m}}.$$

6.3 ACCEPTANCE SAMPLING

As a first application of the urn schemes we consider a problem in acceptance sampling.

EXAMPLE 1. A buyer for a large department store is offered 1000 transistor radios. He knows that these radios have been made by automatic machines and assembly line methods, and that the lot may contain a certain number of defective radios. He decides that he can buy the lot of radios, sell them at a specified price, and make a profit if he has reasonable assurance that the lot does not contain more than 25 defective radios. Both the buyer and the seller realize that the cost of inspecting every one of the lot of 1000 radios would be prohibitive. The buyer consults a statistician and decides on the following course of action. A random sample of 50 radios will be taken from the lot, and the radios in the sample will be thoroughly inspected. If two or fewer defective radios are found in the sample, the buyer will buy the lot; if more than two defectives are found in the sample, the buyer will reject the lot. We shall now investigate the buyer's procedure.

It will be useful to treat the general problem rather than the special one in the example, and it will be convenient to introduce the following notation:

$L =$ the lot to be sampled for possible acceptance,
$N =$ lot size,
$n =$ sample size,
$X =$ number of defectives in a sample,
$c =$ the "acceptance number" (If $X > c$, the lot is rejected; if $X \leq c$, the lot is accepted.),
$M =$ actual number of defectives in the lot,
$M_0 =$ maximum acceptable number of defectives in the lot,
$p = M/N =$ the lot fraction defective,
$p_0 = M_0/N =$ the maximum acceptable lot fraction defective.

The drawing of a sample of size n from the lot L of N objects may be treated as a case of unordered drawings from an urn. Thus, as in urn scheme (i) in Section 6.2, there are $\binom{N}{n}$ samples. Since the samples are random samples by hypothesis, each of the $\binom{N}{n}$ samples is equally likely. Thus the sample space S contains $\binom{N}{n}$ different outcomes, and the probability of each of these outcomes is

$$\frac{1}{\binom{N}{n}}. \tag{1}$$

We shall now investigate certain events in this sample space S. We shall use $X = k$ as an abbreviation for the statement "the set of all outcomes in S which are samples containing exactly k defectives." Thus $X = k$ is a short notation for an event in S. The $n + 1$ events $X = 0, X = 1, X = 2, \ldots, X = n$ are disjoint, and their union is S. The probability of each elementary event in $X = k$ is given by (1); hence, we can find $P(X = k)$ by finding the number of elementary events in $X = k$. A sample in $X = k$ consists of k defective and $n - k$ good items from the lot L. The k defective items can be selected from the M defective items in L in $\binom{M}{k}$ different ways (see Section 4.3), and the $n - k$ good items can be selected from the $N - M$ good items in $\binom{N-M}{n-k}$ ways. By the principle of sequential counting, the number of different ways to form a sample in $X = k$ is

$$\binom{M}{k}\binom{N - M}{n - k}. \tag{2}$$

Hence,

$$P(X = k) = \frac{\binom{M}{k}\binom{N-M}{n-k}}{\binom{N}{n}}. \tag{3}$$

The lot L is accepted if the number of defectives in the sample of size n does not exceed c. Observe that

$$(X \le c) = (X = 0) \cup (X = 1) \cup \cdots \cup (X = c), \tag{4}$$

and that the events on the right in (4) are disjoint. Then, by property (3) of a probability function (see Definition 5.1 and Theorem 5.2),

$$P(X \le c) = \sum_{k=0}^{c} P(X = k) = \sum_{k=0}^{c} \frac{\binom{M}{k}\binom{N-M}{n-k}}{\binom{N}{n}}. \tag{5}$$

Equation (5) gives the probability that the lot L will be accepted if it does, in fact, contain M defectives. Since $M = Np$ (see the notation at the beginning of this section), Eq. (5) can also be written in the following form:

$$P(X \le c) = \sum_{k=0}^{c} \frac{\binom{Np}{k}\binom{N-Np}{n-k}}{\binom{N}{n}} = f(p). \tag{6}$$

Thus $f(p)$ is the probability that the lot L will be accepted when the lot fraction defective is p.

EXAMPLE 2. Consider an example in which the lot size N is ten, and the acceptance number c is one for a sample of size $n = 3$. Then $f(p)$ is $f(M/10)$, and

$$f(M/10) = \sum_{k=0}^{1} P(X = k) = \frac{\binom{M}{0}\binom{10-M}{3}}{\binom{10}{3}} + \frac{\binom{M}{1}\binom{10-M}{2}}{\binom{10}{3}}. \tag{7}$$

The table in Fig. 6.1 shows the values of $f(p)$ corresponding to the eleven possible values of M. If M is zero or one, the probability that the lot will be accepted is one because a sample cannot contain more than one defective in these two cases. If M is nine or ten, the probability that the lot will be accepted is zero because a sample of size three must contain more than one defective in these two cases.

The probability of acceptance is high even when M is fairly large. For example, $f(0.5) = 0.5$; this result is interpreted to mean the following. If $M = 5, n = 3$, and $c = 1$, then in many repetitions of the acceptance sampling experiment we would expect the lot to be accepted in about one-half of the cases and rejected in about one-half of the cases.

The function f described above is called the OC (*operating characteristic*) function for the given acceptance plan. The operating characteristic function is determined by the values of N (over which there is usually no control), and of n and c, which can be chosen by the buyer.

M	$f(M/10)$
0	1
1	1
2	$\frac{56}{60}$
3	$\frac{49}{60}$
4	$\frac{40}{60}$
5	$\frac{30}{60}$
6	$\frac{14}{60}$
7	$\frac{11}{60}$
8	$\frac{4}{60}$
9	0
10	0

Fig. 6.1. Table of values of $f(M/10)$ for $N = 10, n = 3$, and $c = 1$.

The reader should observe an important fact about the probabilities in the table in Fig. 6.1. As M increases, the probabilities $f(M/10)$ decrease monotonically. It is intuitively obvious that this statement should be true, even in the general case, for it says, "the greater the number M of defectives, the less likely the lot L is to be accepted."

The buyer establishes a number of M_0 as the maximum acceptable number of defectives in the lot L; if $M > M_0$, the buyer wishes to reject the lot. If the number of defectives is M_0, then

$$p_0 = M_0/N$$

and

$$f(p_0) = \sum_{k=0}^{c} \frac{\binom{Np_0}{k}\binom{N - Np_0}{n - k}}{\binom{N}{n}}. \tag{8}$$

As shown in Example 2, $f(p)$ decreases as M increases. Therefore the probability of accepting an undesirable lot (a lot with $M > M_0$) is less than $f(p_0)$, where $f(p_0)$ is given by (8). The probability $f(p_0)$ is called the *buyer's risk*. The buyer usually protects himself against buying lots of poor quality (lots with $M > M_0$)

by demanding a small value for $f(p_0)$. In the acceptance sampling procedure, however, it is to be expected that the buyer will accept lots of poor quality $(M > M_0)$ in a certain fraction [less than $f(p_0)$] of the cases.

The acceptance sampling procedure also has certain disadvantages from the point of view of the seller. The lot L may be rejected by the buyer when, in fact, the number of defectives M is less than M_0. The lot will be rejected if $X > c$. Thus if $p < p_0$, the probability that the lot will be rejected when it should have been accepted is

$$\sum_{k=c+1}^{n} P(X = k) = \sum_{k=c+1}^{n} \frac{\binom{Np}{k}\binom{N-Np}{n-k}}{\binom{N}{n}} = F(p). \qquad (9)$$

The probability $F(p)$ is called the *seller's risk* and denoted by $F(p)$. More advanced books, however, usually reserve the name "seller's risk" for a slightly different and more useful quantity. (In this connection, see Exercise 6 of Section 8.2.) Observe from (6) and (9) that

$$F(p) = 1 - f(p). \qquad (10)$$

EXERCISES

1. A random sample of 100 items is taken from a lot, and the lot is accepted if the sample contains at most one defective item. Calculate the probability of accepting the following:
   (a) a lot of 20,000 items, 1000 of which are defective;
   (b) a lot of 2000 items, 100 of which are defective;
   (c) a lot of 200 items, 10 of which are defective;
   (d) a lot of 100 items, 1 of which is defective.

2. Assume that the lot size N is eight and consider the acceptance rule defined by the acceptance number $c = 1$ for a sample size $n = 4$. Find the value of $f(M/8)$ for $M = 0, 1, 2, \ldots, 8$.

3. Repeat Exercise 2 but with the sample size $n = 5$. Compare the values of $f(M/8)$ in this exercise with those computed in Exercise 2. Compute also the values of $f(M/8)$ for samples of size $n = 6$ and $n = 8$.

4. A buyer considers the purchase of a certain lot of 100 items. As usual, the number of defectives is unknown, but the buyer wishes to reject the lot if it contains more than five defectives. The buyer decides on the following acceptance rule. A random sample of size $n = 10$ is drawn and inspected. If the number X of defectives is greater than one, the buyer rejects the lot. Obtain an estimate (the maximum value) for the probability that the buyer will accept a lot of poor quality, that is, a lot with $M > 5$.

5. Find the buyer's risk for the problem described by Example 1 at the beginning of this section.

6.4 ZOOLOGICAL SAMPLE CENSUS: TWO SIMPLE MODELS

Frequently it is necessary to estimate the (unknown) size of a population which cannot be counted. For example, it may be necessary to estimate the number of fish in a lake. This section describes two models which have been used to estimate the size of a population of this kind. Both models are very simple ones—too simple to yield the best results in applications to the real world. Nevertheless, they do illustrate the use of probability theory in solving important problems.

Model I: Direct Sampling. Consider the problem of estimating the number of fish in a lake. The following procedure has been proposed for solving this problem. First, catch 1000 fish from the lake. Mark each of these fish with a red spot, and then return the 1000 fish to the lake. Later, catch 1000 fish from the lake again, and count the number that are marked with red spots. Apply probability theory to this information (perhaps 100 have red spots!) to obtain an estimate of the number of fish in the lake. This procedure can be analyzed with the help of the urn models treated in Section 6.2. We may think of the lake as an urn, the unmarked fish as white balls, and the marked fish as black balls. Then the second catch of fish corresponds to a sample of balls drawn from an urn containing white and black balls. To arrive at an estimate of the number of fish in the lake, it is necessary to make two assumptions: (a) the number of fish in the lake does not change between the two samplings (the two catches), and (b) the second catch of fish is a random sample drawn from the population of all fish in the lake.

Further discussion of the example just given will be postponed until the general problem has been treated. It will be convenient to introduce the following notation:

N = the (unknown) number of fish in the lake,
M = the number of marked fish (predetermined),
n = the number of fish in the second catch (predetermined),
k = the number of marked fish in the second catch.

In this model the number n is determined in advance, but the number k is *not* determined in advance.

The probability of catching exactly k marked fish in a sample of size n is

$$\frac{\binom{N-M}{n-k}\binom{M}{k}}{\binom{N}{n}}. \tag{1}$$

This formula is the same formula as (3) in Section 6.3 with one important difference. In (1), N is the unknown (but fixed) number of fish in the lake, but N in formula (3) of Section 6.3 is the known lot size.

It is instructive to consider the size of the expression (1) for various possible values of N. Consider again the example above in which $M = 1000$, $n = 1000$, and $k = 100$. In this case, N is at least 1900 (1000 fish were marked and 900 unmarked fish were caught in the second catch). If $N = 1900$ (that is, if all fish in the lake were caught on one or the other of the two catches), then the expression (1) becomes

$$\frac{\binom{1900 - 1000}{1000 - 100}\binom{1000}{100}}{\binom{1900}{1000}} = \frac{\binom{900}{900}\binom{1000}{100}}{\binom{1900}{1000}} = \frac{\binom{1000}{100}}{\binom{1900}{1000}}. \tag{2}$$

Methods more advanced than those available in this book are required to calculate or estimate this number, but W. Feller [1, p. 44] estimates it to be of the order of magnitude of 10^{-430}, which is a very small number indeed. Thus it seems very unlikely that there are only 1900 fish in the lake. If $N = 100,000$, however, then (1) is

$$\frac{\binom{100,000 - 1000}{1000 - 100}\binom{1000}{100}}{\binom{100,000}{1000}} = \frac{\binom{99,000}{900}\binom{1000}{100}}{\binom{100,000}{1000}}.$$

This number is of the order of magnitude of 10^{-65}, which is again a very small number. Thus it seems highly doubtful that there are as few as 1900 fish in the lake or as many as 100,000. It should be remembered, however, that the actual number of fish in the lake could be either one of these extremes. Events with small probabilities do occur, but "events with small probabilities happen with about the expected frequency."

The problem remains: how shall we use formula (1) to obtain an estimate of the number of fish in the lake? It should be clear that there is no way to calculate the actual value of N since it is impossible to obtain complete information from partial information. The only procedure possible is to choose some number as an estimate of the unknown number N. The number we shall choose as the estimate of N is one which is recommended by probability considerations, and is that value of N for which the probability in formula (1) is as large as possible (maximum). Let us now investigate the problem of finding the values of N for which the probability (1) has its maximum value.

Define $p_k(N)$ as

$$p_k(N) = \frac{\binom{N - M}{n - k}\binom{M}{k}}{\binom{N}{n}}. \tag{3}$$

We shall now investigate the ratio

$$\frac{p_k(N)}{p_k(N-1)},$$

which is known as the *likelihood ratio*. From (3) we find that

$$\frac{p_k(N)}{p_k(N-1)} = \frac{\left[\binom{N-M}{n-k}\binom{M}{k}\right]/\binom{N}{n}}{\left[\binom{N-1-M}{n-k}\binom{M}{k}\right]/\binom{N-1}{n}}$$

$$= \frac{(N-M)!(N-1-M-n+k)!(N-1)!(N-n)!}{(N-1-M)!(N-M-n+k)!N!(N-1-n)!}$$

$$= \frac{(N-M)(N-n)}{(N-M-n+k)(N)}. \tag{4}$$

The procedure we have adopted for estimating N is based on the following considerations. If the ratio (4) is greater than 1, then $p_k(N) > p_k(N-1)$ and, on intuitive grounds, we prefer N to $N-1$ as an estimate of the number of fish in the lake. If the ratio (4) is less than 1, then $p_k(N) < p_k(N-1)$, and we prefer $N-1$ to N as an estimate of the number of fish in the lake. Thus the preferred value of N is the one for which $p_k(N)$ has its maximum value.

From (4) we find that

$$\frac{p_k(N)}{p_k(N-1)} > 1$$

if and only if

$$\frac{(N-M)(N-n)}{(N-M-n+k)(N)} > 1.$$

Solve this inequality for N; a straightforward calculation shows that this inequality is satisfied if and only if

$$N < \frac{nM}{k}.$$

A similar calculation shows that

$$\frac{p_k(N)}{p_k(N-1)} < 1 \qquad \text{if and only if} \qquad N > \frac{nM}{k}.$$

Thus we have shown that

$$p_k(N-1) < p_k(N) \qquad \text{if and only if} \quad N < \frac{nM}{k},$$

$$p_k(N-1) > p_k(N) \qquad \text{if and only if} \quad N > \frac{nM}{k}.$$

These inequalities show that $p_k(N)$ is monotonically increasing for $N < nM/k$ and monotonically decreasing for $N > nM/k$. If nM/k is not an integer, $p_k(N)$ has its maximum value at the largest integer less than nM/k. If nM/k is an integer, then

$$p_k\left(\frac{nM}{k} - 1\right) = p_k\left(\frac{nM}{k}\right)$$

and $p_k(N)$ takes on its maximum value at $(nM/k) - 1$ and also at nM/k. Define $\hat{N}$ to be nM/k if nM/k is an integer, and define $\hat{N}$ to be the largest integer less than nM/k if nM/k is not an integer. The number $\hat{N}$ is called the *maximum likelihood estimate* of N, and $\hat{N}$ is accepted as an estimate of the number of fish in the lake.

In the example considered above, $n = 1000$, $M = 1000$, $k = 100$, and $\hat{N} = nM/k = 10{,}000$. From Eq. (3) we find that $p_{100}(10{,}000)$ is approximately 0.044. A probability of 0.044 may not seem very large, but it should be remembered that $p_{100}(10{,}000)$ is the probability of obtaining exactly 100 marked fish in a random sample of size 1000 taken from a lake which contains 1000 marked fish and 9000 unmarked fish.

Model II: Inverse Sampling. The problem, as before, is to estimate the unknown number of fish in a lake. The first step in Model II is the same as the first step in Model I: catch a sample of fish from the lake, mark them, and return them to the lake. There is a difference in the second step, however. In Model II, the size of the second sample is not specified in advance. Instead, the second sample is enlarged one at a time until the number of marked fish in the sample reaches a predetermined number. It will be convenient to explain the notation as follows:

$N = $ the (unknown) number of fish in the lake,
$M = $ the number of marked fish (predetermined),
$n = $ the number of fish in the second catch,
$k = $ the number of marked fish in the second catch (predetermined).

Thus k is determined in advance in Model II, but n is not. The second sample (catch) is enlarged one at a time until k marked fish have been caught. The size of the sample at this point is n.

We shall now consider an urn problem as a simplified model of the fish in the lake. We assume that the urn contains N balls (fish) of which M are black balls (marked fish) and $N - M$ are white balls (unmarked fish). We consider an experiment in which balls are drawn from the urn one at a time until exactly k black balls have been obtained. It is clear that the minimum number of draws that can produce k black balls is k; furthermore, $N - M + k$ is the maximum number of draws required to obtain k black balls since the urn contains only $N - M$ white balls. Thus the sample space S for this experiment can be taken as the set $\{k, k + 1, \ldots, n, \ldots, N - M + k\}$.

To complete the problem of estimating N, we shall first compute the probability $P(\{n\})$ that the experiment terminates at the nth draw. Then, as in Model I, we shall choose as our estimate $\hat{N}$ of N that value of N for which $P(\{n\})$ has its maximum value.

Since (S, P) is not an equally likely probability space, the calculation of $P(\{n\})$ by direct methods is not easy. We shall compute $P(\{n\})$ by an indirect method which employs a different experiment with a different sample space.

Consider again the urn which contains N balls, of which M are black and $N - M$ are white. We shall now investigate an experiment in which $N - M + k$ balls are drawn at random, by successive selection without replacement, from the urn. The sample space S' for this experiment consists of all ordered $(N - M + k)$-tuples $(a_1, a_2, \ldots, a_n, \ldots, a_{N-M+k})$ that can be formed in the manner stated from the N balls in the urn. There are $(N)_{N-M+k}$ of these ordered $(N - M + k)$-tuples, and they are all equally likely. Observe that

$$(N)_{N-M+k} = (N)_n (N - n)_{N-M+k-n}. \tag{5}$$

Let P' be the equally likely probability function defined on $\Pi(S')$. Then

$$P'(A) = \frac{N(A)}{(N)_{N-M+k}} = \frac{N(A)}{(N)_n(N - n)_{N-M+k-n}}, \tag{6}$$

where $N(A)$ is the number of $(N - M + k)$-tuples in A.

Let A_n be the event in S' which consists of all ordered $(N - M + k)$-tuples $(a_1, a_2, \ldots, a_n, \ldots, a_{N-M+k})$ which satisfy the following two conditions: (a) exactly $k - 1$ balls in the $(n - 1)$-tuple $(a_1, a_2, \ldots, a_{n-1})$ are black, and (b) the ball a_n is black. From the descriptions of the two experiments it follows that

$$A_k \cup A_{k+1} \cup \cdots \cup A_n \cup \cdots \cup A_{N-M+k} = S',$$
$$A_i \cap A_j = \emptyset, \qquad i \neq j,$$
$$P(\{n\}) = P'(A_n). \tag{7}$$

Thus to obtain $P(\{n\})$, we calculate $P'(A_n)$. To find $P'(A_n)$, we calculate $N(A_n)$ and use Eq. (6).

We shall now count the number of $(N - M + k)$-tuples in A_n [see conditions (a) and (b) above]. There are $\binom{M}{k-1}$ ways to select a combination (unordered sample) of $k - 1$ black balls from the M black balls in the urn to be the $k - 1$ black balls in $(a_1, a_2, \ldots, a_{n-1})$. There are $\binom{N-M}{n-k}$ ways to select a combination of $(n - 1) - (k - 1) = n - k$ white balls from the $N - M$ white balls in the urn to be the $n - k$ white balls in $(a_1, a_2, \ldots, a_{n-1})$. By the principle of sequential counting there are $\binom{M}{k-1}\binom{N-M}{n-k}$ ways to select combinations of black and white balls. Any given set of $n - 1$ black and white balls can be arranged in the $n - 1$ positions in $(a_1, a_2, \ldots, a_{n-1})$ in $(n - 1)!$ ways. Thus there are $\binom{M}{k-1}\binom{N-M}{n-k}(n - 1)!$ ways to form $(a_1, a_2, \ldots, a_{n-1})$. After $k - 1$ black balls have been selected from the M black balls in the urn to form $(a_1, a_2, \ldots, a_{n-1})$, there are $M - k + 1$ ways to select a black ball from the urn to be the black ball a_n in $(a_1, a_2, \ldots, a_{n-1}, a_n)$. Thus there are $\binom{M}{k-1}\binom{N-M}{n-k}(n - 1)!(M - k + 1)$ ways to form $(a_1, a_2, \ldots, a_n)$. There remain $N - n$ balls in the urn. There are $(N - n)_{N-M+k-n}$ ways to fill the $N - M + k - n$ positions in $(a_{n+1}, \ldots, a_{N-M+k})$ by successive selection without replacement from the $N - n$ balls in the urn. Thus, finally, we have shown that there are

$$
\binom{M}{k-1}\binom{N-M}{n-k}(n - 1)!(M - k + 1)(N - n)_{N-M+k-n}
$$

ways to form ordered $(N - M + k)$-tuples which satisfy conditions (a) and (b). This number is $N(A_n)$. Then by Eq. (6)

$$
P'(A_n) = \frac{\binom{M}{k-1}\binom{N-M}{n-k}(n - 1)!(M - k + 1)}{(N)_n},
$$

and by Eq. (7)

$$
P(\{n\}) = \frac{\binom{M}{k-1}\binom{N-M}{n-k}(n - 1)!(M - k + 1)}{(N)_n}. \tag{8}
$$

Consider again the drawing of the second sample of fish. Let $p_n(N)$ be the probability that the kth marked fish is obtained on the nth draw if there are N fish in the lake. Then from the urn model we see that $p_n(N) = P(\{n\})$ and hence

$$
p_n(N) = \frac{\binom{M}{k-1}\binom{N-M}{n-k}(n - 1)!(M - k + 1)}{(N)_n}. \tag{9}
$$

As in Model I, we shall choose as our estimate $\hat{N}$ of N that value of N which gives $p_n(N)$ its maximum value. To find this maximum, consider $p_n(N)/p_n(N - 1)$. From Eq. (9) we have

$$
\frac{p_n(N)}{p_n(N - 1)} = \frac{(N - M)(N - n)}{(N - M - n + k)N}. \tag{10}
$$

By the same calculations as those in Model I above, we find

$$
p_n(N - 1) < p_n(N) \qquad \text{if and only if} \quad N < nM/k,
$$
$$
p_n(N - 1) > p_n(N) \qquad \text{if and only if} \quad N > nM/k.
$$

As before, these considerations lead us to choose $\hat{N}$ to be nM/k if nM/k is an integer, and to choose $\hat{N}$ to be the largest integer less than nM/k if nM/k is not an integer. The two models lead to the same estimate for N.

EXAMPLE 1.   As the first step in estimating the number of fish in a lake, 250 fish are caught, marked, and returned to the lake. After sufficient time has elapsed so that the marked fish are randomly distributed in the lake, fish are taken from the lake until 50 marked fish have been caught. If the 50th marked fish is the 500th fish caught, then $\hat{N} = 500 \cdot 250/50 = 2500$.

Extensions and modifications of Models I and II are discussed briefly in the bibliographical notes at the end of this chapter. Most of the extensions are designed to take into account such naturally occurring events as births, deaths, immigration, and emigration.

EXERCISES

1. To estimate the number of fish in a certain lake, 500 fish were caught, marked, and returned to the lake. After a short time fish were caught from the lake one at a time until 200 marked fish had been caught. If the 200th marked fish was the 2000th fish caught, estimate by the methods of Model II the number of fish in the lake. Can you apply the methods of Model I to the data already collected to obtain another estimate of the number of fish in the lake? If so, what estimate does Model I give?

2. A certain lake contains two different kinds of fish. Can the methods of this section be used to estimate the number of fish of each kind in the lake? If so, explain how.

3. If you were required to estimate the number of automobiles that drive over a certain highway each morning, would you do so by the methods explained in this section? Explain your answer.

4. A game warden wished to estimate the number of rabbits in a wild life preserve. He caught 100 rabbits and marked the ear of each one with a purple spot. Later he caught a random sample of 200 rabbits in the preserve and found that 9 of them had marked ears. How many rabbits are there in the preserve?

5. Show that Models I and II estimate N to have a value such that the proportion of marked fish in the lake is the same as the proportion of marked fish in the second sample. Does this result lead you to believe that Models I and II give reasonable estimates for N?

6. The methods of this section can be used to estimate the (unknown) number of defectives in a given lot of objects. It will be convenient to use the following notation:
    $N = $ the (known) lot size,
    $n = $ sample size,
    $k = $ number of defectives in the sample,
    $M = $ actual number (unknown) of defectives in the lot.
    (a) Show [see Eq. (3) in Section 6.3] that the probability of k defectives in the sample of size n drawn from a lot of size N which contains M defectives is

$$\frac{\binom{M}{k}\binom{N-M}{n-k}}{\binom{N}{n}}.$$

(b) Choose as the estimate $\hat{M}$ of M that value of M which gives the probability in (a) its maximum value. Show that this estimate for M leads to choosing $\hat{M}$ as the largest integer equal to or less than

$$\frac{(N + 1)k}{n}.$$

7. An inspector for an automobile manufacturer finds one defective car door in a random sample of 25 selected from a lot of 1000 car doors. Estimate the number of defective car doors in the lot of 1000.

8. A veterinarian finds two diseased chickens in a random sample of 100 selected from a lot of 2000 chickens. Estimate the number of diseased chickens in the lot of 2000 chickens.

9. A pearl diver finds one pearl in a random sample of 75 oysters. If he has 2500 oysters, estimate the number of pearls he will find.

10. Show that

$$\frac{\binom{M}{k-1}\binom{N-M}{n-k}(n-1)!(M-k+1)}{(N)_n} = \frac{\binom{M}{k-1}\binom{N-M}{n-k}}{\binom{N}{n-1}}\frac{(M-k+1)}{(N-n+1)}.$$

Give a plausible argument to explain why the two sides of this equation should be equal [see Eq. (8)].

11. Show that Eq. (10) is true.

12. Show that

$$\binom{N-M}{n-0}\binom{M}{0} + \binom{N-M}{n-1}\binom{M}{1} + \cdots + \binom{N-M}{n-n}\binom{M}{n} = \binom{N}{n},$$

where N, M, and n are fixed positive integers, and $N > M$, $n \leq M$, and $n \leq N - M$. [*Hint:* Let $S = \{0, 1, \ldots, k, \ldots, n\}$, where k denotes the number of marked fish in a sample of size n, be a sample space for Model I. Use Eq. (1) and the fact that $P(S) = 1$. Observe that the formula is true also for $N \geq M$ and $n \leq N$ provided that the convention is made that $\binom{l}{j} = 0$ for $j > l$.]

6.5 POLYA'S URN SCHEME

In Section 6.2 we considered urn models in which there was sampling both with and without replacement. In this section we shall investigate a generalization of these earlier sampling schemes from urns; this generalization was mentioned in Section 6.2.

Consider an urn which contains n white and m black balls. A ball is drawn at random. The ball is replaced in the urn, and in addition i balls of the same color and j balls of the other color are added. The urn now contains $n + m + i + j$ balls.

A second ball is drawn at random from the urn, and balls are replaced and added to the urn as before. The entire procedure is repeated indefinitely or until it is forced to terminate. It should be observed that i and j are fixed integers, and that either one or both may be negative. If i or j is negative, the procedure may come to an end because all balls have been removed from the urn. Some important special cases of this urn model are the following.

(i) $i = -1$ and $j = 0$. Since the ball drawn is returned to the urn but one of the same color is removed in this case, it is the same as sampling without replacement. This urn model was discussed extensively in Section 6.2.

(ii) $i = 0$ and $j = 0$. Since the ball drawn is returned to the urn but no balls of either color are added in this case, it is the same as sampling with replacement. This urn model also was discussed extensively in Section 6.2.

(iii) $i > 0$ and $j = 0$. This urn model is known as *Polya's urn scheme*; it was proposed by George Polya as a mathematical model for the spreading of a contagious disease. After each drawing, the number of balls of the color drawn increases, but the number of balls of the other color remains unchanged. Thus the drawing of a ball of either color increases the probability of obtaining a ball of that color at the next drawing. Thus Polya's urn scheme provides a probability model, although not a perfect one, for the study of the spreading of a contagious disease since each occurrence of the disease increases the probability of further occurrences.

EXAMPLE 1.   Consider two drawings from an urn according to Polya's urn scheme. We shall first construct an appropriate probability space (S, P). Let S be the set of ordered pairs (a_1, a_2) in which a_1 is the first ball drawn and a_2 is the second ball drawn. By the principle of sequential counting,

$$N(S) = (n + m)(n + m + i),$$

since there are $(n + m)$ ways to choose the first ball and $(n + m + i)$ ways to choose the second ball. Each ordered pair (a_1, a_2) in S is equally likely since each drawing is a random drawing; hence, for each elementary event $\{(a_1, a_2)\}$ in S we define

$$P(\{(a_1, a_2)\}) = \frac{1}{(n + m)(n + m + i)} . \tag{1}$$

Finally, if A is any event in S and $N(A)$ is the number of elements in S, then

$$P(A) = \frac{N(A)}{(n + m)(n + m + i)} . \tag{2}$$

Consider the following questions about the probabilities of certain events.
(1) What is the probability that the first ball drawn is black?
(2) What is the probability that both of the balls drawn are black?
(3) What is the probability that the second ball drawn is black?

In preparation for answering these questions, let us introduce some notation. Let W_1, W_2, B_1, B_2 be events in S which are defined by

$$W_i = \{(a_1, a_2) \mid (a_1, a_2) \in S, \ a_i \text{ is white}\},$$

$$B_i = \{(a_1, a_2) \mid (a_1, a_2) \in S, \ a_i \text{ is black}\}. \tag{3}$$

Consider question (1). The probability of drawing a black ball on the first draw is $m/(n + m)$, because there are $n + m$ balls in the urn and m of them are black. This calculation, however, has not employed the probability space (S, P). Question (1) is more properly answered by computing $P(B_1)$. Since B_1 is the collection of ordered pairs (a_1, a_2) in S in which a_1 is a black ball and a_2 is unrestricted, we have

$$N(B_1) = m(n + m + i)$$

by the principle of sequential counting. Then by Eq. (2)

$$P(B_1) = \frac{m(n + m + i)}{(n + m)(n + m + i)} = \frac{m}{n + m}. \tag{4}$$

As expected, the two calculations of the probability that the first ball drawn is black give the same result.

Consider question (2). Since B_1 contains all ordered pairs (a_1, a_2) for which a_1 is black, and B_2 contains all ordered pairs for which a_2 is black, it follows that $B_1 \cap B_2$ contains exactly those ordered pairs in which both balls are black. Thus the answer to question (2) is $P(B_1 \cap B_2)$. We can find this probability by computing $N(B_1 \cap B_2)$ and using Eq. (2). If a black ball is drawn on the first draw, there are $m + i$ ways to draw a black ball on the second draw. Then $N(B_1 \cap B_2) = m(m + i)$ and

$$P(B_1 \cap B_2) = \frac{m(m + i)}{(n + m)(n + m + i)}. \tag{5}$$

Consider question (3); it asks for the value of $P(B_2)$. The calculation of this probability is somewhat more difficult since the number of black balls in the urn at the second drawing is not the same in all cases. In some cases, a white ball is drawn first; in other cases, a black ball is drawn first. We proceed as follows. Since $(W_1 \cup B_1) = S$ and $(W_2 \cup B_2) = S$, we have $(W_1 \cup B_1) \cap (W_2 \cup B_2) = S$. Then

$$(W_1 \cap W_2) \cup (W_1 \cap B_2) \cup (B_1 \cap W_2) \cup (B_1 \cap B_2) = S. \tag{6}$$

Furthermore, it is easy to show that the four sets on the left in Eq. (6) are disjoint. Next, observe that

$$B_2 = S \cap B_2 = (W_1 \cup B_1) \cap B_2 = (W_1 \cap B_2) \cup (B_1 \cap B_2). \tag{7}$$

Since the two sets in (7) are disjoint, it follows from Eq. (3) in Section 5.3 that

$$P(B_2) = P(W_1 \cap B_2) + P(B_1 \cap B_2). \tag{8}$$

Since $N(W_1 \cap B_2) = nm$ and $N(B_1 \cap B_2) = m(m + i)$, we find from Eq. (2) that

$$P(W_1 \cap B_2) = \frac{nm}{(n + m)(n + m + i)},$$

$$P(B_1 \cap B_2) = \frac{m(m + i)}{(n + m)(n + m + i)}.$$

(9)

Thus finally,

$$P(B_2) = \frac{nm}{(n + m)(n + m + i)} + \frac{m(m + i)}{(n + m)(n + m + i)} = \frac{m}{n + m}.$$ (10)

We have thus shown that $P(B_2) = P(B_1)$ [see Eqs. (10) and (4)]. This same phenomenon was encountered in Example 4 of Section 6.2 in connection with a different type of urn scheme. The fact that $P(B_1) = P(B_2)$ may seem to contradict the earlier statement that Polya's urn scheme is a probability model for the spread of a contagious disease. It does not, however, because if the disease has occurred (a black ball has been drawn on the first draw), then the probability of occurrence of the disease (the probability of a black ball on the second draw) does increase from $m/(n + m)$ to $(m + i)/(n + m + i)$.

(iv) $i = 0$ and $j > 0$. This model has been proposed by B. Friedman [2] for use in the study of industrial safety. An accident in an industrial plant is usually followed by a period of emphasis on safety, and the probability of an accident actually decreases. After a period in which no accidents occur, the safety campaign lags, and the probability of an accident increases. The computations of various probabilities in this case are similar to those in case (iii).

(v) $i = -1$ and $j = 1$. This model is the Ehrenfest model of heat exchange between two isolated bodies. Although we shall not investigate this model further, it is in order to point out that this model and several other urn models have proved useful in the study of statistical physics.

EXERCISES

1. (a) Consider Example 1 again. Continue the calculations begun there and show that

$$P(W_1 \cap W_2) = \frac{n(n + i)}{(n + m)(n + m + i)}, \qquad P(W_1 \cap B_2) = \frac{nm}{(n + m)(n + m + i)},$$

$$P(B_1 \cap W_2) = \frac{mn}{(n + m)(n + m + i)}, \qquad P(B_1 \cap B_2) = \frac{m(m + i)}{(n + m)(n + m + i)}.$$

(b) Using the fact that $P(S) = 1$, prove the following identity:

$$n(n + i) + 2nm + m(m + i) = (n + m)(n + m + i).$$

(c) Give a second proof of this identity.

(d) What is the name of this identity in the special case in which $i = 0$?

2. Consider the general urn model described at the beginning of this section. The urn contains n white balls and m black balls. If a ball is drawn, the ball is replaced in the urn and i balls of the same color and j balls of the other color are added. Show that a suitable sample space S, in the case in which two balls are drawn, consists of all ordered pairs (a_1, a_2), where a_1 is the first ball drawn and a_2 is the second ball drawn. If A is an event in S which contains $N(A)$ elements, show that

$$P(A) = \frac{N(A)}{(n + m)(n + m + i + j)}.$$

(a) Define events W_1, W_2, B_1, B_2 as in equations (3). Show that

$$P(B_1) = \frac{m}{n + m},$$

$$P(B_2) = \frac{n(m + j) + m(m + i)}{(n + m)(n + m + i + j)}.$$

Hence, prove that

$$P(B_2) = P(B_1)$$

if and only if $j = 0$ or $n = m$.

(b) Verify that the following probabilities are correct:

$$P(W_1 \cap W_2) = \frac{n(n + i)}{(n + m)(n + m + i + j)},$$

$$P(W_1 \cap B_2) = \frac{n(m + j)}{(n + m)(n + m + i + j)},$$

$$P(B_1 \cap W_2) = \frac{m(n + j)}{(n + m)(n + m + i + j)},$$

$$P(B_1 \cap B_2) = \frac{m(n + i)}{(n + m)(n + m + i + j)}.$$

(c) Prove the identity

$$n(n + i) + n(m + j) + m(n + j) + m(n + i) = (n + m)(n + m + i + j).$$

Show that this identity reduces to the identity in Exercise 1 if $j = 0$. Show that this identity becomes a special case of the binomial theorem if $i = 0$ and $j = 0$.

3. Consider the general urn model described at the beginning of this section in the case in which three balls are drawn (see also Exercise 2). Show that a suitable sample space S consists of all ordered triples (a_1, a_2, a_3), where a_1 is the first ball drawn, a_2 is the second, and a_3 is the third. If A is an event in S which contains $N(A)$ elements, show that

$$P(A) = \frac{N(A)}{(n + m)(n + m + i + j)(n + m + 2i + 2j)}.$$

(a) Define events W_1, W_2, W_3 and B_1, B_2, B_3 by

$$W_i = \{(a_1, a_2, a_3) \,|\, (a_1, a_2, a_3) \in S, \ a_i \text{ is white}\},$$
$$B_i = \{(a_1, a_2, a_3) \,|\, (a_1, a_2, a_3) \in S, \ a_i \text{ is black}\}$$

[see equations (3)]. Prove that the following eight events are disjoint and that their union is S:

$$
\begin{array}{ll}
W_1 \cap W_2 \cap W_3, & W_1 \cap W_2 \cap B_3, \\
W_1 \cap B_2 \cap W_3, & W_1 \cap B_2 \cap B_3, \\
B_1 \cap W_2 \cap W_3, & B_1 \cap W_2 \cap B_3, \\
B_1 \cap B_2 \cap W_3, & B_1 \cap B_2 \cap B_3.
\end{array}
$$

(b) Show that $N(S) = (n + m)(n + m + i + j)(n + m + 2i + 2j)$, and then establish the formulas:

$$P(W_1 \cap W_2 \cap W_3) = \frac{n(n + i)(n + 2i)}{N(S)},$$

$$P(W_1 \cap W_2 \cap B_3) = \frac{n(n + i)(m + 2j)}{N(S)},$$

$$P(W_1 \cap B_2 \cap W_3) = \frac{n(m + j)(n + i + j)}{N(S)},$$

$$P(W_1 \cap B_2 \cap B_3) = \frac{n(m + j)(m + i + j)}{N(S)},$$

$$P(B_1 \cap W_2 \cap W_3) = \frac{m(n + j)(n + i + j)}{N(S)},$$

$$P(B_1 \cap W_2 \cap B_3) = \frac{m(n + j)(m + i + j)}{N(S)},$$

$$P(B_1 \cap B_2 \cap W_3) = \frac{m(m + i)(n + 2j)}{N(S)},$$

$$P(B_1 \cap B_2 \cap B_3) = \frac{m(m + i)(m + 2i)}{N(S)}.$$

(c) Use the results in (b) to prove that

$$P(B_1) = \frac{m}{n + m},$$

$$P(B_2) = \frac{n(m + j)(n + i + j)}{N(S)} + \frac{n(m + j)(m + i + j)}{N(S)} + \frac{m(n + i)(m + 2j)}{N(S)}$$
$$+ \frac{m(m + i)(m + 2i)}{N(S)},$$

$$P(B_3) = \frac{n(n + i)(m + 2j)}{N(S)} + \frac{n(m + j)(m + i + j)}{N(S)} + \frac{m(n + j)(m + i + j)}{N(S)}$$
$$+ \frac{m(m + i)(m + 2i)}{N(S)}.$$

(d) In the special case in which $j = 0$, prove that $P(B_1) = P(B_2) = P(B_3)$. [*Hint:* Use the results of (c). If $j = 0$, then

$$P(B_2) = \frac{m[n(n + i) + 2n(m + i) + (m + i)(m + 2i)]}{N(S)}.$$

Set $j = 0$ in the identity in Exercise 2(c). Then

$$n(n + i) + 2nm + m(m + i) = (n + m)(n + m + i).$$

This identity is valid for all n, m, and i. Replace m by $m + i$, and we have the identity

$$n(n + i) + 2n(m + i) + (m + i)(m + 2i) = (n + m + i)(n + m + 2i).$$

If this identity is used to simplify the expression for $P(B_2)$, we find that

$$P(B_2) = \frac{m[(n + m + i)(n + m + 2i)]}{(n + m)(n + m + i)(n + m + 2i)} = \frac{m}{n + m}.$$

If $j = 0$, then

$$P(B_3) = \frac{m[n(n + i) + 2n(m + i) + (m + i)(m + 2i)]}{(n + m)(n + m + i)(n + m + 2i)} = \frac{m}{n + m}.$$

Thus, if $j = 0$, then $P(B_1) = P(B_2) = P(B_3)$.]

(e) Obtain an identity from the formulas in part (b) by using the fact that $P(S) = 1$. If $i = 0$ and $j = 0$, show that this identity reduces to a special case of the binomial theorem.

4. Consider Polya's urn scheme in the case in which k balls are drawn. A suitable sample space S consists of all ordered k-tuples $(a_1, a_2, \ldots, a_r, \ldots, a_k)$, where a_r is the rth ball drawn. Show that

$$N(S) = (n + m)(n + m + i) \ldots (n + m + (k - 1)i).$$

For use in this exercise alone, it will be convenient to define the symbol $[l]_s$ by

$$[l]_s = l(l + i)(l + 2i) \ldots (l + (s - 1)i), \qquad s = 1, 2, \ldots,$$
$$[l]_0 = 1.$$

Then $N(S) = [n + m]_k$. If A is any event in S, show that

$$P(A) = \frac{N(A)}{[n + m]_k}.$$

(a) Let $(a_1, a_2, \ldots, a_k)$ and $(b_1, b_2, \ldots, b_k)$ be any two outcomes in S in which there are exactly $(k - r)$ white balls and r black balls (the white and black balls may be arranged in different orders in the two k-tuples). Show that

$$P(\{(a_1, a_2, \ldots, a_k)\}) = P(\{(b_1, b_2, \ldots, b_k)\}) = [n]_{k-r}[m]_r/N(S).$$

(b) Define $A(k - r, r)$, for $r = 0, 1, 2, \ldots, k$, to be the event in S which consists of all outcomes $(a_1, a_2, \ldots, a_k)$ in which there are exactly $k - r$ white balls and r black balls. Show that

$$A(k - s, s) \cap A(k - t, t) = \emptyset, \qquad s \neq t,$$
$$\bigcup_{r=0}^{k} A(k - r, r) = S.$$

(c) Use part (a) of this exercise to prove that

$$P(A(k - r, r)) = \frac{\dbinom{k}{r} [n]_{k-r}[m]_r}{[n + m]_k}.$$

(d) Use parts (b) and (c) of this exercise to prove that

$$\sum_{r=0}^{k} \binom{k}{r} [n]_{k-r}[m]_r = [n + m]_k.$$

Show that this formula, in the special case in which $i = 0$, is

$$\sum_{r=0}^{k} \binom{k}{r} n^{k-r} m^r = (n + m)^k.$$

Thus the binomial identity is a special case of a more general identity.

(e) Let B_k be the event in S in which a black ball is drawn on the kth draw. Show that

$$P(B_k) = \frac{m}{n + m}.$$

[*Hint:* Let $B(k - r, r - 1)$, for $r = 1, 2, \ldots, k$, be the event in S which consists of k-tuples $(a_1, a_2, \ldots, a_k)$ such that a_k is a black ball and $(a_1, a_2, \ldots, a_{k-1})$ contains $(r - 1)$ black balls and $(k - r)$ white balls. Show that the events

$$B(k - 1, 0), B(k - 2, 1), \ldots, B(0, k - 1)$$

are disjoint and that

$$B_k = \bigcup_{r=0}^{k} B(k - r, r - 1).$$

Also show that

$$P(B(k - r, r - 1)) = \frac{\binom{k - 1}{r - 1} [n]_{k-r}[m]_{r-1}(m + (r - 1)i)}{[n + m]_k}.$$

Use these two results to show that

$$P(B_k) = \frac{\sum_{r=1}^{k} \binom{k - 1}{r - 1} [n]_{k-r}[m]_{r-1}(m + (r - 1)i)}{[n + m]_k}.$$

Observe that

$$[m]_{r-1}(m + (r - 1)i) = [m]_r = m[m + i]_{r-1}$$

for $r = 1, 2, \ldots, k$, and that

$$[n + m]_k = (n + m)[n + m + i]_{k-1}.$$

Use these results to show that

$$P(B_k) = \frac{m}{n + m} \frac{\sum_{r=1}^{k} \binom{k - 1}{r - 1} [n]_{k-r}[m + i]_{r-1}}{[n + m + i]_{k-1}}.$$

Make a change of variable in the summation by setting $r - 1 = t$. Then

$$P(B_k) = \frac{m}{n + m} \frac{\sum_{t=0}^{k-1} \binom{k - 1}{t} [n]_{(k-1)-t}[m + i]_t}{[n + m + i]_{k-1}}.$$

Use the first identity in part (d) of this exercise to show that

$$P(B_k) = \frac{m}{n + m} \cdot$$

The proof is complete.]

6.6 CELL OCCUPANCY PROBLEMS

Cell occupancy problems are concerned with placing objects (called marbles, balls, or chips) in cells (boxes or urns). The cell occupancy problems are closely related to the urn model problems studied earlier in this chapter. In Section 4.6 we investigated certain counting problems connected with cell occupancy problems. In this section we shall study the related probability problems by using the results obtained for urn schemes to find solutions for the cell occupancy problems.

Consider the problem of distributing k marbles into n cells. (We shall use the terms "marbles" and "cells" in discussing cell occupancy problems so we can distinguish these objects from the "balls" and "urns" in urn problems.) We shall always assume that the cells are distinguishable, and hence, for convenience, we shall assume that they are labeled $1, 2, \ldots, n$. There are many different cell occupancy problems corresponding to the various restrictions that can be imposed on the number of marbles that are permitted to be placed in any one cell. We shall not investigate all these problems but only the following two types.

(a) An unrestricted number of marbles may be placed in each of the n cells.

(b) At most one marble may be placed in each of the n cells.

The cell occupancy problems determined by (a) and (b) are known as placing marbles in cells *without exclusion* and *with exclusion*, respectively. There are clearly many other possible cell occupancy problems. One such problem is specified by the rule that at most 10 marbles may be placed in each of the n cells. Another more complicated problem is characterized by the rule that at most k marbles may be placed in the kth cell.

When we place a marble in a cell, in effect we choose a cell. Thus, placing k marbles randomly into n cells amounts to choosing successively the k cells to contain the marbles. In cell occupancy problem (a), any cell may be selected to receive any marble; hence, this problem is exactly the same as the problem of drawing successively with replacement from an urn containing n objects (cells). In problem (b), a cell is no longer available to receive a marble after one marble has been placed in it; thus this problem is the same as the problem of drawing successively without replacement from an urn containing n objects.

To summarize, each of the two cell occupancy problems has been reduced to a problem of selecting objects from an urn, where the objects in the urn are the cells in the cell occupancy problem. Furthermore, placing the marbles in the cells without exclusion corresponds to sampling with replacement, and placing the marbles in the cells with exclusion corresponds to sampling without replacement.

	Cell occupancy problem	Urn problem
	Cells	Balls
Correspondence	Selecting k cells from the n cells to receive the k marbles (or, equivalently, placing the k marbles in k cells)	Selecting k balls from the n balls in the urn
	Without exclusion	With replacement
	With exclusion	Without replacement

Fig. 6.2. Some correspondences between cell occupancy problems and urn problems.

Figure 6.2 summarizes these correspondences between cell occupancy problems and urn problems.

It has been shown that a cell occupancy problem can be interpreted as an urn problem. Similarly, an urn problem can be converted into a cell occupancy problem—a problem concerned with placing marbles in cells.

At this point the reader should reread Section 4.6. The examples in that section show that, for cell occupancy problems, it makes a great deal of difference whether the marbles are distinguishable or indistinguishable. Figure 4.17 shows that the number of ways of placing 3 distinguishable objects into 2 cells is $2^3 = 8$, and that the number of ways of placing 3 indistinguishable objects into 2 cells is $\binom{4}{3} = 4$.

If the marbles are distinguishable, then to each placement of the k marbles into the n cells there corresponds a k-tuple $(a_1, a_2, \ldots, a_k)$, where a_i denotes the number of the cell occupied by marble i. That is, in order to place the k marbles in the n cells, it is necessary to select a cell for the first marble, a cell for the second marble, etc. Although the marbles may not be placed in the cells in the order in which the marbles are numbered, it is always necessary to select a cell for the first marble (marble 1), and there is no loss in generality in assuming that this marble is placed first. In general, we may assume that the marbles are placed in the order in which they are numbered. Thus, if the marbles are distinguishable, the cell occupancy problem is equivalent to ordered sampling from an urn.

If the marbles are indistinguishable, then the placing of the k marbles in the n cells does not determine an ordered k-tuple $(a_1, a_2, \ldots, a_k)$ as described in the last paragraph. Instead, there corresponds an unordered set $\{a_1, a_2, \ldots, a_k\}$, where a_i is the number of a cell into which a marble has been placed (observe that the a_i in $\{a_1, a_2, \ldots, a_k\}$ need not be distinct). But $\{a_1, a_2, \ldots, a_k\}$ is an unordered sample of k cells drawn from the n cells. Thus the placing of indistinguishable marbles in cells corresponds to drawing unordered samples of balls

	Cell occupancy problem	Urn problem
Correspondence	Distinguishable marbles	Ordered sample
	Indistinguishable marbles	Unordered sample

Fig. 6.3. Two further correspondences between cell occupancy problems and urn problems.

from an urn. Figure 6.3 exhibits the two additional correspondences (see Fig. 6.2) between cell occupancy problems and urn problems described in the last two paragraphs.

It is now easy to compute the number of ways of distributing the k marbles into the n cells.

(i) Distinguishable marbles, any number placed in a cell (placement without exclusion). If the marbles are placed in the cells at random, there are n^k equally likely ways of placing the k marbles in the n cells without exclusion since there are n^k equally likely ways of selecting k balls with replacement from an urn containing n balls.

(ii) Distinguishable marbles, at most one in a cell (placement with exclusion). There are $(n)_k$ equally likely ways to place the marbles in the cells since there are $(n)_k$ equally likely ways to select k balls without replacement from an urn containing n balls.

(iii) Indistinguishable marbles, any number placed in a cell (placement without exclusion). By Theorem 4.11 there are $\binom{k+n-1}{k}$ ways to place k indistinguishable marbles in n cells without exclusion. If the marbles are placed in the cells at random, each of the $\binom{k+n-1}{k}$ ways is equally likely.

(iv) Indistinguishable marbles, at most one in a cell (placement with exclusion). The problem is equivalent to drawing an unordered sample of size k from an urn containing n objects. Thus there are $(n)_k/k! = \binom{n}{k}$ ways to place, with exclusion, k indistinguishable marbles in n cells. If the marbles are placed in the cells at random, each of the $\binom{n}{k}$ ways is equally likely.

Figure 6.4 summarizes the facts stated in (i), (ii), (iii), and (iv). Furthermore, the figure shows the relationships which exist between placing k marbles in n cells and selecting k balls from an urn containing n balls.

EXAMPLE 1. Let k marbles be placed at random in n cells numbered $1, 2, \ldots, n$. If $k < n$, what is the probability that each of the cells numbered 1 to k contains exactly 1 ball?

The answer to the question will clearly depend on the nature of the marbles (are they distinguishable or indistinguishable?) and the manner in which they

Cell occupancy problem	The number of ways of distributing k marbles into n distinguishable cells		
Marbles are	Distinguishable	Indistinguishable	
Distributed without exclusion	n^k	$\binom{k + n - 1}{k}$	Drawn with replacement
Distributed with exclusion	$(n)_k$	$\binom{n}{k}$	Drawn without replacement
	Ordered	Unordered	Samples are
	Number of ways of selecting samples of size k from an urn containing n distinguishable balls		Urn problem

Fig. 6.4. The number of ways to distribute marbles in cells and draw samples from an urn, and relationships between cell occupancy problems and urn problems.

are distributed in the cells (with or without exclusion). The four situations are described in cases (i), (ii), (iii), and (iv) above. Let A be the set of outcomes in which each of the cells numbered 1 to k contains exactly one marble. Then $N(A) = k!$ if the marbles are distinguishable since $k!$ is the number of ways to arrange k distinguishable objects in k positions. The result is the same whether we assume distribution with or without exclusion since we have specified that each cell is to contain exactly one marble. If the marbles are indistinguishable, then $N(A) = 1$ since there is only one way to put k indistinguishable objects into k specified cells. Then

$$P(A) = \frac{k!}{n^k},$$
if k distinguishable marbles are distributed without exclusion;

$$P(A) = \frac{k!}{(n)_k},$$
if k distinguishable marbles are distributed with exclusion;

$$P(A) = \frac{1}{\binom{k + n - 1}{k}},$$
if k indistinguishable marbles are distributed without exclusion;

$$P(A) = \frac{1}{\binom{n}{k}},$$
if k indistinguishable marbles are distributed with exclusion.

It should be noted that $P(A)$ is the same in cases (ii) and (iv).

EXAMPLE 2. Consider an experiment in which six marbles are placed at random into five cells. Marbles are placed in cells one at a time until a marble is placed in a cell which already contains a marble. Compute the probabilities that the second, third, fourth, fifth, and sixth marbles are placed in occupied cells.

It is clear that the second ball placed is the first one that can be placed in an occupied cell. Also, it should be clear that the problem does not depend in any way on whether the marbles are distinguishable or indistinguishable. Furthermore, the problem is basically one in which marbles are placed in cells with exclusion, since the distribution stops when a marble is placed in an occupied cell for the first time. Let A_k be the event which consists of all outcomes in which: (a) the kth marble placed falls into an occupied cell, and (b) the first $k - 1$ marbles placed fall into unoccupied cells. The problem in Example 2 is to calculate $P(A_k)$ for $k = 2, 3, 4, 5, 6$. The marbles can be considered as distinguishable or indistinguishable in the calculation of $P(A_k)$; the results will be the same in the two cases. We shall assume that the marbles are distinguishable. In Exercise 14 the reader is asked to calculate $P(A_k)$ on the assumption that the marbles are indistinguishable.

If the marbles are distinguishable, the number of ways of placing k marbles in n cells is n^k. The number $N(A_k)$ of elements in A_k is calculated as follows. The first $k - 1$ marbles are placed in $k - 1$ distinct cells; there are

$$n(n - 1) \ldots (n - (k - 1) + 1) = (n)_{k-1}$$

ways to do so. Then the kth marble is placed in a cell that is already occupied; there are $k - 1$ such cells. Then $N(A_k) = (n)_{k-1}(k - 1)$, and hence

$$P(A_k) = \frac{(n)_{k-1}(k - 1)}{n^k}, \qquad k = 2, 3, \ldots, n + 1. \tag{1}$$

Equation (1) gives the probabilities in the general case. For the special case in Example 2 we have:

$$P(A_2) = \frac{(5)_1(2 - 1)}{5^2} = \frac{1}{5},$$

$$P(A_3) = \frac{(5)_2(3 - 1)}{5^3} = \frac{5 \cdot 4 \cdot 2}{5^3} = \frac{8}{25},$$

$$P(A_4) = \frac{(5)_3(4 - 1)}{5^4} = \frac{5 \cdot 4 \cdot 3 \cdot 3}{5^4} = \frac{36}{125},$$

$$P(A_5) = \frac{(5)_4(5 - 1)}{5^5} = \frac{5 \cdot 4 \cdot 3 \cdot 2 \cdot 4}{5^5} = \frac{96}{625},$$

$$P(A_6) = \frac{(5)_5(6 - 1)}{5^6} = \frac{5 \cdot 4 \cdot 3 \cdot 2 \cdot 1 \cdot 5}{5^6} = \frac{24}{625}.$$

The reader can verify without difficulty that

$$P(A_2) + P(A_3) + P(A_4) + P(A_5) + P(A_6) = 1.$$

The problem in Example 2 and its generalization [see Eq. (1)] is another example of a waiting time problem. We wait until a cell is occupied for the second time.

A simple example of this waiting time problem (see Example 2) occurs in coupon collecting. Coupons are collected until a duplicate is obtained. What are the probabilities for the waiting time? Each coupon collected corresponds to placing a marble in a cell, and the number k, where $k - 1$ coupons are collected before a duplicate is obtained, is the waiting time.

The next example contains another variation of the cell occupancy problem. In this variation each cell is required to contain a predetermined number of marbles.

EXAMPLE 3. Let 6 marbles be distributed randomly into 3 cells without exclusion (any number of marbles in each cell). What is the probability that the first cell contains 2 marbles, the second 3 marbles, and the third cell 1 marble?

As usual, there are two solutions to this problem depending on whether the marbles are assumed to be distinguishable or not. Assume first that the marbles are not distinguishable. Let A be the event which consists of distributions of the marbles as specified; then $N(A) = 1$. The total number of ways of distributing the 6 marbles in the three cells is $\binom{6+3-1}{6} = \binom{8}{6} = 28$. Thus $P(A) = \frac{1}{28}$. If the marbles are distinguishable, then there are 3^6 ways of distributing the marbles into the 3 cells. To find $N(A)$, observe that we are forming a three-part classification by putting 2 marbles into the first cell, 3 marbles into the second, and 1 marble into the third (see Section 4.5). There are $\binom{6}{2, 3, 1}$ ways of forming this classification. Then

$$P(A) = \frac{\binom{6}{2, 3, 1}}{3^6} = \frac{20}{243}.$$

The next example is closely related to the last one.

EXAMPLE 4. An urn contains 3 distinguishable balls. A sample of size 6 is drawn with replacement from the urn. What is the probability that the first ball was drawn twice, the second ball three times, and the third ball once?

This problem is the urn problem which corresponds to the cell occupancy problem in Example 3. The drawing of a sample of 6 from the urn containing 3 balls is the same as the placing of 6 marbles into 3 cells. Thus, if the sample is unordered, the probability is $\frac{1}{28}$; if the sample is ordered, the probability is $\frac{20}{243}$.

Examples 3 and 4 can be generalized. First, we shall state the completely general case of the cell occupancy problem as follows. Let k marbles be placed at random and without exclusion into n cells so that the first cell contains k_1 marbles, the second contains k_2 marbles, . . . , and the nth contains k_n marbles, where $k_1 + k_2 + \cdots + k_n = k$. If the marbles are indistinguishable, the probability of this event is

$$\frac{1}{\dbinom{k+n-1}{k}}.$$

If the marbles are distinguishable, the probability of this event is

$$\frac{\dbinom{k}{k_1, k_2, \ldots, k_n}}{n^k}.$$

Observe that some of the k_i may be zero. The urn sampling problem which corresponds is the following. A random sample of k balls is selected with replacement from an urn which contains n balls. The probability that the first ball is selected k_1 times, the second is selected k_2 times, . . . , and the nth is selected k_n times is

$$\frac{1}{\dbinom{k+n-1}{k}}, \qquad \text{if the sample is unordered,}$$

and

$$\frac{\dbinom{k}{k_1, k_2, \ldots, k_n}}{n^k}, \qquad \text{if the sample is ordered.}$$

EXERCISES

1. Seven marbles are given: they are red, orange, yellow, green, blue, indigo, and violet.
   (a) In how many ways can the seven marbles be placed with exclusion in four cells? In seven cells? In ten cells?
   (b) In how many ways can the seven marbles be placed without exclusion in four cells? In seven cells? In ten cells?

2. Seven indistinguishable white marbles are given.
   (a) In how many ways can the seven white marbles be placed with exclusion in four cells? In seven cells? In ten cells?
   (b) In how many ways can the seven white marbles be placed without exclusion in four cells? In seven cells? In ten cells?

3. In how many ways can seven distinguishable workmen be assigned, one workman per job, to four jobs? To seven jobs? To ten jobs?

4. In how many ways can seven indistinguishable workmen be assigned, one workman per job, to four jobs? To seven jobs? To ten jobs?

5. Consider again the marbles in Exercise 1.
   (a) If the seven marbles are placed with exclusion but at random in ten cells, what is the probability that the marbles are in cells 1, 2, . . . , 7?

(b) If the seven marbles are placed without exclusion but at random in ten cells, what is the probability that the marbles are in cells 1, 2, . . . , 7?

6. Consider again the marbles in Exercise 2.
    (a) If the seven marbles are placed with exclusion but at random in ten cells, what is the probability that the marbles are in cells 1, 2, . . . , 7?
    (b) If the seven marbles are placed without exclusion but at random in ten cells, what is the probability that the marbles are in cells 1, 2, . . . , 7?

7. A foreman has six men to assign to three jobs. The three jobs are written on three cards which are then placed in a hat. The first man draws a card from the hat, records his job, and returns the card to the hat. Each of the other five men draws a card and receives a random assignment to a job in the same way.
    (a) If the six men are considered distinguishable with respect to the jobs, find the probability that two men are assigned to the first job, three men are assigned to the second job, and one man is assigned to the third job.
    (b) Solve part (a) of this exercise on the assumption that the six men are indistinguishable with respect to the three jobs.
    (c) If there are ten distinguishable men and five jobs, find the probability that two are assigned to the first, third, and fifth jobs, three to the second job, and one to the fourth job.
    (d) Solve part (c) of this exercise on the assumption that the ten men are indistinguishable with respect to the five jobs.

8. One of three distinguishable men (Brown, Jones, and Smith) is assigned by lot to a certain task on each of six successive days. Find the probability that Brown receives the assignment twice, Jones three times, and Smith once.

9. A game is played as follows. The player draws at random one chip from an urn which contains ten blue chips, ten red chips, and ten white chips. If the player draws a blue chip, he receives a first prize. If he draws a red chip, he receives a second prize. If he draws a white chip, he receives a third prize. If a certain player plays the game six times, what is the probability that he receives a first prize twice, a second prize three times, and a third prize once?

10. Each box of a certain breakfast cereal contains one of ten different coupons. The coupons are randomly distributed in boxes of the cereal. The Jones household collects the coupons from the boxes of cereal bought at random. Let A_k be the event that the first $k - 1$ coupons are different, but the kth coupon is a duplicate of one of the first $k - 1$ coupons. Find $P(A_k)$ for $k = 2, 3, . . . , 10, 11$. What is the probability that the Jones household obtains a duplicate coupon before the eleventh has been collected? By the time the eleventh coupon has been collected?

11. Use Eq. (1) to show that $P(A_2) = 1/n$, that is, that the probability of placing the first and second marbles in the same cell is $1/n$.

12. Consider the problem of placing marbles in cells until two marbles occupy the same cell [see Example 2 and Eq. (1)]. Show that the probability that the first repetition occurs *after* the kth placement is $(n)_k/n^k$.

13. Use Exercise 12 to obtain another solution of the birthday problem in Example 7 of Section 6.2.

14. In Example 2 we derived Eq. (1) by assuming that the marbles were distinguishable. Give an alternative proof of the formula in Eq. (1) by assuming that the marbles are indistinguishable.

15. Consider the problem of randomly distributing, without exclusion, k indistinguishable marbles into n cells. Show that the probability of exactly m cells remaining empty is

$$\frac{\binom{n}{m}\binom{k-1}{n-m-1}}{\binom{n+k-1}{k}}.$$

16. Consider again the problem in Exercise 15. Show that the probability of at least m cells remaining empty is

$$\sum_{j=m}^{n}\frac{\binom{n}{j}\binom{k-1}{n-j-1}}{\binom{n+k-1}{k}}.$$

17. Consider again the problem in Exercise 15. Show that the probability of a given cell containing exactly i marbles is

$$\frac{\binom{n+k-i-2}{k-i}}{\binom{n+k-1}{k}}.$$

18. Consider Exercise 15 again.
    (a) If 5 indistinguishable marbles are randomly distributed, without exclusion, into 3 cells, what is the probability that at least one cell remains empty? That exactly one cell remains empty?
    (b) If 8 indistinguishable marbles are randomly distributed, without exclusion, into 5 cells, what is the probability that at least two cells remain empty? That exactly two cells remain empty?

19. Find the probability in Exercise 18(a) that the first cell contains exactly one marble. Exactly three marbles. Exactly five marbles.

20. Find the probability in Exercise 18(b) that the fourth cell contains exactly one marble. Exactly four marbles. Exactly eight marbles.

21. Each box of a certain breakfast cereal contains one of a series of five coupons. The coupons are randomly distributed in boxes of the cereal bought by a certain family.
    (a) What is the probability that the first five boxes of cereal bought by the family contain a complete set of the coupons?
    (b) What is the probability that the first ten boxes contain a complete set of coupons?
    (c) The family buys k boxes of the cereal. For each k there is a certain probability that the family has a complete set of coupons. Show that this probability increases as k increases.

22. An unordered sample of size k is drawn with replacement from an urn containing n balls. What is the probability that a specified ball is drawn i times?

23. An advertising agency wishes to test the effectiveness of its campaign among people living in small towns. The agency employs ten people in a certain small town to make telephone inquiries. If there are 450 telephones in the town, and if each of the ten employees makes only one telephone call (the number called being selected at random in each case) what is the probability that no person receives two of the telephone calls?

24. A publisher feels that a book is set in type satisfactorily if not more than one typographical error appears on each page. If a certain book is 300 pages long, and if there are 50 typographical errors in it, what is the probability that the book has been satisfactorily set?

6.7 MATCHING PROBLEMS

Two examples will serve to introduce the reader to the subject of matching problems.

EXAMPLE 1.   Three cells labeled 1, 2, 3 and three marbles, also labeled 1, 2, 3, are given. The marbles are placed in the cells with one marble in each cell. What is the probability that a match occurs, that is, what is the probability that the number on a marble is the same as the number on the cell in which it is placed?

There are six ways of placing the marbles in the cells. If the first, second, and third positions in a 3-tuple represent the first, second, and third cells, the six ways to put the three marbles into the three cells are

$$(1, 2, 3) \quad (1, 3, 2) \quad (2, 3, 1) \quad (2, 1, 3) \quad (3, 1, 2) \quad (3, 2, 1).$$

If the marbles are placed in the cells at random, each of the six ways is equally likely. Matches occur in four of the six cases; hence, the probability of at least one match is $\frac{4}{6}$. Furthermore, in one case there are exactly three matches, and in three cases there is exactly one match. (If there are two matches, then obviously there are three matches.) Finally, the probability of no matches is $\frac{1}{3}$.

EXAMPLE 2.   The hat-check girl in a restaurant checks the hats of n men, but she accidently loses the identifying check slips. As a result, she returns the hats to the n men at random. What is the probability that no man receives his own hat?

This problem, of course, is a generalization of the problem in Example 1 in which each man represents a cell and the random returning of the hats corresponds to placing the marbles in the cells with exclusion. To solve this problem we must find the probability of no matches when n marbles numbered $1, 2, \ldots, n$ are placed into n cells numbered $1, 2, \ldots, n$. Let $p(n)$ denote the probability that no matches occur, and let $a(n)$ denote the number of ways in which the hats can be returned without any matches occurring. Then, since there are $n!$ equally likely ways of returning the hats,

$$p(n) = a(n)/n!. \tag{1}$$

We shall calculate $p(n)$ by first obtaining a recursion relation for $a(n)$ and hence for $p(n)$, and then solving the recursion relation for $p(n)$. To find the recursion relation for $a(n)$, we proceed as follows. Assume that no man receives his own hat. The nth man then has the hat of some other man, say the ith man, where $1 \leq i \leq n - 1$. There are $n - 1$ ways for the nth man to have the hat of another man. If no man receives his own hat, then the nth man receives the ith man's hat, and either the ith man receives the nth man's hat or he does not. These two events are disjoint, and hence $a(n)$ equals $(n - 1)$ times the sum of the number of ways each of the two events can occur. If the ith man receives the nth man's hat, the ith man and the nth man have traded hats, and the other $n - 2$ men receive each other's hats. The number of ways the $n - 2$ men can receive each other's hats is $a(n - 2)$, since $a(n - 2)$ is the number of ways $n - 2$ men can exchange hats so that no man receives his own hat. If the ith man does not receive the nth man's hat (but the nth man does receive the ith man's hat), then we consider the $n - 1$ men $1, 2, \ldots, n - 1$ who receive hats numbered $1, 2, \ldots, i - 1$, $n, i + 1, \ldots, n - 1$ so that no man receives his own hat and so that the ith man does not receive the nth man's hat. Since the nth man does receive the ith man's hat, the nth man's hat plays the same role that would be played by the ith man's hat. Recall that $a(n - 1)$ is the number of ways that $n - 1$ men can exchange hats so that no man receives his own hat; then $a(n - 1)$ is the number of ways the $n - 1$ hats $1, 2, \ldots, i - 1, n, i + 1, \ldots, n - 1$ can be distributed among the men $1, 2, \ldots, n - 1$ so that no man receives his own hat, *and* the ith man does not receive the nth man's hat. We have thus shown that

$$a(n) = (n - 1)[a(n - 2) + a(n - 1)]. \tag{2}$$

If we substitute this value for $a(n)$ in Eq. (1), we obtain

$$p(n) = (n - 1)\left[\frac{a(n - 2)}{n!} + \frac{a(n - 1)}{n!}\right] = (n - 1)\left[\frac{p(n - 2)}{n(n - 1)} + \frac{p(n - 1)}{n}\right]$$

$$= \frac{1}{n}[p(n - 2) + (n - 1)p(n - 1)]$$

$$= \frac{1}{n}[p(n - 2) - p(n - 1)] + p(n - 1).$$

Therefore

$$p(n) - p(n - 1) = -(1/n)[p(n - 1) - p(n - 2)]. \tag{3}$$

The recursion relation for $p(n)$ which we set out to find is given by Eq. (3), and the problem can now be completed by finding the solution of this equation.

To solve Eq. (3), set $P(n) = p(n) - p(n-1)$. Then Eq. (3) becomes

$$P(n) = -(1/n)P(n-1). \tag{4}$$

Next observe that $p(1) = 0$ and $p(2) = 1/2!$, and hence that $P(2) = p(2) - p(1) = 1/2!$. A recursive solution of Eq. (4) shows that

$$P(n) = \frac{(-1)^n}{n!}, \qquad n \geq 2. \tag{5}$$

From the definition of $P(n)$ we have

$$\sum_{k=2}^{n} [p(k) - p(k-1)] = \sum_{k=2}^{n} P(k),$$

and by simplifying the expression on the left we obtain

$$p(n) - p(1) = P(2) + P(3) + \cdots + P(n-1) + P(n).$$

Now $p(1) = 0$, and the value of $P(k)$ is given by Eq. (5). Thus we find that

$$p(n) = \frac{1}{2!} - \frac{1}{3!} + \cdots + \frac{(-1)^{n-1}}{(n-1)!} + \frac{(-1)^n}{n!}.$$

The preferred standard form for $p(n)$ is the following:*

$$p(n) = 1 - \frac{1}{1!} + \frac{1}{2!} - \frac{1}{3!} + \cdots + \frac{(-1)^{n-1}}{(n-1)!} + \frac{(-1)^n}{n!}. \tag{6}$$

The complement of the event in which there are no matches is the event in which there are one or more matches. If $q(n)$ denotes the probability of one or more matches, then

$$q(n) = 1 - p(n) = \frac{1}{1!} - \frac{1}{2!} + \frac{1}{3!} - \cdots - \frac{(-1)^{n-1}}{(n-1)!} - \frac{(-1)^n}{n!}.$$

An illustration of this type of matching occurred in early ESP (extra sensory perception) experiments. A test to determine whether or not an experimental subject had ESP was conducted as follows. The person being tested was given a deck of cards numbered, say, from 1 to n, which were randomly shuffled, and which were presented face down. He was asked to arrange them in order without looking at them, that is, to match them with cells numbered 1 to n. The number of matches he made was then compared with the number in a random placement of the cards to see whether he achieved any "significant" improvement over pure chance.

---

* This formula for $p(n)$ can be derived more directly by the method of inclusion and exclusion; see Feller [1, p. 89].

Matching problems have been employed also in attempts to relate a person's individual characteristics with the person. For example, a handwriting expert might be given ten samples of handwriting along with the pictures of the ten people who wrote the samples and asked to match them. To decide whether the expert has any true ability, we need to know the probabilities for random identifications. Random identification here would correspond to matches in the random placing of ten marbles (handwriting samples) into ten cells (pictures), where each cell can hold at most one object. The probability of random identifications of handwriting is the same as the probability of the corresponding number of matches (cases in which a marble is placed in a cell with the same number as the marble).

In Example 2 we calculated the probability of the occurrence of no matches (and hence of one or more matches). We shall now calculate the probability of exactly k matches if n marbles, numbered 1 to n, are placed randomly into n cells, numbered 1 to n, in such a way that one and only one marble is placed into each cell. Let A_k be the event in which exactly k matches occur; we shall calculate the number of ways, $N(A_k)$, this event can happen. There are $\binom{n}{k}$ ways to select the k cells in which the matches occur. For each selection of k cells in which matches occur, the remaining $n - k$ cells must contain no matches. Hence, $n - k$ marbles are distributed into the $n - k$ corresponding cells in such a way that no matches occur. In the notation of Example 2, this distribution can be made in $a(n - k)$ ways. Thus

$$N(A_k) = \binom{n}{k} a(n - k). \tag{7}$$

By Eq. (1), $a(j) = j!p(j)$, and $p(j)$ can be obtained from Eq. (6). From these results we find that

$$a(n - k) = (n - k)!\left[1 - \frac{1}{1!} + \frac{1}{2!} - \frac{1}{3!} + \cdots + \frac{(-1)^{n-k}}{(n - k)!}\right],$$

and that

$$N(A_k) = \binom{n}{k} a(n - k) = \binom{n}{k} (n - k)!\left[1 - \frac{1}{1!} + \frac{1}{2!} - \frac{1}{3!} + \cdots + \frac{(-1)^{n-k}}{(n - k)!}\right]$$

$$= (n)_k \left[1 - \frac{1}{1!} + \frac{1}{2!} - \frac{1}{3!} + \cdots + \frac{(-1)^{n-k}}{(n - k)!}\right]. \tag{8}$$

Then

$$P(A_k) = \frac{N(A_k)}{n!} = \frac{(n)_k}{n!}\left[1 - \frac{1}{1!} + \frac{1}{2!} - \frac{1}{3!} + \cdots + \frac{(-1)^{n-k}}{(n - k)!}\right]$$

$$= \frac{1}{k!}\left[1 - \frac{1}{1!} + \frac{1}{2!} - \frac{1}{3!} + \cdots + \frac{(-1)^{n-k}}{(n - k)!}\right]. \tag{9}$$

Since we have now obtained a formula for the probability of exactly k matches, we can compute the probability of k or more matches.

EXAMPLE 3. A handwriting expert correctly matches 5 out of 10 handwriting samples with 10 character sketches of those who wrote the handwriting samples. Has the handwriting expert made more matches than would occur by pure chance? We have $n = 10$ in this example, and there are 5 matches. By Eq. (9) the probability of 5 matches is

$$\frac{1}{5!}\left[1 - \frac{1}{1!} + \frac{1}{2!} - \frac{1}{3!} + \frac{1}{4!} - \frac{1}{5!}\right].$$

We shall compute the probability of 5 or more matches since we want to know the probability that a result as good as, or better than, 5 matches would occur by chance. The probability [see Eq. (9)] of 5 or more matches is

$$P(A_5) + P(A_6) + \cdots + P(A_{10}) = 0.0037.$$

This probability is interpreted to mean that the handwriting expert has achieved a result that would occur by chance only 37 times in 10,000 trials. The result suggests that the handwriting expert has some ability.

The probability of k or more matches [see Eq. (9)] in the general case is

$$P(A_k) + P(A_{k+1}) + \cdots + P(A_n). \tag{10}$$

This quantity is not easy to compute, but for small values of n and k it has been tabulated (see the paper by Chapman [3] which is mentioned in the bibliographical notes at the end of this chapter).

Most of the actual ESP experiments employ a special deck of 25 cards called Zener cards after Professor K. E. Zener of the Duke University Department of Psychology. These cards are imprinted with five symbols: a circle, a rectangle, a plus sign, wavy lines, and a star. Each symbol appears on five cards. As these cards are turned up, a "percipient" (who does not see the cards) lists his guesses in sequence. Some of the experimental subjects were able to score as many as 16 or 17—and even 22 or 23—correct matches. To evaluate the significance of these results, it is necessary to calculate the probabilities for various numbers of matches to occur in random guessing.

Another matching problem which is almost identical with the ESP experiment is a card game played in Las Vegas. A standard deck of playing cards, which contains 4 suits of 13 denominations in each suit, is shuffled, and the cards are dealt one at a time and face up. At the same time the player calls off the denominations in the order ace, two, three, . . . , queen, king. A match is said to occur if the denomination of the card turned up is the same as the denomination called by the player (the suits need not match). The player wins if no matches occur and loses if matches do occur (the game stops at the first match). What is the probability that the player wins? It has been shown that this probability is approximately $1/e^4$, where $e = 2.718 \ldots$ It is not easy to establish this result (see the bibliographical notes at the end of this chapter for a reference to a treatment of this problem).

The ESP experiment and the Las Vegas gambling games are special cases of a more general matching problem. This problem employs a deck of mn cards of m suits of n denominations each; the denominations in each suit are numbered from 1 to n. The deck is shuffled, and the cards are dealt one at a time and face up. Simultaneously, the player counts, m times, from 1 to n. A match occurs if the denomination called by the player is the same as the denomination on the card turned up. What is the probability of k matches? In Example 2 we solved this problem for $m = 1$. In Example 4 we shall solve it for arbitrary m and $n = 2$.

EXAMPLE 4. Consider the matching problem for arbitrary m and $n = 2$. In this case there are m suits but only two denominations. It is convenient to label the suits with the numbers $1, 2, \ldots, m$, and to label the denominations with the colors red and black. The colors red and black are called alternately as each card is turned up until red has been called m times and black has been called m times. What is the probability of exactly k matches?

To calculate this probability, we consider a $2m$-tuple $(r, b, r, b, \ldots, r, b)$, where r and b denote red and black, respectively. This $2m$-tuple contains the colors in the order in which they are called by the player. The deck that is turned up yields a $2m$-tuple also, $(a_1, a_2, \ldots, a_{2m})$, where each a_i is either r or b, and m of the a_i's are r's and m are b's. A match occurs when a_i is the same as the ith entry in the standard $2m$-tuple $(r, b, r, b, \ldots, r, b)$. Since the suits are not required to match, we can ignore the suits and consider merely that m cards are red (indistinguishable) and m cards are black (indistinguishable). By Theorem 4.10, there are $\binom{2m}{m}$ distinguishable arrangements of $2m$ objects of which m are (indistinguishable) of one kind and m are (indistinguishable) of another kind. Each of these arrangements is equally likely, so to each one we assign the probability

$$\frac{1}{\binom{2m}{m}}.$$

We shall now calculate the probability of exactly k matches. We shall show that an odd number of matches cannot occur, and that an even number $2k$ of matches occurs in $\binom{m}{k}^2$ ways. (The reader may wish to consider the special cases in which there are 0, 1, or 2 matches; the calculations in these special cases should help to convince him that the results stated for the general case are correct.) Thus the probability of $1, 3, 5, \ldots,$ or $2m - 1$ matches is 0, and the probability of $2k$ matches, $k = 0, 1, 2, \ldots, m$, is

$$\frac{\binom{m}{k}^2}{\binom{2m}{m}}. \tag{11}$$

We shall now prove the assertions made in the last paragraph. Assume that exactly k matches with red cards have occurred. Thus we have a $2m$-tuple which has exactly k r's in the odd (red) positions. It follows that there are $m - k$ b's in the odd (red) positions, for otherwise there would be more than k red matches. Then there are left exactly $m - (m - k) = k$ b's and $m - k$ r's to fill the even (black) positions. Thus there are also k matches with black cards, and the total number of matches is $2k$. These results prove not only that the total number of matches is even, but also that the number of red matches is equal to the number of black matches. Next, we shall count the number of ways in which k red matches and k black matches can occur. If there are k red matches, then the m odd positions in a $2m$-tuple are filled with k (indistinguishable) red cards and $m - k$ (indistinguishable) black cards. By Theorem 4.10 the number of distinguishable arrangements of the red and black cards in the m odd positions is $\left(_{k, m-k}^{m}\right) = \binom{m}{k}$. In the m even positions of a $2m$-tuple there are k (indistinguishable) black cards and $m - k$ (indistinguishable) red cards. As before, there are $\left(_{k, m-k}^{m}\right) = \binom{m}{k}$ distinguishable arrangements of the kind described. Thus there are

$$\binom{m}{k}\binom{m}{k} = \binom{m}{k}^2$$

ways of forming a $2m$-tuple which gives exactly $2k$ matches, and the probability of exactly $2k$ matches is

$$P(2k \text{ matches}) = \frac{\binom{m}{k}^2}{\binom{2m}{m}} . \tag{12}$$

By adding probabilities in the usual way, we find that the probability of more than l matches is

$$\sum_{(l/2)<k\leq m} \frac{\binom{m}{k}^2}{\binom{2m}{m}} . \tag{13}$$

We have not solved the matching problem for all values of m (suits) and n (denominations), but we have calculated the probabilities for random matches in two special cases. The probabilities in some other special cases have been tabulated and can be found in an article by Gilbert [4] referred to in the bibliographical notes at the end of this chapter.

EXERCISES

1. Five marbles, numbered 1, 2, 3, 4, 5, are placed at random in five cells numbered 1, 2, 3, 4, 5, one marble being placed in each cell.
   (a) Compute the probabilities of 0, 1, 2, 3, 4, and 5 matches.
   (b) Find the number of matches which has the largest probability.

2. Consider a problem similar to Exercise 1 in which there are n marbles and n cells.
   (a) Show that it is not possible to have exactly $n - 1$ matches.
   (b) Use Eq. (9) to show that the probability of exactly $n - 1$ matches is 0.

3. The probability $P(A_k)$ in Eq. (9) depends on both k and n.
    (a) Compute the probability $P(A_2)$ for $n = 2, 3, \ldots, 8$. Does $P(A_2)$ increase monotonically as n increases? Do your calculations suggest that $P(A_2)$ has a limit as n becomes infinite?
    (b) Find the limit of $P(A_2)$ as n becomes infinite. [*Hint:* It is shown in calculus that

$$\lim_{n \to \infty} \left[1 - \frac{1}{1!} + \frac{1}{2!} - \frac{1}{3!} + \cdots + \frac{(-1)^{n-k}}{(n-k)!} \right] = \frac{1}{e},$$

    where $e = 2.718 \ldots$]
    (c) Find $\lim_{n \to \infty} P(A_k)$ for $k = 0, 1, 2, \ldots$

4. An English class studied ten different authors. On an examination the professor quoted ten passages, with one passage from each of the ten authors, and asked the class to identify the author of each. A certain student identified correctly the author of five of the passages. Does this result indicate that the student had studied the course, or is it likely that he got five correct answers by guessing?

5. A secretary types five letters and addresses five envelopes. Just as she is about to put the letters in the envelopes the telephone rings. While she is answering it, she absent mindedly puts the letters in the envelopes at random. What are the probabilities that 0, 1, 2, 3, 4, or 5 letters are placed in the correct envelopes?

6. Consider three families each consisting of four persons. If four of the twelve members of these families have a contagious disease, what is the probability that
    (a) only one family will have to be quarantined,
    (b) exactly two families will have to be quarantined,
    (c) at least two families will have to be quarantined?

7. Show, in two ways, that

$$\binom{m}{0}^2 + \binom{m}{1}^2 + \cdots + \binom{m}{m}^2 = \binom{2m}{m}.$$

    [*Hint:* (a) Use formula (11) and the fact that $P(S) = 1$. (b) Observe that $\binom{2m}{m}$ is the number of ways of choosing m objects from $2m$ objects, and that

$$\binom{m}{k}^2 = \binom{m}{k}\binom{m}{m-k}.$$

Relate these two facts.]

8. Consider the following experiment. An urn contains $2m$ balls, m red and m black. A sample of size m is drawn. Assume that k of the m balls are red.
    (a) Show that k of the balls remaining in the urn are black.
    (b) Show that the probability of a sample of size m which contains k red balls is

$$\frac{\binom{m}{k}^2}{\binom{2m}{m}}.$$

    (c) Relate this experiment to the matching problem discussed in Example 4.

9. Consider the following experiment. There are two cells, numbered 1 and 2, and $2m$ marbles, of which m are red and m are black. The $2m$ marbles are placed at random into the cells with the stipulation that neither cell will hold more than m marbles. A match is said to occur if a red marble is placed in cell 1 or a black marble is placed in cell 2.
   (a) Show that, if there are exactly k matches in cell 1, then there are exactly k matches in cell 2.
   (b) Use the result of (a) to show that only an even number of matches can occur.
   (c) Find the probability that exactly $2k$ matches occur.
   (d) Relate this experiment with the experiment in Example 4 and the experiment in Exercise 8.

10. A handwriting expert is given ten samples of handwriting, five from doctors and five from bankers. He is asked to identify the profession of each person from the handwriting sample. We assume that the handwriting expert knows there are five samples from each profession. What is the probability of six correct answers if the expert guesses randomly?

11. A handwriting expert is given ten samples of handwriting, four from doctors and six from bankers. The expert is told how many samples there are from each profession, and he is asked to identify the profession of each person from the samples.
   (a) Prove that there can be only an even number of correct matches by showing that if k doctors have been correctly identified, then $k + 2$ bankers have been correctly identified.
   (b) Use the results of part (a) to calculate the probabilities of $0, 1, 2, \ldots, 10$ correct matches if the expert guesses randomly. We assume, of course, that he must identify four persons as doctors and six persons as bankers.

12. Generalize Exercise 11 by considering the case in which there are $2n$ people, with $m \leq n$ of one profession and $2n - m$ of another profession. Show that, if exactly k of the first profession are correctly identified, then exactly $k + (2n - 2m)$ of the second profession are correctly identified. Use this result to find the various probabilities for matches and compute the probabilities in the case of random guessing.

13. More generally, discuss the problem in Exercise 12 in the case in which there are N persons, of which m are doctors and $N - m$ are bankers. [*Hint:* Since Exercise 12 treats the case in which N is an even integer, there remains only the case in which N is an odd integer.]

BIBLIOGRAPHICAL NOTES

Other discussions of urn models, cell occupancy problems, and matching problems can be found in the books by Feller [1] and Parzen [5]. The acceptance sampling model is standard; other accounts are available in many books on statistics. The zoological sample census models follow the treatment given in the paper by Bailey [6]; this paper also contains modifications made in order to estimate the birth- and death-rates. Further extensions and developments may be found by consulting later papers such as those by D. G. Chapman [7], Darroch [8], and Parker [9]; these, when all the references in them are traced back, will supply a large amount of literature on the problem. The urn schemes of Section 6.5 follow the development given in Feller [1] in which more emphasis is placed on the applications of this scheme to the physical sciences. See also Friedman [2]. The treatment of cell occupancy problems as presented here follows that given in Parzen [5]. D. W. Chapman [3] gives tables for evaluating the expression (10) of Section 6.7 when k and n are small; the numerical answer to Example 3 of Section 6.7 was obtained by using these tables. This paper also derives Eq. (9) of Section 6.7 by using the principle of inclusion and exclusion. The treatment given in Example 4 of Section 6.7 was suggested by the article by Gilbert [4] which also contains tables of certain probabilities for some other special cases of the matching problem.

BIBLIOGRAPHY

1. W. FELLER, *An Introduction to Probability Theory and its Applications*, Vol. I, 2nd ed. New York: Wiley, 1957.
2. B. FRIEDMAN, "A Simple Urn Model," *Communications on Pure and Applied Mathematics* **2**, 59–70 (1949).
3. D. W. CHAPMAN, "The Statistics of the Method of Correct Matchings," *American Journal of Psychology* **46**, 287–289 (1934).
4. E. J. GILBERT, "The Matching Problem," *Psychometrika* **21**, 253–266 (1956).
5. E. PARZEN, *Modern Probability Theory and Its Applications*. New York: Wiley, 1960.
6. N. T. J. BAILEY, "On Estimating the Size of Mobile Populations from Recapture Data," *Biometrika* **38**, 293–306 (1951).
7. D. G. CHAPMAN, "The Estimation of Biological Populations," *Annals of Mathematical Statistics* **25**, 1–15 (1954).
8. J. N. DARROCH, "The Multiple-Recapture Census. I. Estimation of a Closed Population," *Biometrika* **45**, 343–359 (1958).
9. R. A. PARKER, "On the Estimation of Population Size, Mortality, and Recruitment," *Biometrics* **19**, 318–323 (1963).

CHAPTER 7

Conditional Probabilities
and Independence

7.1 INTRODUCTION

This chapter treats three basic ideas of probability theory. The first is the idea of *conditional probability*, in which additional information becomes available after an experiment has begun—information which must be incorporated into the calculation of probabilities. The second major idea of the chapter is the concept of *independent events*. For two such events, the occurrence of one does not affect the probability of the occurrence of the other. In this chapter we will explain in detail the usefulness of both conditional probability and independence of events in enabling us to calculate the probability of the event "*A* and *B*" as the product of two other probabilities which are often easier to calculate. The third major idea of the chapter is that of *independent trials*. This concept is related to, but different from, the concept of independent events. The concept of independent trials is of great importance in analyzing experiments which consist of the repetition, under identical conditions, of a specified experiment. Again, the details will be supplied in the course of the chapter.

7.2 CONDITIONAL PROBABILITY

In the applications of probability theory it often happens that some additional information is either known or assumed about the possible outcomes of an experiment. This information must be used to "correct" the assignment of probabilities. Such a correction procedure is illustrated by the following example.

EXAMPLE 1. Consider an acceptance sampling experiment in which a lot L of five items contains three good items and two defective ones. A random sample of three items is drawn from the lot. Inspection of the sample is begun, and a defective item is discovered before it is completed. Making use of the information that the sample contains one defective item, find the probability that the sample contains exactly two defective items. The numbers in the example are unrealistically small for the sake of illustration.

1. $\{G_1, G_2, D_1\}$ 4. $\{G_1, G_2, D_2\}$ 7. $\{G_1, D_1, D_2\}$
2. $\{G_1, G_3, D_1\}$ 5. $\{G_1, G_3, D_2\}$ 8. $\{G_2, D_1, D_2\}$
3. $\{G_2, G_3, D_1\}$ 6. $\{G_2, G_3, D_2\}$ 9. $\{G_3, D_1, D_2\}$
                          10. $\{G_1, G_2, G_3\}$

Fig. 7.1. Samples of three items drawn from the lot L: $\{G_1, G_2, G_3, D_1, D_2\}$.

The first solution of this problem is one which uses first principles only. Let the lot L of five items be denoted by $\{G_1, G_2, G_3, D_1, D_2\}$. The ten samples of three items each which can be drawn from L are shown in the figure above. The original experiment consists of drawing samples of three items each from L. The sample space S consists of ten elementary events, and there is a probability function P, defined over $\Pi(S)$, which has the value $\frac{1}{10}$ for each elementary event. The information that the sample contains at least one defective item creates a new situation, and one point of view toward the new situation is that the original experiment has now been replaced by a different experiment. The sample $\{G_1, G_2, G_3\}$ is not a possible outcome in the new experiment. The new sample space consists of all samples of three items which contain at least one defective. Thus the new sample space consists of the samples marked 1, 2, . . . , 9 in Fig. 7.1. Let this subset of S be denoted by B.

Each sample in the original experiment is equally likely, and it seems reasonable that the nine samples in the new experiment are equally likely also. Thus each elementary event in B is assigned probability $\frac{1}{9}$. The event "the sample contains two defectives" consists of the three elementary events (samples) marked 7, 8, 9; let this event be denoted by A. The probability that the sample contains two defectives is thus $3(\frac{1}{9}) = \frac{1}{3}$. Before the information was obtained that the sample contains one defective, the probability that the sample contains two defectives was $\frac{3}{10}$.

The solution which has been given involves the construction of a new sample space $S'(= B)$ and the definition of a new probability function P'. We have found the answer to our problem to be $P'(A) = \frac{1}{3}$.

There is a second solution to the problem which, in most cases, avoids the construction of a new sample space S' and probability function P'. Before presenting this second solution, a few comments on terminology are in order. First, the probability function P' is commonly denoted by $P(\ \mid B)$, and $P(A \mid B) = P'(A)$ for any event A contained in $B(= S')$. Second, the function $P(\ \mid B)$ should not be confused with the function P, although the two are certainly closely related. In fact, it is this relationship which we propose to exploit. The third comment is that the symbol $P(A \mid B)$ is read "the probability of A, given B."

Let us return to the second solution of the problem in Example 1. Let A once more be the event in S which consists of the three elementary events (samples) marked 7, 8, 9 in Fig. 7.1. The reader has undoubtedly observed already that

$$P'(A) = \frac{10}{9} \cdot \frac{3}{10} = \frac{1}{P(B)} \cdot P(A) = \frac{P(A)}{P(B)}.$$

Furthermore, it is easy to verify that, for any event C in S',

$$P'(C) = P(C \mid B) = \frac{P(C)}{P(B)}.$$

Hence, in this example, we have $P(C \mid B)$ proportional to $P(C)$, that is, we have $P(C \mid B) = kP(C)$ with the constant $k = 1/P(B)$. In fact, if we require that $P(C \mid B) = kP(C)$ for some constant k and every subset C of B, then $k = 1/P(B)$. To prove this statement, set $C = B$. Then $P(B \mid B) = kP(B)$. But $P(B \mid B) = P'(B) = P'(S') = 1$ (since the total probability is 1) and hence $kP(B) = 1$ and $k = 1/P(B)$. Thus we have shown that $P'(A)$ in Example 1 can be calculated as follows:

$$P'(A) = P(A \mid B) = \frac{P(A)}{P(B)} = \frac{\frac{3}{10}}{\frac{9}{10}} = \frac{1}{3}.$$

Example 1 suggests how to define the probability $P(A \mid B)$ of an event A, given B, in the case of a general probability space (S, P). There are two cases to consider. First, if A is a subset of B, we define $P(A \mid B)$ so that it is proportional to $P(A)$. Then $P(A \mid B) = kP(A)$ for $A \subset B$. If $A = B$, then $1 = P(B \mid B) = kP(B)$, and $k = 1/P(B)$. Thus

$$P(A \mid B) = \frac{P(A)}{P(B)}, \quad A \subset B.$$

Second, if A is any subset of S, we observe that $A \cap B$ is a subset of B and define $P(A \mid B)$ to have the value given to $P(A \cap B \mid B)$ in the first case. These considerations suggest the following definition.

Definition 7.1. Let (S, P) be a probability space, and let B be an event in S such that $P(B) \neq 0$. If A is any event in S, then $P(A \mid B)$ is defined by the equation

$$P(A \mid B) = \frac{P(A \cap B)}{P(B)}, \tag{1}$$

and $P(A \mid B)$ is called the *conditional probability* of A, given B. The conditional probability is not defined if $P(B) = 0$.

EXAMPLE 2. An unbiased die is thrown once and an even number is obtained. What is the probability that the number is divisible by 3?

Let $S = \{1, 2, \ldots, 6\}$, and set $P(\{x\}) = \frac{1}{6}$ for each x in S. Let $A = \{3, 6\}$, the event which consists of numbers divisible by 3, and let $B = \{2, 4, 6\}$, the given event. Then

$$P(A \mid B) = \frac{P(A \cap B)}{P(B)} = \frac{P(\{6\})}{\frac{1}{2}} = \frac{\frac{1}{6}}{\frac{1}{2}} = \frac{1}{3}.$$

EXAMPLE 3. A committee of three people is selected at random from a group $\{a, b, c, d, e, f\}$ of six people. Find the conditional probability that a and b are selected, given that b has been selected.

The sample space S consists of the $C_6(3)$ combinations of six objects taken three at a time. Since committees are selected at random, each elementary event $\{x\}$ in S is equally likely, that is, $P(\{x\}) = 1/C_6(3)$. Let A be the event consisting of all committees which include a and b, and let B be the event consisting of all committees that include b. To solve this problem, we compute $P(A \mid B)$ as given by Eq. (1).

We observe first that $A \subset B$ since a committee which contains a and b certainly contains b. Then $A \cap B = A$. We observe next that if a and b have been chosen, then there are $C_4(1)$ ways to select the third person for the committee. Thus A contains $C_4(1)$ elements, and

$$P(A) = C_4(1)/C_6(3).$$

Finally, we must compute $P(B)$. Observe that B^c consists of the $C_5(3)$ committees which do not contain b as a member. Hence, the number of elements in B is $C_6(3) - C_5(3)$, and

$$P(B) = \frac{C_6(3) - C_5(3)}{C_6(3)}.$$

Thus

$$P(A \mid B) = \frac{P(A \cap B)}{P(B)} = \frac{P(A)}{P(B)} = \frac{C_4(1)}{C_6(3) - C_5(3)} = \frac{2}{5}.$$

In Definition 7.1 the function $P(\ \mid B)$ was defined on $\Pi(S)$, the power set of S. We have spoken of $P(\ \mid B)$ as a probability function, but is it? We shall now show that $P(\ \mid B)$ is indeed a probability function on $\Pi(S)$. To do so, we must show that $P(\ \mid B)$ has the three properties required of a probability function by Definition 5.1:

$P(A \mid B) \geq 0$ for every A in $\Pi(S)$;

$P(S \mid B) = 1$;

$P(A_1 \cup A_2 \mid B) = P(A_1 \mid B) + P(A_2 \mid B)$ if $A_1 \cap A_2 = \emptyset$.

Since $P(A \cap B) \geq 0$ and $P(B) \geq 0$, Eq. (1) shows that $P(\ |B)$ has the first of the properties listed here. Also, $P(\ |B)$ has the second property since

$$P(S \mid B) = \frac{P(S \cap B)}{P(B)} = \frac{P(B)}{P(B)} = 1.$$

Finally, since P is a probability function, we have

$$P(A_1 \cup A_2 \mid B) = \frac{P((A_1 \cup A_2) \cap B)}{P(B)} = \frac{P((A_1 \cap B) \cup (A_2 \cap B))}{P(B)}$$

$$= \frac{P(A_1 \cap B) + P(A_2 \cap B)}{P(B)} = P(A_1 \mid B) + P(A_2 \mid B).$$

We have thus shown that $(S, P(\ |B))$ is a probability space. It follows automatically that $P(\ |B)$ has all the properties of a probability function. For example,

$$P(A_1 \cup A_2 \mid B) = P(A_1 \mid B) + P(A_2 \mid B) - P(A_1 \cap A_2 \mid B)$$

for any two sets A_1 and A_2 in S.

In the last paragraph we showed that $P(\ |B)$ is a probability function on S. It is also easy to show that, if the domain of $P(\ |B)$ is restricted so that A belongs to $\Pi(B)$, then $P(\ |B)$ thus restricted is a probability function on B, that is, $(B, P(\ |B))$ is also a probability space. This latter probability space is the one that was first constructed in Example 1. Both points of view are useful. Furthermore, since $P(A \mid B)$ for $A \subset B$ has the same value in each of the probability spaces $(S, P(\ |B))$ and $(B, P(\ |B))$, no ambiguity results. Consequently, we shall use the interpretation and the probability space which lead to the easiest computations.

From Eq. (1) we obtain

$$P(A \cap B) = P(A \mid B)P(B), \qquad P(B) \neq 0. \tag{2}$$

This equation is extremely useful because it enables us to calculate the probability of "A and B" in terms of $P(A \mid B)$ and $P(B)$—two probabilities which are often easy to calculate.

EXAMPLE 4. An urn contains five white and four black balls. Two balls are drawn from the urn at random, in succession, and without replacement. What is the probability that a white ball is obtained on each drawing?

This type of problem has been analyzed in Section 6.2. Instead of using the methods applied in that section (which involved a rather elaborate discussion of the probability space), we shall use Eq. (2) to give a very simple solution. Let W_i denote the event in which a white ball is drawn on the ith drawing. Then the problem is to calculate $P(W_1 \cap W_2)$. In Eq. (2), let $A = W_2$ and $B = W_1$; then

$$P(W_1 \cap W_2) = P(W_2 \cap W_1) = P(W_2 \mid W_1)P(W_1).$$

Now $P(W_1) = \frac{5}{9}$ since five of the nine balls in the urn are white. Furthermore, if one white ball has been drawn (we are given W_1), there are four white and four black balls left in the urn and each of them is equally likely to be drawn on the second drawing. Thus $P(W_2 \mid W_1) = \frac{4}{8}$, and Eq. (2) gives $P(W_1 \cap W_2) = \frac{4}{8} \cdot \frac{5}{9} = \frac{5}{18}$.

This example illustrates the power of Eq. (2) to make calculations of probabilities of the form $P(A \cap B)$ very simple provided that $P(A \mid B)$ and $P(B)$ are easy to calculate. Furthermore, in many cases Eq. (2) enables us to avoid completely the specification of a sample space because the probabilities of the events to be calculated are so simple that no specification of the sample space is really necessary.

It is interesting to observe (as we did in Example 4) in connection with Eq. (2) that $P(A \cap B) = P(B \cap A)$. Then

$$P(A \cap B) = P(B \cap A) = P(B \mid A)P(A) \tag{3}$$

if $P(A) \neq 0$. Thus, in computing $P(A \cap B)$, we can condition either on B or on A, that is, we can assume that either B or A is given and use the corresponding Eq. (2) or Eq. (3). We choose the equation for which the calculation of the probabilities is easier. By combining Eq. (2) and Eq. (3), any one of the four probabilities $P(A)$, $P(B)$, $P(A \mid B)$, and $P(B \mid A)$ can be calculated in terms of the other three (see Exercises 12 and 13). Also, Eqs. (2) and (3) can be generalized; see, for example, Exercise 14.

EXAMPLE 5. In Example 1 of Section 6.5 an urn is given which contains n white and m black balls. Two balls are drawn according to Polya's urn scheme. Thus a ball is drawn at random, replaced, and i balls of the same color are added to the urn. Then a second ball is drawn at random. One of the questions asked in Example 1 is the following: what is the probability that a black ball is drawn on each of the two drawings? The method of conditional probability will now be employed to give a second solution.

As before, let B_i denote the event in which a black ball is drawn on the ith drawing. Then $B_1 \cap B_2$ is the event in which a black ball is drawn on each of the two drawings. By Eq. (3),

$$P(B_1 \cap B_2) = P(B_2 \mid B_1)P(B_1) = \frac{m + i}{n + m + i} \frac{m}{n + m} = \frac{m(m + i)}{(n + m)(n + m + i)},$$

for, if a black ball is drawn on the first drawing, there are $n + m + i$ balls in the urn for the second drawing and $m + i$ of them are black. This value for $P(B_1 \cap B_2)$ is the same as that given in Eq. (5) of Section 6.5.

In Example 1 of Section 6.5 observe that $(m + i)/(n + m + i)$ is the probability that a case of the disease occurs, given that a case of the disease has occurred. The probability $(m + i)/(n + m + i)$ is merely the conditional probability $P(B_2 \mid B_1)$.

The method used above to calculate $P(B_1 \cap B_2)$ can be used to compute also $P(B_1 \cap W_2)$, $P(W_1 \cap B_2)$, and $P(W_1 \cap W_2)$ (see Exercises 1, 2, and 3 of Section 6.5).

EXAMPLE 6. In Model II of Section 6.4 fish are caught from a lake until a specified number, k, of marked fish are caught. As before, let $P(\{n\})$ denote the probability of the following event: there are exactly $k - 1$ marked fish among the first $n - 1$ fish caught, and the nth fish caught is a marked fish. The value of $P(\{n\})$ is given by Eq. (8) of Section 6.4. We shall now give a simpler calculation of $P(\{n\})$ by using the method of conditional probability.

The event $\{n\}$ is the following event: (a) there are exactly $k - 1$ marked fish among the first $n - 1$ fish caught, and (b) the nth fish caught is a marked fish. Let B denote the event described in (a) and let A be the event described in (b). Then $A \cap B$ is exactly the event which we have denoted by $\{n\}$, and

$$P(\{n\}) = P(A \cap B) = P(A \mid B)P(B).$$

Next, we see that

$$P(B) = \frac{\dbinom{N - M}{n - k}\dbinom{M}{k - 1}}{\dbinom{N}{n - 1}},$$

since $\binom{N}{n-1}$ samples of $n - 1$ fish can be formed from the N fish in the lake and $\binom{N-M}{n-k}\binom{M}{k-1}$ of these samples contain $k - 1$ marked fish selected from the M marked fish and $(n - 1) - (k - 1) = n - k$ unmarked fish selected from the $N - M$ unmarked fish in the lake. Furthermore,

$$P(A \mid B) = \frac{M - k + 1}{N - n + 1},$$

for, if the event B has happened, there are $N - n + 1$ fish left in the lake and $M - k + 1$ of them are marked fish. Then

$$P(\{n\}) = P(A \cap B) = P(A \mid B)P(B) = \frac{M - k + 1}{N - n + 1} \frac{\dbinom{N - M}{n - k}\dbinom{M}{k - 1}}{\dbinom{N}{n - 1}}.$$

It can be shown easily that this value of $P(\{n\})$ is the same as that given in Eq. (8) of Section 6.4 (see Exercise 10 of Section 6.4).

EXERCISES

1. Mr. Smith says, "I have two children and at least one of them is a boy." What is the probability that the other child is a boy? If Mr. Smith has two children and the oldest is a boy, what is the probability that he has two boys?

2. After the cards have been dealt in a game of bridge (each player receives 13 cards from an ordinary deck), Mrs. X exclaims: "I have an ace this time!"
   (a) What is the probability that Mrs. X has exactly two aces?
   (b) If she had said, "I have the ace of spades!", what is the probability she has exactly two aces?

3. A file cabinet in a civil service office has three drawers each of which has (exactly) two compartments. The first drawer contains secret material in each compartment, the second contains confidential material in each compartment, but the third contains secret material in one compartment and confidential material in the other.
   (a) A drawer is chosen at random. What is the probability that it contains both confidential and secret material?
   (b) A drawer is chosen at random, and a compartment in it is selected at random. Secret material is found in this compartment. What is the probability that the other compartment of this drawer contains confidential material?

4. The probability that a certain radio signal on a satellite is operating is 0.9. The probability that a signal (this radio signal) is received on the ground is 0.8. Find the probability that the radio signal is received, given that the signal is working.

5. John tosses a true coin and says: "The probability is very high that I will throw a head next time since I have thrown ten tails in a row." What is the probability he will throw a head on the next toss?

6. A book shelf contains eleven novels, thirteen books on science, four books on philosophy, and two history books. If five books are selected at random from the shelf, what is the probability that (exactly) three novels are selected, given that (at least) (a) two novels are selected? (b) one is a history book? (c) one is a novel and one is a book on science?

7. A deck of cards consists of the jack, queen, king, and ace of spades, and all thirteen hearts. Two cards are drawn at random from this deck. Find the probability that the two cards drawn include (a) a spade, given that one card is a heart; (b) two jacks, given that one card is the jack of spades; (c) two different suits; (d) two different suits, given that one card is a spade.

8. Find the probability that Bill will be the tenth student called to recite in a certain class if there are 25 students in the class and the instructor calls them at random (never asking the same student twice).

9. A special deck consists of the 13 spades in a regular deck of 52 cards. Three cards are drawn at random from the special deck.
   (a) Find the probability that the three cards are face cards, given that two are face cards.
   (b) Find the probability that the three cards contain a face card, given that two are not face cards.
   (c) Find the probability that the three cards include the jack, given that two of the cards are not the jack.

10. Work Exercise 1(a) of Section 6.5 using conditional probability.

11. Work Exercise 2(b) of Section 6.5 using conditional probability.

12. A clerk who works on the third floor believes that one out of every 64 customers who comes to his department buys a card table. The probability that a customer buys folding chairs if he buys a card table is $\frac{1}{2}$. The probability that a customer buys a card table given that he buys folding chairs is $\frac{1}{4}$. What is the probability that a customer in the department buys folding chairs? [*Hint:* See Exercise 13.]

13. Use Eqs. (2) and (3) to show that $P(A \mid B)P(B) = P(B \mid A)P(A)$, and hence that

(a) $P(A \mid B) = \dfrac{P(B \mid A)P(A)}{P(B)}$,   (b) $P(A) = \dfrac{P(A \mid B)P(B)}{P(B \mid A)}$.

It is assumed in (a) and (b) that all of the symbols are defined and that none of the denominators is zero.

14. Prove the following theorem. If (S, P) is a probability space, and if A, B, C are any three events such that $P(C) \neq 0$ and $P(B \cap C) \neq 0$, then

$$P(A \cap B \cap C) = P(A \mid B \cap C)P(B \mid C)P(C).$$

7.3 BAYES' THEOREM

In 1763 there appeared in *The Philosophical Transactions* of the Royal Society an essay by the late Rev. Thomas Bayes, F.R.S., entitled "An Essay Toward Solving a Problem in the Doctrine of Chances." This essay contains a statement and proof of a proposition which has since been developed further, and which today is known as Bayes' Theorem. Although the original proposition seems to have been the equation

$$P(B \mid A) = \frac{P(A \mid B)P(B)}{P(A)}, \tag{1}$$

a slightly different version is known today as Bayes' Theorem. We shall derive from Eq. (1) the equation that is known as Bayes' Theorem, and we shall illustrate its usefulness with several recent and quite diverse applications.

Equation (1) can be derived as follows from the definition of conditional probability (see Definition 7.1) and Eq. (2) in Section 7.2:

$$P(B \mid A) = \frac{P(B \cap A)}{P(A)} = \frac{P(A \cap B)}{P(A)} = \frac{P(A \mid B)P(B)}{P(A)}.$$

This equation can be used to compute the probability of the event B, given A, in terms of the probability of A, given B, and the probabilities of A and B.

EXAMPLE 1. An urn contains five white and four black balls. A ball is drawn and laid aside, its color unnoted. A second ball is drawn, and its color is black. What is the probability that the first ball drawn was black?

The first step in solving this problem is to introduce some notation. As usual, let B_i denote the event in which a black ball is drawn on the ith drawing, and let W_i denote the event in which a white ball is drawn on the ith drawing. In this notation, the answer to the problem is $P(B_1 \mid B_2)$. By Eq. (1),

$$P(B_1 \mid B_2) = \frac{P(B_2 \mid B_1)P(B_1)}{P(B_2)}.$$

We see that Eq. (1) permits us to reverse the order of the events B_1 and B_2 in the conditional probabilities. Both $P(B_2 \mid B_1)$ and $P(B_1)$ are easy to compute; we find that $P(B_2 \mid B_1) = \frac{3}{8}$ and $P(B_1) = \frac{4}{9}$. Also, the results in Section 6.2 show that $P(B_2) = P(B_1)$. Thus

$$P(B_1 \mid B_2) = P(B_2 \mid B_1) = \tfrac{3}{8}.$$

In solving the problem in Example 1 we used the fact that $P(B_2) = P(B_1)$. We shall show next how this result can be established by using conditional probabilities. The result is a useful one, because the value of $P(A)$ in the denominator of Eq. (1) is frequently not easy to compute by straightforward methods. If, in the example, the outcome of the first draw were known, it would be easy to calculate the probability of the event B_2. The outcome of the first draw is either a black ball (B_1) or a white ball (W_1). Hence $S = B_1 \cup W_1$, and

$$B_2 = B_2 \cap S = B_2 \cap (B_1 \cup W_1) = (B_2 \cap B_1) \cup (B_2 \cap W_1).$$

The events $(B_2 \cap B_1)$ and $(B_2 \cap W_1)$ are disjoint, and hence

$$P(B_2) = P(B_2 \cap B_1) + P(B_2 \cap W_1). \tag{2}$$

Since each of the terms on the right-hand side of Eq. (2) is the probability of the intersection of two sets, the probability can be computed in terms of conditional probabilities. From Eq. (2) above and Eq. (2) of Section 7.2 we find

$$P(B_2) = P(B_2 \mid B_1)P(B_1) + P(B_2 \mid W_1)P(W_1) = \tfrac{3}{8} \cdot \tfrac{4}{9} + \tfrac{4}{8} \cdot \tfrac{5}{9} = \tfrac{4}{9} = P(B_1). \tag{3}$$

Equation (3) is a special case of a theorem which is important in its own right.

Theorem 7.1. Let (S, P) be any probability space, and let A be any event in S. Let $B_1, B_2, \ldots, B_n$ be events in S such that

$$B_i \cap B_j = \emptyset, \qquad i \neq j,$$

$$\bigcup_{i=1}^{n} B_i = S,$$

$$P(B_i) \neq 0, \qquad i = 1, 2, \ldots, n.$$

Then

$$P(A) = P(A \mid B_1)P(B_1) + P(A \mid B_2)P(B_2) + \cdots + P(A \mid B_n)P(B_n). \tag{4}$$

The usefulness of this theorem results from the fact that it is often possible to choose the events $B_1, B_2, \ldots, B_n$ so that all the probabilities on the right-hand side of Eq. (4) are easy to calculate. To apply the theorem, $B_1, B_2, \ldots, B_n$ must satisfy the three hypotheses of the theorem, but once these restrictions have been satisfied, the freedom of choice which remains can be employed to simplify the calculations of the probabilities on the right-hand side of Eq. (4).

Proof of Theorem 7.1. Let $B_1, B_2, \ldots, B_n$ be sets which satisfy the hypotheses of the theorem. Then

$$A = A \cap S = A \cap \bigcup_{i=1}^{n} B_i$$

$$= \bigcup_{i=1}^{n} (A \cap B_i).$$

Since $B_1, B_2, \ldots, B_n$ are disjoint, the sets $(A \cap B_1), (A \cap B_2), \ldots, (A \cap B_n)$ are disjoint also. Then

$$P(A) = \sum_{i=1}^{n} P(A \cap B_i).$$

If we replace $P(A \cap B_i)$ in this equation by $P(A \mid B_i)P(B_i)$ [see Eq. (2) in Section 7.2], Eq. (4) is the result.▲

The following example illustrates the usefulness of Eq. (4).

EXAMPLE 2. The grocery store in Example 4 of Section 6.2 offers 1000 quarts of milk for sale. The 1000 quarts consist of 900 fresh quarts and 100 day-old quarts. A housewife selects a quart of milk at random after another customer has selected at random a quart of milk of unknown character. What is the probability that the housewife selects a day-old quart of milk?

Let G_i denote the event in which a fresh quart of milk is selected on the ith drawing (selection of a quart of milk), and let D_i denote the event in which a day-old quart is selected on the ith drawing. Then $P(D_2)$ is the answer to the problem in Example 2. Observe that $G_1 \cup D_1 = S$ since either a fresh quart or a day-old quart is selected on the first drawing. Then, by Eq. (4),

$$P(D_2) = P(D_2 \mid G_1)P(G_1) + P(D_2 \mid D_1)P(D_1)$$

$$= \tfrac{100}{999} \cdot \tfrac{900}{1000} + \tfrac{99}{999} \cdot \tfrac{100}{1000} = \tfrac{1}{10} = P(D_1).$$

This calculation is simpler in many ways than the one given in Example 4 of Section 6.2.

The statement known as Bayes' Theorem results from combining Eq. (1) and Eq. (4).

Theorem 7.2 (*Bayes' Theorem*). Let (S, P) be any probability space, and let $B_1, B_2, \ldots, B_n$ be events in S such that

$$B_i \cap B_j = \emptyset, \quad i \neq j,$$

$$\bigcup_{i=1}^{n} B_i = S,$$

$$P(B_i) \neq 0, \quad i = 1, 2, \ldots, n.$$

Then for each fixed j, $1 \leq j \leq n$, and any event A in S such that $P(A) \neq 0$,

$$P(B_j \mid A) = \frac{P(A \mid B_j)P(B_j)}{\sum_{i=1}^{n} P(A \mid B_i)P(B_i)}. \tag{5}$$

Proof. The proof follows from Eq. (1) and Eq. (4). Since $P(A) \neq 0$ by hypothesis, Eq. (1) gives

$$P(B_j \mid A) = \frac{P(A \mid B_j)P(B_j)}{P(A)}.$$

Next, replace $P(A)$ in this equation by its value from Eq. (4), and the result is Eq. (5).▲

The following example illustrates the use of Bayes' Theorem.

EXAMPLE 3. Two urns are given. Urn 1 contains three white balls and seven black balls, and Urn 2 contains twelve white balls and eight black balls. An urn is selected at random, and a ball is drawn at random from it. The ball drawn is white. What is the probability that it was drawn from Urn 1?
  Let events U_1, U_2, W_1, W_2 be defined as follows:

$$U_1 \quad \text{Urn 1 is selected,}$$
$$U_2 \quad \text{Urn 2 is selected,}$$
$$W_1 \quad \text{a white ball is drawn from Urn 1,}$$
$$W_2 \quad \text{a white ball is drawn from Urn 2.}$$

The question in the problem in Example 3 is the following: what is

$$P(U_1 \mid W_1 \cup W_2)?$$

Since $U_1 \cup U_2$ is the entire sample space S, Bayes' Theorem gives

$$P(U_1 \mid W_1 \cup W_2) = \frac{P(W_1 \cup W_2 \mid U_1)P(U_1)}{P(W_1 \cup W_2 \mid U_1)P(U_1) + P(W_1 \cup W_2 \mid U_2)P(U_2)}.$$

The statement that an urn is selected at random means that $P(U_1) = P(U_2) = \frac{1}{2}$.

Thus, to complete the calculation, it is sufficient to determine $P(W_1 \cup W_2 \mid U_1)$ and $P(W_1 \cup W_2 \mid U_2)$. We find

$$P(W_1 \cup W_2 \mid U_1) = \frac{P((W_1 \cup W_2) \cap U_1)}{P(U_1)}$$

$$= \frac{P(W_1 \cap U_1)}{P(U_1)} = P(W_1 \mid U_1) = \tfrac{3}{10} \, ;$$

$$P(W_1 \cup W_2 \mid U_2) = \frac{P((W_1 \cup W_2) \cap U_2)}{P(U_2)}$$

$$= \frac{P(W_2 \cap U_2)}{P(U_2)} = P(W_2 \mid U_2) = \tfrac{12}{20}.$$

Thus

$$P(U_1 \mid W_1 \cup W_2) = \frac{\tfrac{3}{10} \cdot \tfrac{1}{2}}{\tfrac{3}{10} \cdot \tfrac{1}{2} + \tfrac{12}{20} \cdot \tfrac{1}{2}} = \frac{1}{3} \, .$$

The above examples of the applications of Theorems 7.1 and 7.2 have dealt with urn schemes. The next three examples deal with recent applications of Bayes' Theorem to three very diverse problems.

EXAMPLE 4. Television networks are vitally concerned with the problem of determining the success of their shows before they are presented to the public. The networks pretest their shows by presenting them as previews to random audiences who rate them before they are broadcast nationally. One company that pretests shows (arranges previews and evaluates them) for the major networks claims that its system is 92% accurate. Evaluate the company's claim to accuracy.
    As the first step in evaluating the company's claim to accuracy, we shall translate the claim into a probability statement. Let A denote the event in which a show is unsuccessful when broadcast and let B denote the event in which the show receives a low rating on its pretest. Using this notation, we interpret the company's claim to mean that its methods are 92% accurate in the sense that

$$P(A \mid B) = 0.92, \qquad P(A^c \mid B^c) = 0.92.$$

On first examination, the company's claim seems impressive, but further investigation is in order. What is the probability that an unsuccessful show will receive a high rating on its pretest? To answer this question, we apply Bayes' Theorem to compute $P(B^c \mid A)$:

$$P(B^c \mid A) = \frac{P(A \mid B^c)P(B^c)}{P(A \mid B^c)P(B^c) + P(A \mid B)P(B)} \, .$$

Since $P(A \mid B^c) + P(A^c \mid B^c) = 1$ and $P(A^c \mid B^c) = 0.92$, we find that

$$P(A \mid B^c) = 0.08.$$

For the sake of illustration, assume that $P(B^c) = 0.90$. This assumption seems reasonable since the probability of a good rating on the pretest can be expected to be high because of the presence of stars in the cast and a good script for the first show. Then

$$P(B^c \mid A) = \frac{(0.08)(0.90)}{(0.80)(0.90) + (0.92)(0.10)} = 0.44.$$

This result means that 44% of such unsuccessful shows will nevertheless receive good ratings on their pretests. The company's claim to accuracy should be accepted with some caution. Also, a word of caution is in order in connection with the illustration in this example. We have assumed $P(B^c) = 0.90$, a value which is rather large. Furthermore, it is difficult to determine $P(B^c)$ except by a subjective evaluation.

EXAMPLE 5 (A Conditional Probability Model for Medical Diagnoses). If patient Y is known to have a certain disease, it is easy for the doctor to observe the symptoms associated with this disease. The doctor who must make a diagnosis, however, is faced with the opposite problem. He must determine, from the observable symptoms exhibited by patient Y, the disease which patient Y has. These two situations remind us of Eq. (1), for the information given in one situation is the information sought in the other. How can Bayes' Theorem be used to assist in medical diagnoses?

We shall need some notation to discuss this problem. Let $d_1, d_2, \ldots, d_n$ denote n mutually exclusive diseases and let $s_1, s_2, \ldots, s_m$ denote m clinical findings. These clinical findings will be called symptoms; they include observations such as physical signs of disease and evidence such as electrocardiographic records. The set $\{s_1, s_2, \ldots, s_m\}$ of symptoms will be denoted by X.

We wish to calculate the probability $P(d_j \mid X)$ that a patient who has the symptoms X has the disease d_j. We know from Bayes' Theorem that

$$P(d_j \mid X) = \frac{P(X \mid d_j)P(d_j)}{\sum_{i=1}^{n} P(X \mid d_i)P(d_i)} \tag{6}$$

if $d_1, d_2, \ldots, d_n$ are the only diseases that can occur. Thus, if we can calculate the probabilities on the right-hand side of Eq. (6), we can calculate a probability for each disease, given a set of symptoms X. We shall now explain how these probabilities can be estimated.

The practical solution to the problem of estimating the probabilities on the right-hand side of Eq. (6) is based on relative frequencies. From the population of all persons who have one of the diseases $d_1, d_2, \ldots, d_n$, we select a large but random sample. We then determine the relative frequency of occurrence of each disease d_i in this sample. This relative frequency will be taken as the value of $P(d_i)$. Thus, if $N(d_1, d_2, \ldots, d_n)$ is the number of people in the sample, and if

$N(d_i)$ is the number of people in the sample who have disease d_i, we set

$$P(d_i) = \frac{N(d_i)}{N(d_1, d_2, \ldots, d_n)} \cdot \tag{7}$$

It is clear that $P(d_i)$ is an estimate of the relative frequency of incidence of the disease d_i in the population of people who have exactly one of the diseases $d_1, d_2, \ldots, d_n$. Next, let $N(X, d_i)$ be the number of persons in the sample who have the disease d_i and the symptoms X. Since

$$P(X \mid d_i) = \frac{P(X \cap d_i)}{P(d_i)},$$

we estimate $P(X \mid d_i)$ as follows:

$$P(X \mid d_i) = \frac{N(X, d_i)/N(d_1, d_2, \ldots, d_n)}{N(d_i)/N(d_1, d_2, \ldots, d_n)} = \frac{N(X, d_i)}{N(d_i)} \cdot \tag{8}$$

By substituting the value of $P(d_i)$ in Eq. (7) and the value of $P(X \mid d_i)$ in Eq. (8) into Eq. (6), we obtain a value for $P(d_j \mid X)$. The doctor now compares the values $P(d_1 \mid X)$, $P(d_2 \mid X)$, $\ldots$, $P(d_n \mid X)$ and chooses as the most likely ailment of patient Y the disease which corresponds to the largest of these values. A word of caution is in order again. Medical diagnosis based on this application of Bayes' Theorem is new and untested, and a diagnosis obtained in this manner should be used with care. References to the literature are given in the bibliographical notes at the end of this chapter [1, 2, 3].

EXAMPLE 6 (*The Mosteller-Wallace Model for Determining Disputed Authorship*). Historians have wondered for years whether Alexander Hamilton or James Madison wrote a certain 12 of the 77 *Federalist Papers*. These essays appeared in New York newspapers in 1787 and 1788, and were signed with the pseudonym "Publius." It is known that John Jay wrote five of the 77 papers, that Hamilton wrote 43 papers, and that Madison wrote 14 papers. In addition, there are three papers which are generally considered to be joint papers. The authorship of the other 12 papers is in dispute. F. Mosteller and D. L. Wallace [4], by using Bayes' Theorem, have given a most convincing argument which strongly supports the contention that Madison wrote the 12 disputed papers. We shall give here a short and, of necessity, incomplete account of the methods used by Mosteller and Wallace.

One of the difficulties encountered in the statistical analysis of the authorship of the *Federalist Papers* is the fact that the styles of Hamilton and Madison are similar; both wrote in the ornate style that was popular at the time. However, it has been known for some time that certain words are characteristic of each of the two men. For example, Hamilton uses *while*, but Madison, in similar situations, uses *whilst*. Such words are called *marker* words; the set of marker words includes *upon* (the best one), *while*, *whilst*, and *enough*. If the 12 papers of disputed authorship are considered as a whole, the marker words indicate that Madison probably wrote them. The marker words do not occur often enough in single papers, however, to settle the question of the authorship of individual papers. As a result, certain high-frequency function words such as *an*, *by*, *of*, *this*, and *to* were investigated also. In all, thirty words were considered and for each of these words a rate of appearance per 1000 words was calculated for both Hamilton and Madison from their known papers. This information was used to estimate the probability of x occurrences of a given word in a paper of any given length.

Thus, if we let H denote the event that Hamilton wrote a disputed paper and M denote the event that Madison wrote the paper, then $P(x \mid H)$ and $P(x \mid M)$ have been estimated. Then if the word *of*, for example, appears x times in a paper, we can use Bayes' Theorem to calculate $P(H \mid x)$ and $P(M \mid x)$ as follows:

$$P(H \mid x) = \frac{P(x \mid H)P(H)}{P(x \mid H)P(H) + P(x \mid M)P(M)}, \tag{9}$$

$$P(M \mid x) = \frac{P(x \mid M)P(M)}{P(x \mid H)P(H) + P(x \mid M)P(M)}. \tag{10}$$

The formulas for $P(H \mid x)$ and $P(M \mid x)$ in Eqs. (9) and (10) are merely special cases of Bayes' Theorem. A closer examination of these equations shows that we must know $P(H)$ and $P(M)$, the probabilities that Hamilton and Madison respectively wrote the papers, in order to calculate the desired probabilities. Since $P(H)$ and $P(M)$ are unknown, and since there is no obvious way to estimate these probabilities by means of relative frequencies, Mosteller and Wallace determined them on other grounds, largely historical. To isolate the influence of the subjective choice of $P(H)$ and $P(M)$, they considered the following ratio [see Eqs. (9) and (10)]:

$$\frac{P(H \mid x)}{P(M \mid x)} = \frac{P(H)P(x \mid H)}{P(M)P(x \mid M)} = \frac{P(H)}{P(M)} \cdot \frac{P(x \mid H)}{P(x \mid M)}. \tag{11}$$

Mosteller and Wallace examined separately the likelihood ratio $P(x \mid H)/P(x \mid M)$ and the initial odds $P(H)/P(M)$. The initial odds are determined by prior beliefs, and the likelihood ratio, by the data from the experiment. The quantity $P(H \mid x)/P(M \mid x)$ is called the final odds.

If we have no strong prior beliefs about the authorship of a paper (that is, if the initial odds are approximately one), and if the likelihood ratio is very large or very small, then Eq. (11) indicates rather strongly that Hamilton or Madison, respectively, wrote the paper in question. The initial odds, however, may be the dominant factor if the likelihood ratio is approximately one. For example, if

$$\frac{P(x \mid H)}{P(x \mid M)} = \frac{10^4}{1} \quad \text{and} \quad \frac{P(H)}{P(M)} = \frac{1}{10},$$

then

$$\frac{P(H \mid x)}{P(M \mid x)} = \frac{10^3}{1}$$

and the odds favor Hamilton's authorship. As another example, assume that

$$\frac{P(x \mid H)}{P(x \mid M)} = \frac{2}{1} \quad \text{and} \quad \frac{P(H)}{P(M)} = \frac{1}{10^3};$$

then the final odds of 2/1000 definitely favor Madison's authorship.

Thus far we have indicated how the evidence based on a single word is evaluated, but we have not described how the evidence derived from more than one word is used. In the next section, however, we shall treat independent events, and this concept will enable us to combine the evidence derived from several words. A second point that has not been explained is the method used for assigning values to $P(x \mid H)$ and $P(x \mid M)$. The methods used by Mosteller and Wallace for assigning these probabilities are slightly beyond the scope of this book. The interested reader is urged to consult the book by Mosteller and Wallace [4] which contains, among other things, references to treatments of the techniques used for estimating $P(x \mid H)$ and $P(x \mid M)$.

EXERCISES

1. Two urns of identical appearance contain respectively three white and two black balls and two white and five black balls. One urn is selected and a ball taken from it. What is the probability that this ball is white?

2. An urn contains three white and five black balls. A ball is drawn and laid aside, *its color unnoted.* Then another ball is drawn. Find the probability that this second ball is white. Compare this with the probability that the first ball drawn is white. If the first ball drawn was white, what is the probability that the second ball is white?

3. Suppose that we have two urns, A and B, containing ten black balls and ten white balls, respectively. Five black balls are drawn from urn A, placed in B, and mixed. Then five balls are drawn from B and placed in A. Compare the probability of drawing a white ball from urn A with the probability of drawing a black ball from urn B.

4. Southern Bell is twice as likely to be offered the contract to build a certain rocket as Seymour Aircraft. If Southern Bell is offered the contract, the probability of a successful launch is 0.7, of partial success is 0.1, and of failure is 0.2. If Seymour Aircraft is offered the contract, the probability of success is 0.6; the probabilities of partial success and failure are 0.3 and 0.1, respectively. Assume that the contract

is awarded to one of these corporations and that the launch is successful. What is the probability that the contract was offered to Seymour Aircraft?

5. The probability of success in mathematics is $\frac{4}{5}$ if a student scores above 50 on the placement examination at the beginning of the year. The probability of success if a score between 25 and 50 is recorded is $\frac{1}{2}$; the probability of success is $\frac{1}{5}$ if the score is below 25. One-eighth of the students score above 50, and $\frac{1}{8}$ score below 25. If we know that a student succeeds, what is the probability he scored between 25 and 50 on the placement examination?

6. Three urns of the same appearance have the following proportions of white and black balls:

$$\begin{array}{ll} \text{Urn 1} & \text{1 white, 2 black;} \\ \text{Urn 2} & \text{2 white, 1 black;} \\ \text{Urn 3} & \text{2 white, 2 black.} \end{array}$$

One of the urns is selected and one ball is drawn. It turns out to be white. What is the probability that the third urn was chosen?

7. A tire manufacturer makes three grades of tires: A, B, and C. The same number of grade A and B tires are manufactured, but only half as many of grade C are made as of grade A. It is found that 50% of the people who buy grade A tires buy a second set of tires from the same manufacturer, while 75% of those who buy grade B and 25% of those who buy grade C buy a second set of tires from the manufacturer. What is the probability that a customer returning for a second order of tires will already have a specified grade of tire?

8. A traveler must go by taxicab from his hotel to the airport during the rush hour. There are four different routes, and the probabilities of completing the trip within an hour on the four routes are 0.5, 0.3, 0.1, and 0.1, respectively. The traveler enters a taxicab, makes a random choice of route to the airport, and arrives at the airport within an hour. Find the probability that he took the second route.

9. It is believed that about $\frac{4}{5}$ of the people who apply for a certain skilled labor position are actually well qualified and would be successful in the position. However, due to human error in the process of interviewing and training, $\frac{1}{48}$ of the well-qualified applicants *are not* accepted and $\frac{1}{12}$ of the unqualified applicants *are* accepted. Out of 48 applicants who pass the training program, how many are actually well qualified?

10. Using the information given in Example 6 of Section 6.2, find the probability that the housewife buys a day-old quart of milk if:
(a) replacement policy (a) is in effect,
(b) replacement policy (b) is in effect,
(c) replacement policy (c) is in effect (use conditional probabilities and give a different argument than the one given in Example 6),
(d) replacement policy (d) is in effect,
(e) replacement policy (e) is in effect and the replacement supply is composed of $\frac{1}{10}$ day-old quarts and $\frac{9}{10}$ fresh quarts of milk,
(f) replacement policy (e) is in effect and the replacement supply is composed of $\frac{1}{100}$ day-old quarts and $\frac{99}{100}$ fresh quarts of milk.

7.4 INDEPENDENT EVENTS

The concept of the independence of two events is essential for some of the common applications of the theory of probability. In terms of the applications, two events are independent if the occurrence of one of them does not affect the probability of the occurrence of the other. The following is a formal mathematical definition which at first glance seems unrelated to the preceding statement. Following the definition, however, we shall prove a theorem which shows the close connection between the two statements.

Definition 7.2. Let (S, P) be a probability space and let A and B be events in S. Then A and B are *independent* if and only if

$$P(A \cap B) = P(A) \cdot P(B).$$

Thus $P(A \cap B)$ is easy to calculate if A and B are independent events. In Section 7.2 we derived the formula $P(A \cap B) = P(A \mid B)P(B)$. By combining this formula and the formula $P(A \cap B) = P(A)P(B)$ satisfied by independent events, we obtain the following theorem.

Theorem 7.3. Let (S, P) be a probability space and let A and B be events in S such that $P(B) \neq 0$. Then A and B are *independent* if and only if

$$P(A \mid B) = P(A). \tag{1}$$

This theorem makes two assertions for events B with $P(B) \neq 0$: (1) if A and B are independent events, then the occurrence of the event B does not affect the probability of the occurrence of A, that is, Eq. (1) holds, (2) if the occurrence of B does not affect the probability of the occurrence of A, that is, if Eq. (1) holds, then A and B are independent. Independence of events could have been defined by Eq. (1). However, if we had done so, it would have been necessary to restrict attention to events B such that $P(B) \neq 0$. Thus the definition of independence in Definition 7.2 is mathematically simpler than a definition based on Eq. (1). There is another formula similar to the one in Eq. (1): if $P(A) \neq 0$, then A and B are independent if and only if

$$P(B \mid A) = P(B). \tag{2}$$

Proof of Theorem 7.3. Assume first that $P(B) \neq 0$ and that A and B are independent. Then $P(A \cap B) = P(A)P(B)$ by Definition 7.2, and $P(A \cap B) = P(A \mid B)P(B)$ by Eq. (2) of Section 7.2. Thus $P(A \mid B)P(B) = P(A)P(B)$ and, since $P(B) \neq 0$, $P(A \mid B) = P(A)$. The proof that Eq. (1) is a necessary condition for independence is complete.

Assume next that $P(B) \neq 0$ and that Eq. (1) holds. Then $P(A \mid B) = P(A)$ and, by Eq. (2) of Section 7.2, we have

$$P(A \cap B) = P(A \mid B)P(B) = P(A)P(B).$$

Then by Definition 7.2, A and B are independent. The proof that Eq. (1), together with the hypothesis $P(B) \neq 0$, is a sufficient condition for independence is complete. ▲

There are two ways to prove that two events A and B are independent: (a) prove that $P(A \cap B) = P(A)P(B)$; (b) prove that Eq. (1) is true [if $P(B) \neq 0$] or that Eq. (2) is true [if $P(A) \neq 0$]. Intuition is sometimes helpful in identifying independent events, but it is often misleading. The following examples exhibit a variety of situations.

EXAMPLE 1.   A card is drawn at random from a deck of 52 cards. Show that the two events "drawing an ace" and "drawing a spade" are independent.
    Each card in the deck corresponds to an elementary event; thus S contains 52 elementary events which are equally likely. For each x in S, we set $P(\{x\}) = \frac{1}{52}$. The event A, "drawing an ace," consists of four elementary events; hence $P(A) = \frac{4}{52}$. The event B, "drawing a spade," consists of 13 elementary events; hence $P(B) = \frac{13}{52}$. The event $A \cap B$ consists of a single elementary event, namely, "drawing the ace of spades"; hence $P(A \cap B) = \frac{1}{52}$. Therefore $P(A \cap B) = P(A)P(B)$, and the events A and B are independent.

EXAMPLE 2.   An unbiased coin is tossed twice. Let A be the event "not more than one head," and let B be the event "at least one of each face." Are A and B independent?
    Let $S = \{(H, H), (H, T), (T, H), (T, T)\}$ and assign probability $\frac{1}{4}$ to each of the four elementary events. Then

$$
\begin{aligned}
A &= \{(H, T), (T, H), (T, T)\}, \\
B &= \{(H, T), (T, H)\}, \\
A \cap B &= B, \\
P(A \cap B) &= \tfrac{1}{2}, \\
P(A)P(B) &= \tfrac{3}{4} \cdot \tfrac{1}{2} = \tfrac{3}{8}.
\end{aligned}
$$

Thus the events A and B are not independent.

EXAMPLE 3.   An unbiased coin is tossed three times. Let A be the event "not more than one head," and let B be the event "at least one of each face." Are A and B independent?

Let $S = \{(a, b, c) \mid$ each of a, b, c is either H or $T\}$. Then S contains eight elementary events, each of which is assigned the probability $\frac{1}{8}$. Then

$$
\begin{aligned}
A &= \{(H, T, T), (T, H, T), (T, T, H), (T, T, T)\}, \\
B &= S - \{(H, H, H),(T, T, T)\}, \\
A \cap B &= \{(H, T, T), (T, H, T), (T, T, H)\}, \\
P(A) &= \tfrac{4}{8}, \\
P(B) &= \tfrac{6}{8}, \\
P(A \cap B) &= \tfrac{3}{8}.
\end{aligned}
$$

Therefore $P(A \cap B) = P(A)P(B)$, and the events A and B are independent.

We shall frequently be concerned with the independence of more than two events. The definition of the independence of any number of events is given in Definition 7.3.

Definition 7.3. Let (S, P) be a probability space. The events $A_1, A_2, \ldots, A_n$ in S are *independent* if and only if

$$
P\left(\bigcap_{i=1}^{m} A_{k_i}\right) = P(A_{k_1})P(A_{k_2}) \cdots P(A_{k_m}) \tag{3}
$$

for every set $\{A_{k_1}, A_{k_2}, \ldots, A_{k_m}\}$, $m = 2, 3, \ldots, n$, of m sets selected from the n events.

By Definition 7.3 the events A, B, C are independent if and only if

$$
P(A \cap B \cap C) = P(A)P(B)P(C); \tag{4}
$$

$$
\begin{aligned}
P(A \cap B) &= P(A)P(B), \\
P(A \cap C) &= P(A)P(C), \\
P(B \cap C) &= P(B)P(C).
\end{aligned} \tag{5}
$$

It would be reasonable to assume that equations (5) imply Eq. (4), but unfortunately this is not the case. Furthermore, Eq. (4) does not imply equations (5). The following examples establish these assertions.

EXAMPLE 4. Let $S = \{1, 2, 3, 4, 5, 6, 7, 8\}$ and take $A = \{1, 2, 5, 8\}$, $B = \{2, 3, 6, 8\}$, and $C = \{1, 3, 5, 6\}$. Let $P(\{n\}) = \frac{1}{8}$ for $n = 1, 2, \ldots, 8$. Then A, B, C satisfy equations (5) but not Eq. (4). In fact, $P(A) = P(B) = P(C) = \frac{1}{2}$; $P(A \cap B) = P(A \cap C) = P(B \cap C) = \frac{1}{4}$; and $P(A \cap B \cap C) = 0$.
    This example is a *counterexample* which disproves the conjecture that equations (5) imply Eq. (4).

EXAMPLE 5. Let (S, P) be the probability space defined in Example 4 and take $A = \{1, 2, 3, 8\}$, $B = \{1, 2, 5, 8\}$, and $C = \{4, 6, 7, 8\}$. Then $P(A \cap B \cap C) = \frac{1}{8} = P(A)P(B)P(C)$, since $P(A) = P(B) = P(C) = \frac{1}{2}$. But $P(A \cap B) = \frac{3}{8} \neq P(A)P(B)$, $P(A \cap C) = \frac{1}{8} \neq P(A)P(C)$, and $P(B \cap C) = \frac{1}{8} \neq P(B)P(C)$.

This example is a counterexample which disproves the conjecture that Eq. (4) implies equations (5).

Thus far we have given (a) the mathematical definition of independent events, (b) some consequences of this definition, and (c) some simple examples of independent events. The remaining examples in this section illustrate how the idea of independence can be applied. The major point in connection with applications is that frequently independence is assumed for certain events. This assumption usually simplifies some of the calculations. Whether the assumption is justified or not is a question which cannot be answered with certainty, although there are statistical tests of the appropriateness of the assumption of independence.

EXAMPLE 6. A business firm has two suppliers. When the stock of a hard-to-procure item becomes low, the firm customarily places an order with each supplier in order to increase the probability of getting at least some of the needed item. The firm estimates that the probabilities of receiving the item from the suppliers are 0.6 and 0.7. Does the firm increase its probability of obtaining the scarce item by placing an order with each of the two suppliers?

To answer this question, begin by letting A and B be the events in which the firm receives the item from the first and second suppliers, respectively. We wish to calculate $P(A \cup B)$, since $A \cup B$ is the event in which the firm receives the item from the first supplier, the second supplier, or both. Now $P(A \cup B) = P(A) + P(B) - P(A \cap B) = 0.6 + 0.7 - P(A \cap B)$. If we assume that the events A and B are independent (which means that we assume the difficulties rest with the suppliers rather than the manufacturers), then $P(A \cap B) = P(A)P(B) = (0.6)(0.7) = 0.42$. Thus $P(A \cup B) = 1.3 - 0.42 = 0.88$, and the firm has indeed increased its probability of obtaining the scarce item.

EXAMPLE 7. Modern space technology requires the construction of complex electrical circuits with a high degree of reliability. In some cases, to avoid failure as a result of the failure of a single component, secondary systems are provided for the vital primary systems. If the primary system has a probability of 0.99 of performing satisfactorily, and if the secondary system has a probability of 0.90 of performing satisfactorily, what is the probability that both systems fail?

Let A and B be the events in which the primary and secondary systems, respectively, perform satisfactorily. Since $A^c \cap B^c$ is the event in which both systems fail, the problem asks us to calculate $P(A^c \cap B^c)$. If we assume that A and B are independent, then $P(A^c \cap B^c)$ can be calculated in two ways. The first method employs the fact that A^c and B^c are independent since A and B are independent. This fact is stated in Corollary 7.1. Then $P(A^c \cap B^c) = P(A^c)P(B^c) =$ $(0.01)(0.1) = 0.001$. The second calculation contains a proof that A^c and B^c are independent. Now

$$A^c \cap B^c = (A \cup B)^c, \tag{6}$$

$$\begin{aligned} P(A^c \cap B^c) = P\big((A \cup B)^c\big) &= 1 - P(A \cup B) = 1 - [P(A) + P(B) - P(A \cap B)] \\ &= 1 - P(A) - P(B) + P(A \cap B) = 1 - 0.99 - 0.9 + (0.99)(0.9) \\ &= 0.001. \end{aligned} \tag{7}$$

This result shows that the combined system, which consists of the primary and secondary systems together, is far more reliable (has a smaller probability of failure) than either system alone.

The proof that the complements of independent events are independent is contained in the proof of the following theorem and its corollary.

Theorem 7.4. Let A and B be events in a probability space (S, P). Then A and B are independent if and only if A and B^c are independent.

Corollary 7.1. Let A and B be events in a probability space. Then A and B are independent if and only if A^c and B^c are independent.

The proof of Theorem 7.4 is left as an exercise for the reader (see Exercises 7 and 8). The corollary clearly follows immediately from the theorem.

EXAMPLE 8 [Mosteller-Wallace Model (continued)]. In Example 6 of Section 7.3 we discussed a model proposed by Mosteller and Wallace for determining disputed authorship. In that discussion we indicated how evidence based on the usage of a single word was employed in determining authorship, but we deferred until this section a discussion of how evidence based on the usages of several words could be employed. Clearly, evidence based on several words should be more significant than evidence based on a single word. Mosteller and Wallace achieved this added significance by selecting words whose usages are independent. Here independence means that the event of x occurrences of one word and y occurrences of another word in a paper, given that Hamilton wrote it or that Madison wrote it, are independent events. In symbols, this statement means that Mosteller and Wallace selected words such that

$$P\big((x, y) \mid H\big) = P(x \mid H)P(y \mid H), \tag{8}$$

$$P\big((x, y) \mid M\big) = P(x \mid M)P(y \mid M), \tag{9}$$

where (x, y) denotes the event in which the first word occurs x times and the second word y times. The final odds then are

$$\frac{P\big(H \mid (x, y)\big)}{P\big(M \mid (x, y)\big)} = \frac{P\big((x, y) \mid H\big) \cdot P(H)}{P\big((x, y) \mid M\big) \cdot P(M)} = \frac{P(H)}{P(M)} \cdot \frac{P(x \mid H)}{P(x \mid M)} \cdot \frac{P(y \mid H)}{P(y \mid M)}. \tag{10}$$

Thus the final odds are the product of the initial odds $P(H)/P(M)$ and the likelihood ratios $P(x \mid H)/P(x \mid M)$ and $P(y \mid H)/P(y \mid M)$ for the separate words. The method obviously can be extended so that evidence from more than two words is employed.

As a simple example, assume there are four occurrences of the word *also* and seven occurrences of the word *an* in a given 2000-word paper. Then, using the values given by Mosteller and Wallace, namely,

$$\frac{P(x \mid H)}{P(x \mid M)} = \frac{0.00331}{0.03520},$$

$$\frac{P(y \mid H)}{P(y \mid M)} = \frac{0.0437}{0.1170},$$

we have

$$\frac{P(x \mid H)}{P(x \mid M)} \cdot \frac{P(y \mid H)}{P(y \mid M)} = \frac{0.00331}{0.03520} \cdot \frac{0.0437}{0.1170} = 0.038 = \frac{38}{1000}.$$

These odds are more strongly in favor of Madison's authorship than the odds based on either word alone. The initial odds, $P(H)/P(M)$, could still influence the final odds significantly, however.

Many of the applications of independent events occur in connection with repeated trials of an experiment in which it is assumed that each trial is performed under identical conditions and that the outcome of an earlier trial does not influence the outcome of a later trial. For such experiments it seems reasonable to assume that an event which depends on one trial only is independent of an event which depends on another trial only. The next section is devoted to a discussion of these repeated trials and independent events.

EXERCISES

1. A white die and a black die are rolled. If A is the event "five on the white die" and B is the event "six on the black die," show that A and B are independent events.

2. A true coin is tossed three times. Show that the events corresponding to the statements "the same side turns up" and "at most one head turns up" are independent.

3. The probability that X and Y will live an additional 15 years is 0.8 and 0.7 respectively. Assuming that these events are independent, what is the probability that both X and Y will live an additional 15 years?

4. Find the probability of a head on the fourth and sixth tosses of a coin.

5. An urn contains three red, two white, and five black balls. If three balls are drawn successively, find the probability of a red, white, and black ball in that order if
   (a) the ball drawn is replaced after each drawing;
   (b) the ball drawn is not replaced after each drawing.

6. Let (S, P) be any probability space.
   (a) If A and B are events in S, and if $P(B) = 1$, show that the events A and B are independent. What does this result state about the certain event S?
   (b) If A is any event in S, and if B is any event in S such that $P(B) = 0$, show that A and B are independent events.
   (c) If A and B are disjoint, that is, if $A \cap B = \emptyset$, show that A and B are independent if and only if $P(A)P(B) = 0$. This result shows that, if A and B are independent and $P(A)$ and $P(B)$ are both nonzero, then A and B are *not* disjoint.

7. Prove Theorem 7.4. [*Hint:* $A = A \cap (B \cup B^c) = (A \cap B) \cup (A \cap B^c)$.]

8. Use Theorem 7.4 to give a detailed proof of Corollary 7.1.

9. Urn 1 contains two white and four black balls. Urn 2 has three white and two black balls. One ball is drawn from each of the two urns. What is the probability that (a) both balls are black? (b) one is white and the other is black?

10. A mathematics professor occasionally makes a mistake in class. However, the probability that any particular student in the class will recognize the mistake and point it out to the rest of the class is 0.1 (independent of the other students). What is the minimum number of students necessary in order to be at least 0.95 sure that a mistake will be corrected by a student in the class?

7.5 INDEPENDENT TRIALS

Some of the examples already discussed have dealt with repeated trials. For instance, in Example 2 of Section 7.4 we considered the experiment of tossing a coin twice. We assigned as sample space a set of ordered pairs, and we defined a probability function which agreed with our intuition. In this section we shall consider a slightly different approach to the construction of that probability space. The method used in this section leads to the concept of independent trials.

Let $S_1 = \{H, T\}$, and let P_1 be the probability function on the subsets of S_1 defined by

$$P_1(\{H\}) = p, \qquad P_1(\{T\}) = q,$$

where $p \geq 0$, $q \geq 0$, and $p + q = 1$. Let

$$S = S_1 \times S_1 = \{(x, y) \mid x \in S_1, y \in S_1\} = \{(H, H), (H, T), (T, H), (T, T)\}.$$

This set S is the same as the set S in Example 2 in Section 7.4. Next, for each (x, y) in S define

$$P(\{(x, y)\}) = P_1(\{x\})P_1(\{y\}).$$

This equation defines a function P on the elementary events in S. We can extend P to a function defined for every event A in $\Pi(S)$ by applying Eq. (6) in Section 5.3. This function P defined on $\Pi(S)$ is a probability function if and only if the sum of the probabilities of the elementary events is one. The probabilities of the elementary events are calculated below:

$$P(\{(H, H)\}) = P_1(\{H\})P_1(\{H\}) = p \cdot p = p^2,$$
$$P(\{(H, T)\}) = P_1(\{H\})P_1(\{T\}) = p \cdot q = pq,$$
$$P(\{(T, H)\}) = P_1(\{T\})P_1(\{H\}) = q \cdot p = pq,$$
$$P(\{(T, T)\}) = P_1(\{T\})P_1(\{T\}) = q \cdot q = q^2.$$

The sum of the probabilities of the four elementary events is

$$p^2 + 2pq + q^2 = (p + q)^2 = 1^2 = 1.$$

Thus P is a probability function on S. Observe that $p = q = \frac{1}{2}$ in the case of an unbiased coin, and that the probability of each elementary event in S is $\frac{1}{4}$, as in Example 2 of Section 7.4.

The method we have used to construct the probability space (S, P) in the case of two tosses of a coin can be generalized readily to treat the cases in which the coin is tossed more than twice. For example, if the coin is tossed ten times, then an appropriate sample space is

$$S = S_1 \times S_1 \times \cdots \times S_1 = \{(x_1, x_2, \ldots, x_{10}) \mid x_i \in S_1, 1 \le i \le 10\}.$$

A probability function can be defined on the 2^{10} elementary events in S by setting

$$P(\{(x_1, x_2, \ldots, x_{10})\}) = P_1(\{x_1\})P_1(\{x_2\}) \cdots P_1(\{x_{10}\}),$$

where $(x_1, x_2, \ldots, x_{10}) \in S$. This probability function is the "natural" choice if we assume that the outcome of any toss does not affect the outcome of any other toss, that is, if we assume that the tosses are independent.

In general, we shall assume that there are n probability spaces (S_1, P_1), (S_2, P_2), $\ldots$, (S_n, P_n) corresponding to n experiments (which may be the same or different). We then define the *product probability space* as stated in the following definition.

Definition 7.4. The *product probability space* of the probability spaces (S_1, P_1), (S_2, P_2), $\ldots$, (S_n, P_n) is the probability space (S, P), where

$$S = S_1 \times S_2 \times \cdots \times S_n,$$
$$P(\{(x_1, x_2, \ldots, x_n)\}) = P_1(\{x_1\})P_2(\{x_2\}) \cdots P_n(\{x_n\})$$

for $(x_1, x_2, \ldots, x_n) \in S$. When this probability function P is employed on S, we say that the n *experiments are independent.* If one experiment is repeated n times (that is, if the probability spaces (S_i, P_i) are the same for $i = 1, 2, \ldots, n$), and if the product probability space is employed, then we say that we have n *independent trials* of the experiment.

Of course, it must be shown that P, as defined in Definition 7.4, is a probability function. To give this proof it is sufficient to show that $\sum P(\{(x_1, x_2, \ldots, x_n)\}) = 1$, where the summation extends over all elements $(x_1, x_2, \ldots, x_n)$ in S. This sum can be written as the following $n$fold summation:

$$\sum_{x_1 \in S_1} \sum_{x_2 \in S_2} \cdots \sum_{x_n \in S_n} P(\{(x_1, x_2, \ldots, x_n)\}).$$

The proof is now completed by using the definition of P and the fact that

$$\sum_{x_i \in S_i} P_i(\{x_i\}) = 1.$$

We have

$$\sum P(\{(x_1, x_2, \ldots, x_n)\}) = \sum_{x_1 \in S_1} \sum_{x_2 \in S_2} \cdots \sum_{x_n \in S_n} [P_1(\{x_1\}) P_2(\{x_2\}) \cdots P_n(\{x_n\})]$$

$$= \left[\sum_{x_1 \in S_1} P_1(\{x_1\}) \right] \left[\sum_{x_2 \in S_2} P_2(\{x_2\}) \right] \cdots \left[\sum_{x_n \in S_n} P_n(\{x_n\}) \right]$$

$$= 1 \cdot 1 \cdot \ldots \cdot 1 = 1^n = 1.$$

A conceptually simpler proof can be based on Lemma 7.1 below; this proof will be left to the reader as an exercise.

The concept of independent events was introduced in Section 7.4. The definition of the product probability space (S, P) has been motivated by a desire to obtain a definition for the probability function P such that events in independent experiments correspond to events in S which are independent in the sense of Section 7.4. The definition

$$P(\{(x_1, x_2, \ldots, x_n)\}) = P_1(\{x_1\}) P_2(\{x_2\}) \cdots P_n(\{x_n\})$$

suggests that the elementary events $\{x_1\}, \{x_2\}, \ldots, \{x_n\}$ in $S_1, S_2, \ldots, S_n$ are independent events in S in the sense of Definition 7.3 in Section 7.4, but we wish to investigate the independence of more general events. Let E_i and E_j be events in S which are determined by the ith and jth experiments S_i and S_j respectively. We shall show that, in the probability space (S, P) given by Definition 7.4, we have

$$P(E_i \cap E_j) = P(E_i)P(E_j). \tag{1}$$

To prove this result, we shall need another definition and some preliminary results.

Definition 7.5. An event E_i of the product space S(see Definition 7.4) is determined by the ith experiment if and only if there is a subset C_i of S_i such that

$$E_i = S_1 \times S_2 \times \cdots \times S_{i-1} \times C_i \times S_{i+1} \times \cdots \times S_n.$$

The following examples will illuminate both this definition and Eq. (1).

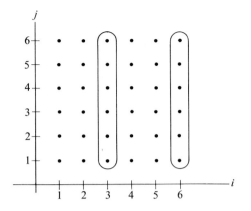

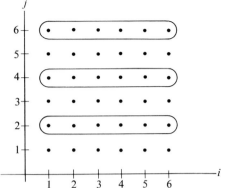

Fig. 7.2. The sample space S and the event A of Example 2 (the elements of A are encircled).

Fig. 7.3. The sample space S and the event B of Example 2 (the elements of B are encircled).

EXAMPLE 1.   Let $S_1 = S_2 = \{H, T\}$, $S = S_1 \times S_2$, and let E_1 be the event that the first of two tosses of a coin results in a head.   Then E_1 is determined by the first experiment since

$$E_1 = \{(H, H), (H, T)\} = \{H\} \times S_2.$$

EXAMPLE 2.   Find the probability of obtaining a multiple of three on the first toss and an even number on the second toss of a die.

An appropriate probability space is the product probability space (S, P) where $S = \{1, 2, \ldots, 6\} \times \{1, 2, \ldots, 6\}$ and $P(\{(i, j)\}) = \frac{1}{36}$ for each element (i, j) in S.   Define the events A and B in S by

$$A = \{(i, j) \mid i = 3, 6;\ 1 \leq j \leq 6\} \qquad \text{(see Fig. 7.2)},$$
$$B = \{(i, j) \mid 1 \leq i \leq 6;\ j = 2, 4, 6\} \qquad \text{(see Fig. 7.3)}.$$

Then A is the event "a multiple of three on the first toss," and B is the event "an even number on the second toss."   We see that

$$A \cap B = \{(i, j) \mid i = 3, 6;\ j = 2, 4, 6\} \qquad \text{(see Fig. 7.4)},$$
$$P(A \cap B) = \frac{6}{36} = \frac{1}{6}.$$

Since $P(A) = \frac{12}{36}$ and $P(B) = \frac{18}{36}$, we find that

$$P(A \cap B) = \frac{1}{6} = \frac{12}{36} \cdot \frac{18}{36} = P(A)P(B).$$

Thus A and B are two events in S for which Eq. (1) is true (with $A = E_i$ and $B = E_j$).   It should be observed that

$$A = \{3, 6\} \times \{1, 2, \ldots, 6\}, \qquad B = \{1, 2, \ldots, 6\} \times \{2, 4, 6\}.$$

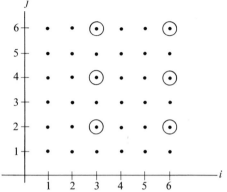

Fig. 7.4. The sample space S and the event $A \cap B$ of Example 2 (the elements of $A \cap B$ are encircled).

Thus according to Definition 7.5, A is determined by the first experiment (tossing the die the first time) and B is determined by the second experiment (tossing the die the second time).

To simplify the exposition, we shall state and prove Lemmas 7.1 and 7.2 and Theorem 7.5 for the special case $n = 2$; thus, $S = S_1 \times S_2$. The reader will find it easy to extend these results to the general case $S = S_1 \times S_2 \times \cdots \times S_n$.

Lemma 7.1. Let (S, P) be the product probability space of (S_1, P_1) and (S_2, P_2) as defined in Definition 7.4. If $C_1 \subset S_1$ and $C_2 \subset S_2$, then

$$P(C_1 \times C_2) = P_1(C_1)P_2(C_2). \tag{2}$$

Proof. Let $x_1, x_2, \ldots, x_k$ be the distinct elements of C_1. Then

$$C_1 \times C_2 = \bigcup_{i=1}^{k} [\{x_i\} \times C_2]. \tag{3}$$

Furthermore, since the x_i are distinct,

$$[\{x_i\} \times C_2] \cap [\{x_j\} \times C_2] = \emptyset, \quad i \neq j, \quad 1 \leq i \leq k, \quad 1 \leq j \leq k.$$

Thus the sets in the union on the right in (3) are disjoint, and

$$P(C_1 \times C_2) = \sum_{i=1}^{k} P(\{x_i\} \times C_2). \tag{4}$$

Let the distinct elements of C_2 be $y_1, y_2, \ldots, y_m$. Then

$$\{x_i\} \times C_2 = \bigcup_{j=1}^{m} \{(x_i, y_j)\}, \quad 1 \leq i \leq k,$$

and

$$\{(x_i, y_j)\} \cap \{(x_i, y_l)\} = \emptyset, \quad j \neq l, \quad 1 \leq j \leq m, \quad 1 \leq l \leq m.$$

Thus

$$P(\{x_i\} \times C_2) = \sum_{j=1}^{m} P(\{(x_i, y_j)\}) = \sum_{j=1}^{m} P_1(\{x_i\})P_2(\{y_j\})$$

$$= P_1(\{x_i\}) \sum_{j=1}^{m} P_2(\{y_j\}) = P_1(\{x_i\})P_2(C_2), \qquad 1 \le i \le k,$$

by Definition 7.4 and the fact that $C_2 = \{y_1, y_2, \ldots, y_m\}$. Substitute the value just obtained for $P(\{x_i\} \times C_2)$ in Eq. (4). We find that

$$P(C_1 \times C_2) = \sum_{i=1}^{k} P_1(\{x_i\})P_2(C_2) = P_2(C_2) \sum_{i=1}^{k} P_1(\{x_i\})$$

$$= P_2(C_2)P_1(C_1) = P_1(C_1)P_2(C_2)$$

since $C_1 = \{x_1, x_2, \ldots, x_k\}$. ▲

Lemma 7.2. If $E_1 = C_1 \times S_2$ and $E_2 = S_1 \times C_2$, then

$$E_1 \cap E_2 = C_1 \times C_2.$$

The proof of this lemma is left as an exercise for the reader.

Theorem 7.5. If E_1 is an event determined by the first experiment, and if E_2 is an event determined by the second experiment, then

$$P(E_1 \cap E_2) = P(E_1)P(E_2), \tag{5}$$

where P is the product probability function.

Proof. From the definitions of E_1 and E_2 there exist subsets C_1 of S_1 and C_2 of S_2 such that

$$E_1 = C_1 \times S_2, \qquad E_2 = S_1 \times C_2.$$

By Lemmas 7.1 and 7.2,

$$P(E_1 \cap E_2) = P(C_1 \times C_2) = P_1(C_1)P_2(C_2). \tag{6}$$

Also, by Lemma 7.1,

$$P(E_1) = P(C_1 \times S_2) = P_1(C_1)P_2(S_2) = P_1(C_1), \tag{7}$$

$$P(E_2) = P(S_1 \times C_2) = P_1(S_1)P_2(C_2) = P_2(C_2). \tag{8}$$

Equation (5) follows directly from Eqs. (6), (7), and (8), and the proof of the theorem is complete. ▲

It should be observed that Eqs. (7) and (8) state that the product probability function assigns the same probability to an event determined by the ith experiment as the probability function P_i for the ith experiment assigns to the corresponding event in S_i.

We shall now consider an important special case. We consider an experiment whose probability space is (S_1, P_1), where $S_1 = \{s, f\}$ and $P_1(\{s\}) = p$, $P_1(\{f\}) = q$, $p + q = 1$. The outcome s is called success, and the outcome f is called failure. Repeated independent trials of this experiment are known as *Bernoulli trials* after the Swiss mathematician J. Bernoulli. If there are n Bernoulli trials, then the product probability space (S, P) is defined by

$$S = S_1 \times S_1 \times \cdots \times S_1$$
$$= \{(x_1, x_2, \ldots, x_n) \mid x_i = s \text{ or } x_i = f, \ 1 \leq i \leq n\},$$
$$P(\{(x_1, x_2, \ldots, x_n)\}) = p^k q^{n-k}.$$

Here we are assuming that $(x_1, x_2, \ldots, x_n)$ is an element of S such that $x_i = s$ for k values of i and $x_i = f$ for the other $n - k$ values of i. Thus k denotes the number of successes in the n trials and $n - k$ denotes the number of failures.

Let A_k, $0 \leq k \leq n$, denote the event in which there are exactly k successes in n Bernoulli trials. Then

$$A_k = \{(x_1, x_2, \ldots, x_n) \mid (x_1, x_2, \ldots, x_n) \in S, \ x_i = s \text{ for } k \text{ values of } i,$$
$$x_i = f \text{ for } n - k \text{ values of } i\}.$$

We wish to find $P(A_k)$. We have shown above that the probability associated with each element of A_k is $p^k q^{n-k}$; to find $P(A_k)$, therefore, we need only count the number of elements in A_k. The number of these elements is equal to the number of distinguishable arrangements of n objects, k of which are (indistinguishable) of one kind ($= s$) and $n - k$ of which are (indistinguishable) of a second kind ($= f$). By Section 4.6, this number is $\binom{n}{k}$. We have thus shown that

$$P(A_k) = \binom{n}{k} p^k q^{n-k}, \qquad k = 0, 1, 2, \ldots, n. \tag{9}$$

These results are summarized in the following theorem.

Theorem 7.6. The probability of exactly k successes in n Bernoulli trials is

$$\binom{n}{k} p^k q^{n-k}, \qquad 0 \leq k \leq n. \tag{10}$$

Here p is the probability of success, q is the probability of failure, at each trial, and $p + q = 1$.

EXAMPLE 3. An unbiased coin is tossed ten times. Compute the probability of exactly five heads.

This experiment can be interpreted as a sequence of ten Bernoulli trials in which success means heads and failure means tails, provided that the tosses are independent. We shall assume that the tosses are independent and make this interpretation. Since the coin is unbiased, we take $p = q = \frac{1}{2}$, and by Theorem 7.6 the probability of exactly five successes is

$$\binom{10}{5}\left(\frac{1}{2}\right)^5\left(\frac{1}{2}\right)^{10-5} = \frac{63}{256}.$$

EXAMPLE 4. An unbiased coin is tossed ten times. What is the probability of at least five heads?

The event "at least five heads" means "exactly five heads, or exactly six heads, . . . , or exactly 10 heads." If E is the event "at least five heads," and if A_k is the event "exactly k heads," then $E = A_5 \cup A_6 \cup \cdots \cup A_{10}$. Since $A_i \cap A_j = \emptyset, i \neq j,$

$$P(E) = \sum_{k=5}^{10} P(A_k) = \sum_{k=5}^{10} \binom{10}{k}\left(\frac{1}{2}\right)^k\left(\frac{1}{2}\right)^{10-k}$$

$$= \left(\frac{1}{2}\right)^{10} \sum_{k=5}^{10} \binom{10}{k} = \frac{319}{512}.$$

As an easy consequence of this result we can compute the probability of less than five heads as follows:

$$P(E^c) = 1 - P(E) = 1 - \tfrac{319}{512} = \tfrac{193}{512}.$$

EXAMPLE 5. What is the probability of exactly four threes in five tosses of an unbiased die?

In this experiment a success means a three appears, and a failure means a three does not appear. The experiment is then a sequence of five Bernoulli trials in which $p = \frac{1}{6}$ and $q = \frac{5}{6}$. By Theorem 7.6, the probability of exactly four successes in five trials is

$$\binom{5}{4}\left(\frac{1}{6}\right)^4\left(\frac{5}{6}\right) = \frac{25}{7776}.$$

If we are interested only in the number of successes (or failures) in n Bernoulli trials, then it is easy to introduce a simpler probability space (S', P') than the product probability space (S, P). Set

$$S' = \{0, 1, 2, \ldots, n\},$$
$$P'(\{k\}) = P(A_k) = \binom{n}{k} p^k q^{n-k}, \qquad 0 \le k \le n.$$

It is necessary to show that (S', P') is a probability space. Since P' is clearly nonnegative and since we define it to be additive, it is sufficient to show that

$$\sum_{k=1}^{n} P'(\{k\}) = 1.$$

Recall the binomial theorem and the fact that $p + q = 1$. Then

$$\sum_{k=0}^{n} P'(\{k\}) = \sum_{k=0}^{n} \binom{n}{k} p^k q^{n-k} = (p + q)^k = 1.$$

Thus (S', P') is a probability space; it is called a *binomial probability space*. The probability $P'(\{k\})$ is denoted by $b(k;n, p)$. The numbers n and p are called *parameters*. The values of $b(k;n, p)$ depend on n and p. After values are specified for n (the number of trials) and p (the probability of success on each trial) corresponding to the given experiment, the only variable is k (the number of successes). Thus $b(k;n, p)$ is the probability of *exactly* k successes in n Bernoulli trials where the probability of success at each trial is p.

EXAMPLE 6. A handwriting expert claims to be able to distinguish between the handwriting of abnormal persons and that of normal persons. To test the claim, the following trial was devised. Ten people were selected who had been diagnosed as psychotics by at least two psychiatrists. For each of the psychotics a control person, who was normal, was matched for age, sex, and education. Handwriting samples for each pair of persons were placed into separate folders and presented to the expert being tested. The expert was required to identify the abnormal sample of each pair. The expert correctly identified six of the ten. What is the probability that the expert would be able to identify at least six correctly just by chance?

If the expert has no ability and is just guessing, we may consider the ten guesses as ten Bernoulli trials with probability $p = \frac{1}{2}$ of success on each trial. Thus we wish to calculate the probability of six or more successes in ten Bernoulli trials where $p = \frac{1}{2}$. In Example 4 we found the probability of five or more successes in ten Bernoulli trials with $p = \frac{1}{2}$ to be $\frac{319}{512}$; hence, the probability of six or more successes is $\frac{319}{512}$ minus $\binom{10}{5}(\frac{1}{2})^{10}$, the probability of exactly five successes. Thus the answer is

$$\tfrac{319}{512} - \tfrac{126}{512} = \tfrac{193}{512} = 0.3770.$$

The expert's performance on the test is not an overwhelming indication of ability.

EXAMPLE 7. In large bureaucracies it is possible for a person who is not really wise to appear wise and to make correct decisions by chance and good luck. Assume that (a) there are m bureaucrats at the same level who are charged with making decisions and whose records can be compared, (b) that there are n important decisions to be made, (c) that each man makes each decision independently, (d) that it is possible to evaluate a decision as being either good or bad, and (e) that the probability p of a correct decision is the same for all decisions and all men. The probability p is called the *competence level*. A man who makes only correct decisions is called "highly competent." What is the probability that at least one man is highly competent? (A man who is highly competent according to this definition is not necessarily wise; it is possible that he is merely lucky.)

The probability that any one of the m men makes only correct decisions is p^n, the probability of n successes in n Bernoulli trials. Next, by our assumptions, the probability that at least one man is highly competent is

$$\sum_{k=1}^{m} \binom{m}{k} (p^n)^k (1 - p^n)^{m-k}, \tag{11}$$

since each man is independent of the other men and all have probability p^n of being highly competent. The direct evaluation of the expression in (11) can be avoided by observing that

$$\sum_{k=1}^{m} \binom{m}{k} (p^n)^k (1 - p^n)^{m-k} = 1 - \binom{m}{0} (p^n)^0 (1 - p^n)^{m-0};$$

hence, the probability that at least one man appears wise is

$$1 - (1 - p^n)^m. \tag{12}$$

For example, if $p = \frac{1}{2}$ (all decisions are random), $n = 3$, and $m = 5$, then (12) becomes $1 - 0.513 = 0.487$; if $p = \frac{1}{2}$, $n = 8$, and $m = 2^8 = 256$, then (12) becomes $1 - 0.367 = 0.633$.

This example will be discussed further in the next chapter, where the idea of mathematical expectation will be used to find the expected number of highly competent men.

EXAMPLE 8. A manufacturer of a vaccine wishes to test his product for purity. Suppose that at a certain stage of production the vaccine contains N live viruses which are not desired; N is unknown, but assumed fixed. If there are V cubic centimeters of vaccine in the batch and the N viruses are distributed uniformly throughout, then there are $m = N/V$ viruses per cubic centimeter. A sample of v cubic centimeters is drawn from the batch, and the number of viruses present in the sample is determined. Two important questions are: (a) What is the probability of k live viruses in the sample? (b) What is a reasonable estimate of the number N of viruses in the batch?

To answer these questions we proceed as follows. Each of the N viruses, being uniformly distributed in the vat, has a probability v/V of being in the sample. If we define a success to mean that a virus is in the sample, and failure to mean that a virus is not in the sample, then we have N Bernoulli trials (one for each virus). The probability of a success at each trial is $p = v/V$ and hence the probability of exactly k successes is

$$\binom{N}{k} p^k q^{N-k}, \qquad q = 1 - p. \tag{13}$$

Often the number, m, of viruses per cubic centimeter, on the average, is known from past experience; in these cases we can replace N by mV and calculate (13) by evaluating

$$\binom{mV}{k} p^k q^{mV-k}. \tag{14}$$

If, however, the number N (and hence the number m) is not known, how do we estimate it? One reasonable way of estimating N is to choose that value of N—denote it by $\hat{N}$—which makes the expression (13) as large as possible; $\hat{N}$ is called the maximum likelihood estimate of N (see Section 6.4). Denote the expression in (13) by $p(N, k)$:

$$p(N, k) = \binom{N}{k} p^k q^{N-k}. \tag{15}$$

Consider the ratio

$$\frac{p(N, k)}{p(N-1, k)} = \frac{\binom{N}{k} p^k q^{N-k}}{\binom{N-1}{k} p^k q^{(N-1)-k}} = \frac{Nq}{N-k}. \tag{16}$$

This ratio is greater than one for $N < k/p$ and less than one for $N > k/p$. (Remember that $1 - q = p$.) Hence, $p(N, k)$, considered as a function of N, is first increasing and then decreasing. Thus its largest value occurs at the greatest integer less than or equal to k/p. [If k/p is an integer, it occurs at both k/p and $(k/p) - 1$.] Hence, we choose as the estimate $\hat{N}$ of N the greatest integer less than or equal to

$$\frac{k}{p} = \frac{k}{v/V} = \frac{kV}{v}.$$

For example, if $V = 100$, $v = 10$, and six live viruses are found in the sample of size v, we have

$$\hat{N} = \frac{6 \cdot 100}{10} = 60.$$

EXERCISES

1. Compute the value of each of the following expressions.

(a) $\displaystyle\sum_{k=0}^{2} \binom{10}{k} \left(\frac{1}{2}\right)^{10}$

(b) $\displaystyle\sum_{k=0}^{2} \binom{10}{k} \left(\frac{1}{4}\right)^k \left(\frac{3}{4}\right)^{10-k}$

(c) $\displaystyle\sum_{k=3}^{10} \binom{10}{k} \left(\frac{1}{2}\right)^{10}$

(d) $\displaystyle\sum_{k=3}^{10} \binom{10}{k} \left(\frac{1}{4}\right)^k \left(\frac{3}{4}\right)^{10-k}$

2. Find the probability of exactly two tails in five tosses of an unbiased coin.

3. Find the probability of exactly two heads in five tosses of an unbiased coin.

4. An automobile agency knows that, if a new car is sold, then the probability is $\frac{2}{3}$ that it is sold on the installment plan. What is the probability that exactly seven out of the next ten new cars sold will be sold on the installment plan?

5. Find the probability of scoring over 75% on a true-false examination of ten questions by merely guessing. (Assume that there is no penalty for wrong answers and that each question is worth the same number of points.)

6. The probability of a defective in a manufacturing process is 0.05. What is the probability that a sample of five items will contain
   (a) no defectives?   (b) one or more defectives?

7. Find the probability that a family of three children will have
   (a) two boys and one girl;   (b) all girls;
   (c) at least one boy.
   (Assume equal probabilities for a boy or a girl.)

8. If you are interested in recording the sum of the dots that appear, does it make any difference whether you throw one die three times or three dice once? What is the probability that the sum on the three dice is three? seventeen?

9. A certain city street department estimates that the probability of a snow storm on any given day in January is 0.1. Every such storm adds $2000 to the cost of maintaining the city streets. What is the probability that more than $10,000 will be spent during January because of the extra maintenance due to snow? (Assume that there can never be more than one storm per day.)

10. Suppose that we plant 15 tulip bulbs which are equally likely to have red, yellow, or purple flowers. What is the probability that we get
    (a) five red, two yellow, and eight purple tulips?
    (b) five red, six yellow, and four purple tulips?
    (c) no yellow flowers?

11. Given that two unbiased coins are tossed three times, find the probability of getting the same number of heads at each toss.

12. Using the information given in Example 6, find the number of correct identifications the handwriting expert would have to make so that the probability of getting at least that many correct by chance would be no more than 0.05?

13. A production line turns out 100 cars a day. It is known from past experience that an average of 5% of these cars have flaws. If ten are examined and three of these have flaws, estimate the number of cars having flaws in the day's run. What would you conclude about the quality on that particular day?

14. In connection with Example 7, how many men would there have to be for the probability of at least one highly competent man to be $\frac{1}{2}$ or more? to be R or more, $0 < R < 1$?

7.6 ELEMENTARY APPLICATIONS TO GENETICS

Probability theory plays an important role in the study of genetics and heredity. Simple models based on the mathematics which we have developed so far can be used to great advantage. Before investigating the mathematics involved, however, we must understand the basic definitions and concepts of genetics. In the following discussion many simplifications have been made which will be readily apparent to the student of genetics. However, these simplifications do not alter the general mathematical reasoning involved.

The theory of heredity or genetics, originated by G. Mendel, may be defined as "the science concerned with that which young organisms inherit from their parents." The carriers of this "inherited something" are known as *genes* and are linked together in chain-like structures called *chromosomes* which are found in all body cells. With the exception of those in the reproductive cells, called *gametes*, these chromosomes always exist in pairs in cells. Genes which occupy the same position on paired chromosomes are assumed to determine the same characteristics (such as eye color) of the individual involved. In the most general case, each gene of a particular pair can assume one of two forms or *alleles*, say A and a. Thus three different pairs, AA, Aa (there is no distinction between Aa and aA), and aa, can be formed. These combinations are known as *genotypes*. In general, one of the alleles (the one represented by the capital letter) is *dominant*, and the other allele is *recessive*. This simply means that an individual with the Aa genotype will have the same physical appearance as an individual with the AA genotype. The different physical appearances are known as *phenotypes*.

At this point a simple illustration should be helpful. Let A be the gene which determines the ability to taste PTC (phenylthiocarbamate), and let a be the gene for nontasting of PTC. Then A is the dominant gene and a is recessive. The following is a table of possible genotypes and their corresponding phenotypes.

Genotype	Phenotype
AA	Taster
Aa	Taster
aa	Nontaster

Thus there are three genotypes and two phenotypes.

However, the reproductive cells (gametes), as mentioned above, do not contain pairs of chromosomes. Instead, each is, in effect, half of a typical body cell and contains only one chromosome (and therefore only one gene) of each type. Thus an AA-genotype produces only gametes of the A-type, an aa-genotype produces only a-gametes, and an Aa-genotype produces A-gametes and a-gametes in equal numbers.

In the process of reproduction, two gametes (one from the male and one from the female) fuse together to form a *zygote*, or fertilized egg cell. (It is from this zygote, by a process of cellular division, that the individual eventually

Mating	Offspring	
	Genotype	Proportion for mating specified
$AA \times AA$	AA	$1 \cdot 1 = 1$
$Aa \times AA$	$\begin{cases} AA \\ Aa \end{cases}$	$\frac{1}{2} \cdot 1 = \frac{1}{2}$ $\frac{1}{2} \cdot 1 = \frac{1}{2}$
$AA \times Aa$	$\begin{cases} AA \\ Aa \end{cases}$	$1 \cdot \frac{1}{2} = \frac{1}{2}$ $1 \cdot \frac{1}{2} = \frac{1}{2}$
$Aa \times Aa$	$\begin{cases} AA \\ Aa \\ aa \end{cases}$	$\frac{1}{2} \cdot \frac{1}{2} = \frac{1}{4}$ $\frac{1}{2} \cdot \frac{1}{2} + \frac{1}{2} \cdot \frac{1}{2} = \frac{1}{2}$ $\frac{1}{2} \cdot \frac{1}{2} = \frac{1}{4}$
$aa \times Aa$	$\begin{cases} aa \\ Aa \end{cases}$	$1 \cdot \frac{1}{2} = \frac{1}{2}$ $1 \cdot \frac{1}{2} = \frac{1}{2}$
$Aa \times aa$	$\begin{cases} aa \\ Aa \end{cases}$	$\frac{1}{2} \cdot 1 = \frac{1}{2}$ $\frac{1}{2} \cdot 1 = \frac{1}{2}$
$aa \times AA$	Aa	$1 \cdot 1 = 1$
$AA \times aa$	Aa	$1 \cdot 1 = 1$
$aa \times aa$	aa	$1 \cdot 1 = 1$

Fig. 7.5. Genotypes and their proportions for various matings.

develops.) Thus each zygote contains a pair of genes which determine a given characteristic—one gene from the father (a paternal gene) and one from the mother (a maternal gene).

The genotype of the zygote depends on chance, and this is the point at which probability theory becomes useful. Let us first look at the various possible matings. (In biology, the symbol $\times$ is used to represent a mating.) Figure 7.5 tabulates the different matings and their possible results. Figure 7.5 indicates that there are six mating possibilities ($AA \times Aa$ is the same as $Aa \times AA$) and that we have assumed that (a) at every occasion, each parental gene has probability $\frac{1}{2}$ of being transmitted, and (b) the successive trials are independent.

A study of Fig. 7.5 gives the impression that genetics can be very complicated, especially when we wish to study whole populations involving many matings. However, if we assume that matings occur randomly in the population (a condition known as *random mating*), our calculations can be greatly simplified by looking at the gametes produced rather than at the genotypes of the parents. For example, if one-half the gametes are A and one-half are a, then clearly we would expect the second generation of our population to be composed of one-fourth AA-individuals, one-half Aa-individuals, and one-fourth aa-individuals.

Let us suppose that the paternal and maternal genes are selected independently and at random from the population of all genes carried by males or females of the parental population. Suppose that the three genotypes AA, Aa, aa occur

Genotype of parent		
AA	Aa	aa
Frequency	d	2h	r

Fig. 7.6. Genotype frequencies.

among males and females in the same frequencies; let d be the frequency of AA, let $2h$ be the frequency of Aa, and let r be the frequency of aa, where $d + 2h + r = 1$. The numbers d, $2h$, r are called the *genotype frequencies*. (See Fig. 7.6.) The numbers $p = d + h$ and $q = h + r$ are called the *gene frequencies* of A and a, respectively. Clearly p is the probability of selecting at random an A gene, and q is the probability of selecting an a gene, where $p + q = 1$.

Now the probability that an offspring belongs to genotype AA is p^2, since the two selections are independent and in each the probability of an A is p. Similarly, the probability that an offspring belongs to genotype aa is q^2, and the probability that an offspring belongs to Aa is $2pq$ since Aa can occur in two ways (either A first and a second, or conversely, each with probability pq). Thus, under random mating conditions, an offspring belongs to the genotypes AA, Aa, and aa with probabilities p^2, $2pq$, and q^2, respectively. (This is illustrated in Fig. 7.7.)

First-generation genotype of offspring (sons and daughters)		
AA	Aa	aa
Frequency	p^2	$2pq$	q^2

Fig. 7.7. Genotype frequencies of first-generation offspring.

Let us note the gene frequencies for the first-generation offspring. The gene frequency of A is $p^2 + pq = p(p + q) = p \cdot 1 = p$, and the gene frequency of a is $pq + q^2 = (p + q)q = 1 \cdot q = q$. Thus the gene frequencies are unchanged. Since the genotype of the first-generation offspring depended only on the gene frequencies, the second-generation offspring (and all succeeding generations) will be of genotypes AA, Aa, aa with probabilities p^2, $2pq$, and q^2 respectively. (See Fig. 7.8.) These results lead us to the following statement, known as the Hardy-Weinberg Law.

Hardy-Weinberg Law. In the case of random mating, gene frequency will remain the same indefinitely and, as a result, the genotype distribution is stable after one generation.

It should be observed that this result is based on a mathematical model which involves certain assumptions. In practice, the assumption of random mating is

Genotype of kth generation $(k \geq 1)$		
	AA	Aa	aa
Frequency	p^2	$2pq$	q^2

Fig. 7.8. Genotype frequencies of the kth generation.

not valid (only approximately for large populations), and deviations will occur. In fact, the gene frequencies p and q will change from generation to generation, and the genetic composition will slowly change. The following examples illustrate the Hardy-Weinberg Law.

EXAMPLE 1. All parents are of type AA. Then $d = 1$, $h = r = 0$, and $p = 1, q = 0$.

EXAMPLE 2. All parents are of genotype Aa. Then $d = r = 0$ and $2h = 1$, and $p = q = \frac{1}{2}$; hence, for the first generation, $p^2 = \frac{1}{4}$, $2pq = \frac{1}{2}$, and $q^2 = \frac{1}{4}$.

EXAMPLE 3. If $d = r = \frac{1}{4}$ and $2h = \frac{1}{2}$, then $p = q = \frac{1}{2}$; and $p^2 = \frac{1}{4}$, $2pq = \frac{1}{2}$, and $q^2 = \frac{1}{4}$ for the first-generation offspring.

EXAMPLE 4. If $d = r = \frac{1}{3}$ and $2h = \frac{1}{3}$, then $p = q = \frac{1}{2}$, and the first-generation of offspring has genotypes AA, Aa, and aa occurring with probabilities $\frac{1}{4}, \frac{1}{2}, \frac{1}{4}$, respectively.

The sex of a human offspring is determined by two chromosomes. Every female has two X chromosomes, and every male has one X and one Y. These chromosomes are called *sex chromosomes*. The mother transmits an X chromosome and the father transmits either an X chromosome or a Y chromosome. Hence, the sex of an offspring is determined by the father, in whom male and female gametes are produced in equal numbers (the numbers are only approximately equal, but for convenience we assume them to be equal).

Previously we said that all genes appear in pairs with the notable exception of those genes carried on the X chromosome of a male, which have no corresponding genes on the Y chromosome. Such genes carried on the X chromosome are called *sex-linked* genes. A female, since she is XX, has a pair of sex-linked genes, but a male, being XY, has only one of each of these genes. This fact has some important consequences. If *sl* denotes a sex-linked gene carried in the X chromosome and if $+$ denotes the other allelomorph, then a woman may be *sl sl*, *sl* $+$, or $++$ with respect to the two alleles *sl* and $+$. On the other hand, a man can only be *sl* or $+$. Thus, for a man, *sl*, if present as either a dominant or recessive gene, always manifests itself in the physical characteristics of the man. There are two possibilities for a woman as follows. If the gene *sl* is dominant, then *sl sl* and *sl* + genotypes exhibit the characteristic; if the gene is recessive, then the characteristic appears only in *sl sl* genotypes.

Typical sex-linked genes that are carried on the *X* chromosome are those causing red-green color blindness, hemophilia, and a rickets-like bone abnormality. Observe that a man cannot pass these hereditary abnormalities on to a son since the son must receive the *Y* chromosome from his father. However, a father can transmit these abnormalities to his daughter, who can pass them on to her son. A mother, even though she may not exhibit these abnormalities herself, can transmit them to a son who will always exhibit the associated physical characteristics.

EXAMPLE 5. Let *a* denote the recessive gene which causes hemophilia and let *A* denote the dominant normal allelomorph. If the mother of a child is known to be a carrier, that is, *Aa*, then the probability that a son will inherit hemophilia is $\frac{1}{2}$, since he will receive either an *A* or an *a* gene from his mother. If the mother is *Aa* and the father is *a*, then a daughter has probability $\frac{1}{2}$ of being *aa*, and hence afflicted with hemophilia (this, for some reason which is still unclear, does not seem to happen). The daughter also has probability $\frac{1}{2}$ of being *Aa*, since she must inherit the *a* gene from her father. On the other hand, a normal father cannot have a daughter who exhibits the disease.

EXAMPLE 6. A color-blind man marries a woman who appears to be normal. What is the probability that a son will be color-blind? That a daughter will be color-blind? That an offspring will be color-blind?

To answer these questions, let *a* denote the recessive gene that causes color blindness. Then the father is *a*, and the mother may be *AA* or *Aa*. Let M_{AA} and M_{Aa} denote the events that the mother is in the genotypes *AA* and *Aa*, respectively. Let C_s and C_d denote the events that a son or a daughter, respectively, are color-blind. Then p_s, the probability that a son is color-blind, is computed thus:

$$p_s = P(C_s \mid M_{AA})P(M_{AA}) + P(C_s \mid M_{Aa})P(M_{Aa}) \tag{1}$$
$$= 0 \cdot \tfrac{1}{2} + \tfrac{1}{2} \cdot P(M_{Aa}) = \tfrac{1}{2}P(M_{Aa}).$$

Similarly, the probability, p_d, that a daughter is color-blind is found thus:

$$p_d = P(C_d \mid M_{AA})P(M_{AA}) + P(C_d \mid M_{Aa})P(M_{Aa}) \tag{2}$$
$$= 0 \cdot \tfrac{1}{2} + \tfrac{1}{2} \cdot P(M_{Aa}) = \tfrac{1}{2}P(M_{Aa}).$$

Since we are assuming either sex is equally likely for an offspring, the probability, p, that an offspring is color-blind is

$$p = p_s \cdot \tfrac{1}{2} + p_d \cdot \tfrac{1}{2} = \tfrac{1}{2}P(M_{Aa}). \tag{3}$$

Equations (1), (2), and (3) all involve the unknown term $P(M_{Aa})$. To calculate this quantity, it is necessary to know the family history of the woman. If the woman comes from a family having no trace of color blindness in the past, then

$P(M_{Aa})$ should be very small and p_s, p_d, and p will also be small. On the other hand, if the woman's mother was known to be Aa and her father was normal, then $p_s = p_d = p = \frac{1}{4}$ since $P(M_{Aa}) = \frac{1}{2}$ in this case. For the effect of mutations, which we are ignoring here, see Example 8.

EXAMPLE 7. Suppose that the man and woman of Example 6 have a family of three children. What is the probability that exactly two of the three children are color-blind?

To solve this problem, we assume that the three children constitute three Bernoulli trials where a success means that a child is color-blind. This assumption seems reasonable (provided that we ignore the possible effects of mutations) since the color blindness of each child depends only on the genes of his parents and since each child has the same probability $p = \frac{1}{2}P(M_{Aa})$ of being color-blind. Thus we are asking for the probability of two successes in three Bernoulli trials with the probability of success being p. The desired probability is

$$\binom{3}{2} p^2(1 - p) = 3p^2(1 - p). \tag{4}$$

If $P(M_{Aa}) = \frac{1}{2}$, then $p = \frac{1}{4}$ and (4) becomes $\frac{9}{64}$.

In the same manner as above we could calculate the probabilities for 0, 1, or 3 color-blind offspring.

Thus far, we have not discussed the possible effect of mutations. These tend to keep the strict Hardy-Weinberg Law from being exactly true and cause shifts in the genetic composition of populations. The following example illustrates that effects due to mutations can be quite spectacular. (This example is based on one on page 115 in the book by Parzen [5].)

EXAMPLE 8. A woman whose family has no history of hemophilia marries a normal man. Their first child, a son, has hemophilia. The parents are then worried that if they have additional male children, these children also willl have hemophilia. Is this worry justified?

At first glance it would appear that since there is no history of hemophilia in the family, the wife is not a carrier, and that the first son was a mutant. Further, it is known that hemophilia mutants occur about once in 50,000 gametes. Thus it would appear that the probability that the second son would have hemophilia should be about $\frac{1}{50000}$, the probability that he is a mutant. Unfortunately, this is not the case if we are willing to assume that the mother could also be a mutant.

We shall employ the notation of Example 6; in addition, let H_i denote the event that the ith son has hemophilia, $i = 1, 2$. Then we wish to calculate

$$P(H_2 \mid H_1) = \frac{P(H_2 \cap H_1)}{P(H_1)}.$$

Let m be the probability of a mutation of the X chromosome (about $\frac{1}{50000}$). Since the mother comes from a family free of hemophilia, it seems reasonable to assume that the only way she could be a carrier is that one of her two X chromosomes has mutated so that she is in the genotype Aa. Since she has two X chromosomes, the probability that exactly one of them is a mutant is $\binom{2}{1} m(1-m) = 2(m - m^2)$. (We can assume that both chromosomes are not mutants, since the mother would then have hemophilia.) Then

$$P(H_1 \cap H_2) = P(M_{Aa} \cap H_1 \cap H_2) + P(M_{AA} \cap H_1 \cap H_2)$$
$$= P(H_2 \mid H_1 \cap M_{Aa})P(H_1 \cap M_{Aa})$$
$$+ P(H_2 \mid H_1 \cap M_{AA})P(H_1 \cap M_{AA})$$
$$= P(H_2 \mid H_1 \cap M_{Aa})P(H_1 \mid M_{Aa})P(M_{Aa})$$
$$+ P(H_2 \mid H_1 \cap M_{AA})P(H_1 \mid M_{AA})P(M_{AA}),$$

since the mother is either AA or Aa. Now we assume that

$$P(H_2 \mid H_1 \cap M_{Aa}) = \tfrac{1}{2},$$
$$P(H_2 \mid H_1 \cap M_{AA}) = m,$$
$$P(H_1 \mid M_{Aa}) = \tfrac{1}{2},$$
$$P(H_1 \mid M_{AA}) = m,$$
$$P(M_{Aa}) = 2m(1 - m),$$
$$P(M_{AA}) = 1 - 2m(1 - m).$$

That the above are assumptions should be apparent because we are neglecting in some the possible effects of mutations (the first and third) and in others we are, of course, ignoring the possibility of earlier but hidden mutations (the fifth). Then

$$P(H_1 \cap H_2) = \tfrac{1}{2} \cdot \tfrac{1}{2} \cdot 2m(1 - m) + m \cdot m \cdot [1 - 2m(1 - m)]$$
$$= \frac{m}{2}(1 - 4m^2 + 4m^3).$$

Next,

$$P(H_1) = P(H_1 \mid M_{Aa})P(M_{Aa}) + P(H_1 \mid M_{AA})P(M_{AA})$$
$$= \tfrac{1}{2} \cdot 2m(1 - m) + m[1 - 2m(1 - m)]$$
$$= m(1 - m) + m - 2m^2 + m^3 = 2m - 3m^2 + m^3.$$

Thus

$$P(H_2 \mid H_1) = \frac{[1 - 4m^2 + 4m^3]}{2[2 - 3m + m^2]}.$$

Then, if $m = \frac{1}{50000}$, $P(H_2 \mid H_1) = 0.25008$, which is approximately $\tfrac{1}{4}$.

EXERCISES

1. Given that parents of genotypes AA and aa are mixed in equal numbers and that there are no parents of genotype Aa, show that
   (a) $d = r = \frac{1}{2}, h = 0$;   (b) $p = q = \frac{1}{2}$;
   (c) the probabilities of first-generation offspring of genotypes AA, Aa, aa are $\frac{1}{4}$, $\frac{1}{2}$, $\frac{1}{4}$, respectively.

2. Given that parents of genotypes AA and aa occur in equal numbers, show that
   (a) $d = r$, $0 < h \leq \frac{1}{2}$;   (b) $p = q = \frac{1}{2}$;
   (c) the probabilities of first-generation offspring of genotypes AA, Aa, aa are $\frac{1}{4}$, $\frac{1}{2}$, $\frac{1}{4}$, respectively.

3. Find the genotype distribution of the second generation in Exercise 1. Find the genotype distribution of the second generation in Exercise 2. Explain your answers.

4. Show that, under random mating, not more than half the population belongs to genotype Aa. When does half the population belong to this genotype?

5. A normal male marries a normal appearing woman. Find the probabilities that
   (a) a son is colorblind,   (b) a daughter is colorblind,
   (c) an offspring is colorblind.

6. Amaurotic idiocy is a fatal condition in infants resulting from a defect in the chemistry of the brain cells. It is caused by a rare recessive gene which is not sex-linked. A young couple have had an amaurotic baby. Find the probability that if they have another baby, it will be affected.

7. Let a be a sex-linked gene and let A be the normal allelomorph. Assume random mating and let the frequencies of the genotypes AA, Aa, and aa in the female population be u, $2v$, w, respectively. Let $p = u + v$, $q = v + w$. Let p' and q' denote the frequencies of the two male genotypes A and a, respectively.
   (a) Given that p'_1 and q'_1 denote the probabilities that a male descendent is of type A and a, respectively, show that $p'_1 = p$ and $q'_1 = q$.
   (b) Given that $u_1, 2v_1, w_1$ denote the probabilities of a female descendent belonging to genotypes AA, Aa, aa, respectively, show that

$$u_1 = pp', \qquad 2v_1 = pq' + qp', \qquad w_1 = qq'.$$

   (c) Using part (b) show that

$$p_1 = u_1 + v_1 = \tfrac{1}{2}(p + p'), \qquad q_1 = v_1 + w_1 = \tfrac{1}{2}(q + q').$$

   (d) Combine (a) and (c) to show that

$$p'_1 - p_1 = \tfrac{1}{2}(p - p'), \qquad q'_1 - q_1 = \tfrac{1}{2}(q - q').$$

   Interpret the above result.
   (e) Continue the process started above to the second generation. [In general, it can be shown that $p_n \to \alpha$, $p'_n \to \alpha$, $q_n \to \beta$, $q'_n \to \beta$, so that $u_n \to \alpha^2$, $2v_n \to 2\alpha\beta$, $w_n \to \beta^2$, where $\alpha = \frac{1}{3}(2p + p')$, $\beta = \frac{1}{3}(2q + q')$. This means that if a recessive sex-linked defect occurs among males with frequency α, it will occur among females with frequency approximately α^2.]

8. Some genes are lethal. For example, platinum fur in foxes is caused by a dominant gene, which we may call P. All PP foxes die during gestation, $P+$ ($+$ denotes the normal allele) foxes have platinum coats, and $++$ foxes have silver coats. This gene is also not sex-linked. (Actually the gene P is dominant for color and recessive for death during gestation.)

   (a) In a $P+ \times P+$ mating, find the probability of a platinum fox. A silver fox.

   (b) In a $P+ \times ++$ mating, find the probability of a platinum fox. A silver fox.

   (c) Let $u = 0$, $2v$, w denote the frequencies with which the genotypes PP, $P+$, $++$, respectively, appear in the total population of platinum and silver foxes. What are the frequencies p and q of the genes P and $+$ in this population?

   (d) Assuming random mating, show that the frequencies u_1, $2v_1$, w_1 of the genotypes PP, $P+$, $++$ in the first generation of offspring will be $u_1 = 0$, $2v_1 = 2pq$, $w_1 = q^2$.

   (e) Use (d) to show that the gene frequencies p_1 and q_1 of the genes P and $+$ in the first generation of offspring will be $p_1 = pq$, $q_1 = pq + q^2 = q$.

   (f) If we let u_n, $2v_n$, w_n denote the frequencies of the genotypes PP, $P+$, $++$ in the nth generation of offspring and let p_n, q_n denote the frequencies of the genes P and $+$ in the nth generation, show that $u_n = 0$, $2v_n = 2p_{n-1}q_{n-1}$, $w_n = q_{n-1}^2$ and that $p_n = p_{n-1}q_{n-1}$, $q_n = q_{n-1}$.

   (g) Use the results of (e) and (f) to show, by induction, that $p_n = pq^n$ and $q_n = q$. This shows that $p_n \to 0$ as n becomes large, and hence the $P+$ genotype will tend to die out unless there are mitigating forces such as nonrandom mating and mutations, which are present in this case.

Exercises 9, 10, and 11 use the concept of a matrix.

9. Denote the genotypes AA, Aa, aa by 1, 2, 3, respectively. Let

$$p_{ij} \ (1 \le i \le 3, \ 1 \le j \le 3)$$

   be the conditional probability of an offspring of genotype j given that the male parent is of genotype i.

   (a) Compute these nine probabilities p_{ij}, assuming that the probabilities for the other parent to be of genotype 1, 2, 3 are p^2, $2pq$, q^2, respectively.

   (b) Form the matrix P_1 whose ijth entry is p_{ij}. What is the sum of the ith row $(1 \le i \le 3)$ of the matrix P_1?

10. Show that the conditional probability of a grandson to be of genotype j, given that the grandfather is of genotype i, is $p_{ij}^{(2)} = p_{i1}p_{1j} + p_{i2}p_{2j} + p_{i3}p_{3j}$. Compare this with the ijth entry of the matrix $P_2 = P_1^2$. What generalizations does this suggest?

11. Show that if a son is of genotype AA, then the (conditional) probability that the father is of genotype Aa is p_{12}, the 1, 2th entry of the matrix P_1. Generalize this by showing that the conditional probability that a father is of genotype j, if it is known that the son is of genotype i, is p_{ij}, the ijth entry of P_1.

12. Consider only $AA \times Aa$ matings.

   (a) Among all families having exactly two children, show that $\frac{1}{4}$ of the families have two AA children, $\frac{1}{2}$ of the families have one AA and one Aa child, and $\frac{1}{4}$ of the families have two Aa children.

(b) Among families having exactly three children, show that $\frac{1}{8}$ will have three AA children, $\frac{3}{8}$ will have two AA and one Aa children, $\frac{3}{8}$ will have one AA and two Aa children, and $\frac{1}{8}$ will have three Aa children.

Note the relation between these proportions and the formal expansion

$$[\tfrac{1}{2}AA + \tfrac{1}{2}Aa]^3 = \tfrac{1}{8}(AA)^3 + \tfrac{3}{8}(AA)^2(Aa) + \tfrac{3}{8}(AA)(Aa)^2 + \tfrac{1}{8}(Aa)^3.$$

[By a formal expansion we mean the following: the binomial expression $[\tfrac{1}{2}x + \tfrac{1}{2}y]^3$ is expanded and the quantity (AA) is substituted for x in the resulting expression and (Aa) is substituted for y.] Compare the coefficients here with the probabilities found in part (b). Obtain a formal expansion for $[\tfrac{1}{2}AA + \tfrac{1}{2}Aa]^2$.

BIBLIOGRAPHICAL NOTES

The conditional probability model for medical diagnoses presented in Example 5 of Section 7.3 was given by Warner, *et al.* [1] and was applied there in a study of congenital heart diseases. Various other models along these lines have appeared in the literature, for example, the papers by Overall and Williams [2] and Overall and Gorham [3]. The model for determining disputed authorship was adapted from material in the book by Mosteller and Wallace [4]. Example 6 of Section 7.5 was given in Pascal and Suttell [6]; the treatment here was suggested by an exercise in Parzen [5]. Example 7 of Section 7.5 was taken from a note by Deutsch and Madow [7]. The book by Parzen [5] was responsible for suggesting two other examples, the first half of Example 8 of Section 7.5 and Example 8 of Section 7.6. In general, the discussion of genetical applications follows along the lines of that given in Feller [8].

BIBLIOGRAPHY

1. H. R. WARNER, A. F. TORONTO, L. G. VEASEY, and R. STEPHENSON, "A Mathematical Approach to Medical Diagnosis," *Journal of the American Medical Association* **177,** 177–183 (1961).
2. J. E. OVERALL and C. M. WILLIAMS, "Conditional Probability Program for Diagnosis of Thyroid Function," *Journal of the American Medical Association* **183,** 307–313 (1963).
3. J. E. OVERALL and D. R. GORHAM, "A Pattern Probability Model for the Classification of Psychiatric Patients," *Behavioral Science* **8,** 108–116 (1963).
4. F. MOSTELLER and D. L. WALLACE, *Inference and Disputed Authorship: The Federalist,* Reading, Mass.: Addison-Wesley, 1964.
5. E. PARZEN, *Modern Probability Theory and Its Application,* New York: Wiley, 1960.
6. G. R. PASCAL and B. SUTTELL, "Testing the Claims of a Graphologist," *Journal of Personality* **16,** 192–197 (1947).
7. K. W. DEUTSCH and W. G. MADOW, "A Note on the Appearance of Wisdom in Large Bureaucratic Organizations," *Behavioral Science* **6,** 72–78 (1961).
8. W. FELLER, *An Introduction to Probability Theory and its Applications,* Vol. I, 2nd ed., New York: Wiley, 1957.

CHAPTER 8

Random Variables

8.1 INTRODUCTION

Often we are not concerned with the actual outcome of an experiment but rather with some real number associated with each outcome. For example, in an acceptance sampling experiment, the buyer is interested in the number of defective items in the sample. Another number associated with the sample is the cost of inspecting it; the cost may be small if a large number of defective items is found early, or it may be large if it is necessary to inspect the entire sample. Thus a number connected with the sample may convey the information of greatest interest. Further, it is often more convenient to work with real numbers than with elements of an arbitrary sample space. Thus in this chapter we define real-valued functions on sample spaces (such functions are called *random variables*), and we study the outcomes of experiments in terms of these functions. Once we have the idea of a random variable we can introduce its distribution and probability functions and calculate its mean and variance. All these concepts have proved useful not only in the theory of probability, but also in its application, as we shall see later. Finally, we prove the law of large numbers which, for repeated Bernoulli trials, shows that the relative frequency and our assignment of probabilities are (or should be) closely related.

We begin by defining a random variable. Chapter 2 of this book treated functions; in the theory of probability some functions are given a new name as stated in the following definition.

Definition 8.1. A *random variable* is a real-valued function whose domain is a sample space.

Capital letters such as X and Y usually denote random variables. A typical element in the sample space S is usually denoted by s, and the real number associated with s in S is denoted by $X(s)$; thus $X = \{(s, X(s)) \mid s \in S, \ X(s) \in R^1\}$.

It is possible to have many different random variables associated with a given sample space. In a given experiment, the choice of the random variable will depend on the problem to be solved.

EXAMPLE 1. Let $S = \{H, T\}$ and define a random variable X as follows: $X(H) = 1$, $X(T) = -1$. A second random variable on the same sample space can be defined as follows: $Y(H) = 1$, $Y(T) = 0$. The random variable X might be used to describe a coin-tossing game in which a penny is won if a head appears, and a penny is lost if a tail appears. Again, Y might be used to describe the game if a penny is won if a head appears, but no money is lost if a tail appears.

EXAMPLE 2. A die is rolled. A penny is won if a number less than four appears, and a penny is lost if the number on the die is four or greater. A random variable to describe the outcome of this experiment might be defined as follows. Let $S = \{1, 2, 3, 4, 5, 6\}$ be the sample space and define $X(1) = X(2) = X(3) = 1$, $X(4) = X(5) = X(6) = -1$. The value of the random variable describes the gain or loss for each element of the sample space.

EXAMPLE 3. Let $S = \{1, 2, \ldots, 6\} \times \{1, 2, \ldots, 6\}$ and define a random variable X on S by setting $X = \{((x, y), x + y) \mid (x, y) \in S\}$. It is clear that X is a random variable, and that the range of X is the set $\{2, 3, \ldots, 12\}$. If one considers the experiment of rolling two dice, then S is an appropriate sample space, and X has for its values the sum of the dots on the faces of the two dice.

EXAMPLE 4. In an acceptance sampling scheme of Section 6.3, we defined a quantity X which is, in fact, a random variable. The function X was actually defined for each sample of size n from a lot L; and, if s denotes a sample of size n which contains k defectives, then $X(s) = k$.

It is sometimes convenient to express an event in terms of a random variable. For example, the event of throwing a seven in a toss of two dice can be expressed in terms of the random variable X and the sample space S of Example 3 as $\{s \mid s \in S, \ X(s) = 7\}$. This event is clearly the following set of outcomes: $\{(x, y) \mid (x, y) \in S, \ x + y = 7\}$. If only the sum of the numbers on the two dice is of interest, then the entire investigation of the experiment concerns the range of X. Events such as $\{s \mid s \in S, \ X(s) = 2 \text{ or } X(s) = 11\}$ are easily defined and studied in terms of X.

In connection with Example 4 above it should be mentioned that in Section 6.3 we talked about such events as "$X = k$." If we consider X as a random variable, which it is, we see that this event is really the event $\{s \mid s \in S, \ X(s) = k\}$. The notation "$X = k$" is just an abbreviation for the above expression which is clearly a description of a subset of the sample space S. But we shall say more about this later.

We actually encountered in Chapter 6 many random variables even though they were not labeled as such. The following example illustrates another such random variable.

EXAMPLE 5. Consider again Example 2 of Section 6.6 and let $S = \{(a_1, a_2, a_3, a_4, a_5, a_6) \mid a_i$ denotes the number of the cell that marble i occupies, $i = 1, 2, \ldots, 6\}$. Then S contains 5^6 elements and is the sample space used in Example 2 of Section 6.6. Define a function X on S by

$$X\big((a_1, a_2, a_3, a_4, a_5, a_6)\big) = k,$$

if $a_1, a_2, \ldots, a_{k-1}$ are distinct and a_k is the same as a_j, $1 \le j \le k - 1$. For example $(1, 2, 5, 3, 1, 2)$ denotes an element of S and means that the first marble has been placed in the first cell, the second marble in the second cell, the third marble in the fifth cell, the fourth marble in the third cell, the fifth marble in the first cell, and the sixth marble in the second cell. Also

$$X\big((1, 2, 5, 3, 1, 2)\big) = 5.$$

The random variable X has for its value the number of the first marble that is put into a cell which is already occupied. The range of X is $\{2, 3, 4, 5, 6\}$, and, if A_k is the event as given in Example 2 of Section 6.6, then

$$A_k = \{(a_1, a_2, \ldots, a_6) \mid (a_1, a_2, \ldots, a_6) \in S, \ X\big((a_1, a_2, \ldots, a_6)\big) = k\}$$

for $k = 2, 3, 4, 5, 6$.

EXERCISES

1. Toss a die once. Define a random variable which would be a natural one to associate with this experiment. Define a second random variable for this experiment.

2. Consider the first random variable in Exercise 1. What are the elements of the set $\{s \mid s \in S, \ X(s)$ is an even number$\}$? What is the probability of this set?

3. In Example 2, find the following sets.
   (a) $\{s \mid s \in S, \ X(s) \ge 0\}$ (b) $\{s \mid s \in S, \ X(s) \le 0\}$
   (c) $\{s \mid s \in S, \ X(s) < 0\}$ (d) $\{s \mid s \in S, \ X(s) \ge -1\}$
   (e) $\{s \mid s \in S, \ X(s) < -1\}$

4. Find the probability of each of the sets in Exercise 3 if the die is assumed to be unbiased.

5. Using the data given in Example 3, find the probabilities for the events

$$\{s \mid s \in S, \ X(s) = i\}$$

for $i = 2, 3, \ldots, 12$. Are these events disjoint? What is the probability of their union?

6. On the basis of the data in Example 3, show that

$$\{s \mid s \in S, \ X(s) > 2\} = \{s \mid s \in S, \ X(s) \leq 2\}^c$$

and that

$$\{s \mid s \in S, \ X(s) \leq 2\} = \{s \mid s \in S, \ X(s) = 1\} \cup \{s \mid s \in S, \ X(s) = 2\}.$$

From these results calculate $P(\{s \mid s \in S, \ X(s) > 2\})$.

7. Using the data given in Example 2 of Section 6.7, let X denote the number of men who receive their correct hats. Show that X is a random variable. What is the domain of X? What is the range of X?

8. If S denotes the domain of the function X in Exercise 7, find

$$P(\{s \mid s \in S, \ X(s) = k\}), \qquad \text{for} \quad k = 0, 1, 2, \ldots, n.$$

9. Using the data from Example 3 of Section 6.7, let X denote the number of correct matches made by the handwriting expert. Show that X is a random variable and find its domain and range.

10. Let S denote the domain of the random variable X of Exercise 9. What is

$$P(\{s \mid s \in S, \ X(s) \geq 5\})?$$

8.2 SOME IMPORTANT RANDOM VARIABLES

There are some random variables which occur so frequently that they have been given special names. In this section we shall discuss briefly three random variables—Bernoulli, binomial, and hypergeometric—which appear often both in the theory of probability and in its applications.

Definition 8.2. A random variable is called a *Bernoulli random variable* if its range is the set $\{0, 1\}$.

EXAMPLE 1. The random variable Y in Example 1 of Section 8.1 is a Bernoulli random variable, but the random variable X in the same example is not a Bernoulli random variable.

Note that a Bernoulli random variable results in a dichotomy of the original sample space. The reason that we insist that the range of a Bernoulli random variable be the set $\{0, 1\}$ rather than some other two-element set will become clearer after we discuss sums of random variables.

Next we define a binomial random variable.

Definition 8.3. A random variable X defined on the sample space S of a probability space (S, P) is called a *binomial random variable* if and only if
(a) the range of X is the set $\{0, 1, 2, \ldots, n\}$ for some integer n, and
(b) $P(\{s \mid s \in S, \ X(s) = k\}) = \binom{n}{k}p^k(1 - p)^{n-k}$, where $0 \leq k \leq n$, for some number p, $0 < p < 1$.

EXAMPLE 2.   Consider an experiment which consists of n Bernoulli trials, that is, n independent experiments which result either in success or failure.   Set $S_1 = \{s, f\}$ and $S = S_1 \times S_1 \times \cdots \times S_1$ (n factors).   Define a random variable X on S as follows: for each $(x_1, x_2, \ldots, x_n)$ in S, $X((x_1, x_2, \ldots, x_n))$ is the number of values of i for which $x_i = s$.   Thus each value of X is one possible number of successes in n Bernoulli trials.   Since (see Section 7.5) the probability of exactly k successes in n Bernoulli trials is $\binom{n}{k}p^k(1-p)^{n-k}$, where p is the probability of success at each trial, we see that

$$P(\{w \mid w \in S,\ X(w) = k\}) = \binom{n}{k} p^k(1-p)^{n-k}, \qquad 0 \le k \le n.$$

(We have used w to denote elements of S here because s has been used to mean a success.)   Thus we have shown that X is a binomial random variable.

EXAMPLE 3.   Consider again Example 6 of Section 7.5 and let X denote the number of correct indentifications made by the handwriting expert.   If he is just guessing, then X is a binomial random variable with $p = \frac{1}{2}$.   If he has some ability, then X may very well still be a binomial random variable with some other (unknown) value of p.   If $p = \frac{1}{2}$, we showed that $P(\{w \mid w \in S,\ X(w) \ge 5\}) = 0.3770$ in that section.

Another common type of random variable is the *hypergeometric random variable*.   We encountered this random variable in Section 6.3 (see also Section 8.1, Example 4).   This random variable arises very naturally when we sample without replacement from a set containing only two kinds of objects.

> **Definition 8.4.**   A random variable X defined on the sample space S of a probability space (S, P) is a *hypergeometric random variable* if and only if
> (a) the range of X is $\{0, 1, 2, \ldots, n\}$ for some integer n, and
> (b) $P(\{s \mid s \in S,\ X(s) = k\}) = \binom{M}{k}\binom{N-M}{n-k}/\binom{N}{n}$, where N and M are fixed integers with $N \ge n$ and $N \ge M$.

The above definition looks somewhat artificial and unnatural.   If, however, one considers the problem of taking a sample of size n without replacement from an urn containing N objects of which M are of one kind and $N - M$ are of a second kind, then the above expression gives the probability of obtaining exactly k objects of the first kind in the sample.

EXAMPLE 4.   A lake contains 2500 fish of which 1000 have been marked with a red spot.   A random sample of 1000 fish is taken without replacement from the lake.   Let X denote the number of marked fish in such a sample.   Then X is a hypergeometric random variable with $n = 1000$, $N = 2500$, and $M = 1000$.   The range of X is $\{0, 1, 2, \ldots, 1000\}$ and

$$P(\{s \mid s \in S,\ X(s) = k\}) = \binom{1000}{k}\binom{1500}{1000-k}\Big/\binom{2500}{1000}.$$

EXAMPLE 5. A production line produces 100 articles a day. Of these, ten are carefully inspected. If there are three defective items among the 100, what are the probabilities of k defectives in the sample of ten?

To solve this problem we let X denote the number of defectives in the sample and note that X is a hypergeometric random variable. Hence

$$P(\{s \mid s \in S, \ X(s) = k\}) = \binom{3}{k}\binom{97}{10-k} \Big/ \binom{100}{10}. \tag{1}$$

Actually, since there are only three defectives in the entire lot, it is impossible to have more than three defectives in the sample. This is, of course, built into Eq. (1) since $\binom{3}{k} = 0$ if $k > 3$.

We have been struggling along with the notation $\{s \mid s \in S, \ X(s) = k\}$ for some time now. It is convenient at this time to introduce new notation to facilitate the exposition. If X is a random variable on a sample space S, we shall write $\{X = x\}$ as an abbreviation for $\{s \mid s \in S, \ X(s) = x\}$. We shall write $P(X = x)$ as an abbreviation for $P(\{X = x\})$. Finally, we shall write $P(s)$ as an abbreviation for $P(\{s\})$. These abbreviations should cause the reader no difficulties and should indeed, in some cases, make the subject more intuitive. In fact, this is exactly the notation that we employed in Section 6.3.

EXAMPLE 6. Consider the random variable X of Example 5. Using the above notation, Eq. (1) states that

$$P(X = k) = \binom{3}{k}\binom{97}{10-k} \Big/ \binom{100}{10}, \qquad \text{for} \quad k = 0, 1, 2, \ldots, 10.$$

Extensions of the above notation to other important cases will be discussed in the next section.

EXERCISES

1. Let X denote the sum of the dots that appear in a toss of a pair of dice. What is $\{X = 7\}$? What is the set $\{X = 3\}$?

2. An urn contains n balls of which np are white and nq are black, where $p + q = 1$. A random sample of size m is taken with replacement. Let X denote the number of white balls drawn. Show that X is a binomial random variable with

$$P(X = k) = \binom{m}{k} p^k q^{m-k},$$

when p and q have the values given above.

3. A football team has probability 0.7 of winning any given game. If the team plays ten games, what is the probability that the team wins all its games? Exactly seven of its games? Explain the fact that there is a relatively small probability that the team will win exactly seven games, when it appears that this would happen, since

$(0.7) \cdot 10 = 7$. What is the probability that the team will win not more than eight nor less than six games?

4. If an operation is successful, on the average, 99 times out of 100, what is the probability that the 100th patient to be operated on will die? What is the probability that at least one patient out of 100 will die?

5. The quality control engineer of a company estimates that the probability of a defective item in the process is 0.01. If 1000 items are made, what is the probability of not more than ten defectives?

6. A manufacturer is interested in knowing the probability that a lot of N items from his production line will be rejected (the terminology is that used in Section 6.3). Assume that the manufacturing process is under control with a *defective fraction p*, that is, items taken from the production line may be considered as coming from Bernoulli trials with probability p of being defective. Since we take a sample of size n, the procedure is equivalent to n successive Bernoulli trials. If a lot is rejected when $X > c$, show that the probability that the lot is rejected is

$$g(p) = \sum_{k=c+1}^{n} \binom{n}{k} p^k (1 - p)^{n-k}.$$

The probability $g(p)$ is called the *seller's risk (manufacturer's risk)* rather than the quantity $F(p)$ mentioned in Section 6.3.

7. Assume that the acceptance number $c = 3$ and the sample size 100 are used in Exercise 6. Compute the manufacturer's risk.

8. In connection with Example 8 of Section 7.5 define a random variable by letting X_N be the number of live viruses in a sample of v cubic centimeters.
   (a) For each N, show that X_N is a binomial random variable. What is the value of p?
   (b) Find $P(X_N = k), k = 0, 1, 2, \ldots, N$.
   (c) Find the ratio $P(X_N = k)/P(X_{N-1} = k)$.
   (d) Describe the events

$$\{X_N = k\} \qquad \text{and} \qquad \{X_{N-1} = k\}.$$

   Are these events defined on the same probability space?
   (e) Find the value (or values) $\hat{N}$ of N which maximizes the probability $P(X_N = k)$ for a fixed k. This value is called the maximum likelihood estimate of N.

8.3 THE INDUCED PROBABILITY SPACE

In Section 7.5, following Example 5, it was shown that it is possible to start with the probability space (S, P) for n Bernoulli trials and construct from it a probability space (S', P') in which $S' = \{0, 1, 2, \ldots, n\}$. The sample space S' is a set of real numbers. Furthermore, this set of real numbers is the range of the random variable X (see Example 2 of Section 8.2) which is the number of successes in the n Bernoulli trials. This construction can be carried out in all cases, as we shall show in the following theorem.

Theorem 8.1. Let X be a random variable whose domain is the sample space S of a probability space (S, P) and let S' be the range of X (S' is a set of real numbers). Define a new function P', on the subsets of S', as follows:

$$P'(A) = P(\{s \mid s \in S, \; X(s) \in A\}), \qquad A \subset S'. \tag{1}$$

Then (S', P') is a probability space which is called the *probability space induced by* X.

Proof. Since "probability space" in this book means "finite probability space," we must first show that S' is a finite set. Next, we must show that the function P' has the three properties of a probability function as stated in Definition 5.1.

To see that S' is finite, observe first that S is finite. Assume that S is the set $\{a_1, a_2, \ldots, a_n\}$, then, since S' is the range of X, $S' = \{X(a_1), X(a_2), \ldots, X(a_n)\}$, and S' contains at most n real numbers. The number of elements in S' may be less than n because the numbers $X(a_1), X(a_2), \ldots, X(a_n)$ may not all be distinct. In any event, however, S' is finite.

Since P is a nonnegative set function, it follows from the definition of P' in Eq. (1) that $P'(A) \geq 0$ for every A in S'. Next, since S' is the range of X, we have $\{s \mid s \in S, \; X(s) \in S'\} = S$; hence

$$P'(S') = P(\{s \mid s \in S, \; X(s) \in S'\}) = P(S) = 1.$$

Thus P' has properties (1) and (2) of Definition 5.1, and it remains only to show that P' is additive, that is, if $A \cap B = \emptyset$, then

$$P'(A \cup B) = P'(A) + P'(B).$$

Let A and B be two disjoint events in S'. Then

$$\begin{aligned}
P'(A \cup B) &= P(\{s \mid s \in S, \; X(s) \in (A \cup B)\}) \\
&= P(\{s \mid s \in S, \; X(s) \in A \text{ or } X(s) \in B\}) \\
&= P(\{s \mid s \in S, \; X(s) \in A\} \cup \{s \mid s \in S, \; X(s) \in B\}).
\end{aligned}$$

Since A and B are disjoint, the sets $\{s \mid s \in S, \; X(s) \in A\}$ and $\{s \mid s \in S, \; X(s) \in B\}$ are also disjoint. Since P is a probability function, it is additive. From the last equation above we obtain

$$\begin{aligned}
P'(A \cup B) &= P(\{s \mid s \in S, \; X(s) \in A\}) + P(\{s \mid s \in S, \; X(s) \in B\}) \\
&= P'(A) + P'(B),
\end{aligned}$$

by the definition of P' in Eq. (1) above. Thus P' is additive and, hence, is a probability function.▲

It may be worth repeating that, since a random variable is a real-valued function, the probability space induced by a random variable is one in which the elements of the sample space are real numbers.

As we mentioned, the binomial probability space (S', P') discussed in Section 7.5 following Example 5 is exactly the probability space induced by the random variable X in Example 2 of Section 8.2.

The induced probability space is useful because it enables us to replace a possibly awkward descriptive sample space S with a sample space of real numbers. Moreover, at times it allows us to forget completely (or ignore completely) the underlying sample space S. Of course, we must remember that the induced space depends on the random variable at hand; if a different random variable is used, we obtain a different induced probability space. The choice of the random variable usually depends on what information contained in the original sample space is useful to us.

EXAMPLE 1. Let (S, P) be any probability space, and let X be a Bernoulli random variable defined on S. Then the induced probability space is given by $S' = \{0, 1\}$ and
$$P'(1) = P(X = 1), \qquad P'(0) = P(X = 0).$$

If we call the event $\{X = 1\}$ a success, then $P'(1) = p$ is the probability of a success.

EXAMPLE 2. In Model II of Section 6.4 we considered a lake containing N fish of which M were marked. Fish were caught until a predetermined number, k, of marked fish were caught. We choose as a sample space S the various possibilities for the number of fish we would have to catch to get exactly k marked fish; thus $S = \{k, k + 1, \ldots, k + N - M\}$. Actually the sample space S is an induced sample space.

To show that the above statement is true, let X be a random variable defined as follows: $X = n$ if it is necessary to catch n fish to get k marked fish. More precisely, X has the value n if there are exactly $k - 1$ marked fish among the first $n - 1$ fish caught and a marked fish is the nth fish caught. Then the range of X is $\{k, k + 1, \ldots, k + N - M\}$. The underlying probability space is an equiprobable space which, in Model II, is denoted by (S', P'), where S' is the set of all $(k + N - M)$-tuples that are possible in selecting successively without replacement. In Model II we set
$$P(n) = P'(\{s \mid s \in S', \ X(s) = n\}) = P'(X = n).$$

(Remember that here P is the induced probability function and P' is the original.) Thus the probability space (S, P) which we used in the model is exactly an induced probability space.

The preceding example shows that in some cases, although we may want to use the induced sample space, it is helpful to know the original sample space in order to assign probabilities. The next example illustrates a situation where we work exclusively with the induced sample space; in fact, the underlying sample space is rather hypothetical at best.

EXAMPLE 3. In Example 6 of Section 7.3 we discussed the Mosteller-Wallace Model for determining disputed authorship. We were interested in such events as "x occurrences of a specified word in an essay containing a certain number of words." If we let X denote the number of such occurrences in a paper, then X is a random variable even though it is not at all clear on what sample space X is defined. (One might consider all possible essays of the given length, for instance.) In this example we used such notation as $P(x \mid H)$ and $P(x \mid M)$ to indicate the conditional probabilities of x occurrences of the word, given that Hamilton and Madison, respectively, wrote the essay. In terms of the random variable X these events would be written $P(X = x \mid H)$ and $P(X = x \mid M)$. In that particular example there is no advantage in using this notation. However, in Example 7 of Section 7.4 we encounter occurrences of two or more words. It is convenient to be able to assign a different random variable to each word. For instance, if we let X denote the number of occurrences of one word and Y denote the number of occurrences of another word, then the events "x occurrences of the first word" and "y occurrences of the second" are unambiguously given by $\{X = x\}$ and $\{Y = y\}$, respectively. In that example we assumed that $\{X = x\}$ and $\{Y = y\}$ are independent. Equations (8) and (9) of that section become

$$P(\{X = x\} \cap \{Y = y\} \mid H) = P(X = x \mid H)P(Y = y \mid H),$$
$$P(\{X = x\} \cap \{Y = y\} \mid M) = P(X = x \mid M)P(Y = y \mid M).$$

Note that if we do not use the random variable notation, $P(3 \mid H)$ is ambiguous and could mean either $P(X = 3 \mid H)$ or $P(Y = 3 \mid H)$. Thus the random variable notation proves useful just in keeping track of different types of quantities.

The above discussion suggests the following problem. Given a (finite) subset S' of the real numbers and a probability function P' defined on the subsets of S', is it always possible to find a probability space (S, P) and a random variable X such that (S', P') is the probability space induced by X? The answer to this question is yes; however, the construction we shall give is not very interesting, especially from the point of view of applications.

We can construct such a probability space (S, P) by letting $S = S'$, $P = P'$, and X be the function such that $X(s) = s$ for each s. Then it is trivial to check that the range of X is S' and that $P'(A) = P(\{s \mid s \in S, X(s) \in A\})$. In fact, $\{s \mid s \in S, X(s) \in A\} = A$ since $X(s) = s$, and hence $P'(A) = P(A) = P(\{s \mid s \in S, X(s) \in A\})$. As noted before, this construction is not of great interest. We usually use the induced space because its sample space is composed of real numbers, a fact which facilitates the assignment of values to certain outcomes (see Section 8.5).

EXERCISES

1. Suppose that a random variable X is such that $X(s) = a$, a constant, for each $s \in S$. Find the induced probability space (S', P'). What must be the value of $P'(\{a\})$?

2. Let X be a hypergeometric random variable. Describe the induced probability space.

3. Find the induced probability space corresponding to the random variable X in Exercise 7 of Section 8.1.

4. Find the induced probability space corresponding to the random variable X in Exercise 9 of Section 8.1.

5. A pair of unbiased dice are rolled. If X denotes the sum of the dots which appear on the two dice, find the probability space (S', P') induced by X.

6. A fair coin is flipped twice. If X denoted the number of heads which appears, find the probability space induced by X.

7. A balanced die is thrown. If the number which appears is less than four, it is tossed again. Let X be the sum of the numbers which appear if the die is tossed twice or the number which appears on the first toss if it is thrown only once.
   (a) Find a sample space S for the experiment.
   (b) Find the probability space (S', P') induced by X.

8.4 DISTRIBUTION FUNCTIONS AND PROBABILITY FUNCTIONS

Frequently we wish to compute the probability that a random variable has a value less than or equal to some specified number, rather than the probability that X is equal to a given number. For example, we may be interested in the probability of the occurrence of five or fewer defectives in a lot of 1000 manufactured items for which it is known that the probability that each item is defective is p, where $0 < p < 1$. This problem leads to a binomial probability space with $n = 1000$ and p as given. If we define X as the number of defectives in the lot, then the desired probability is $P(X \leq 5)$.

In general, if X is defined on the sample space S of a probability space (S, P), then the event "X is less than or equal to a given number x" is the subset of S which consists of all those elements s of S for which $X(s) \leq x$, that is, the set $\{s \mid s \in S, X(s) \leq x\}$. This event is usually shortened to $\{X \leq x\}$ for convenience. Furthermore, the probability of this event is usually denoted by

$$F(x) = P(\{s \mid s \in S, X(s) \leq x\}) = P(X \leq x).$$

Definition 8.5. Let X be a random variable defined on the sample space S of a probability space (S, P). Then the function F whose value for each real number x is $F(x) = P(X \leq x)$ is called the (*cumulative*) *distribution function* for the random variable X. If more than one random variable is under consideration, it is customary to denote the distribution function of X by F_X in order to indicate its dependence on X.

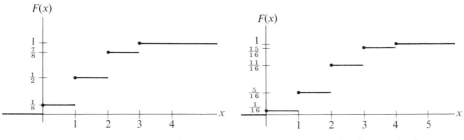

Fig. 8.1. Graph of F in Eq. (1) for $n = 3$ and $p = \frac{1}{2}$.

Fig. 8.2. Graph of F in Eq. (1) for $n = 4$ and $p = \frac{1}{2}$.

The distribution functions of binomial random variables are tabulated for many values of the parameters n and p. If X is a binomial random variable,

$$F(x) = P(X \le x) = \sum_{k=0}^{[x]} \binom{n}{k} p^k(1 - p)^{n-k}, \qquad (1)$$

where the symbol $[x]$ denoted the greatest integer less than or equal to x. For example, if $x = \frac{7}{2}$, $[x] = [\frac{7}{2}] = 3$; if $x = 3$, $[x] = [3] = 3$; if $x = 0.1$, $[x] = [0.1] = 0$; if $x = -2$, $[x] = [-2] = -2$; if $x = -2.5$, $[x] = [-2.5] = -3$. The formula in Eq. (1) for $F(x)$ is true provided that it is understood that whenever $[x] < 0$, the quantity on the right-hand side of Eq. (1) has the value zero.

Figures 8.1 and 8.2 show the graphs of the function F in (1) for two sets of values of n and p. These functions are frequently called *step functions* because of the appearance of their graphs.

Actually, for finite probability spaces (which are the only ones we are considering), the distribution function of a random variable X is always a step function. Moreover, as shown in the above figures, the distribution function increases as we go from left to right. The principal facts about distribution functions are summarized in the following theorem.

Theorem 8.2. Let X be a random variable defined on the sample space S of a (finite) probability space (S, P). Let $x_1 < x_2 < \cdots < x_n$ be the distinct points in the range of X arranged in increasing order. Then the distribution function F of X has the following properties:
(a) $F(x) = 0$ for $x < x_1$, $F(x) = 1$ for $x \ge x_n$, $0 \le F(x) \le 1$ for $x_1 \le x \le x_n$;
(b) $F(x) \le F(y)$ if $x \le y$;
(c) $P(x < X \le y) = F(y) - F(x)$;
(d) $F(x_k) = F(x_{k-1}) + P(X = x_k)$ for $k = 2, 3, \ldots, n$.

Proof. To show that (a) is true, note that $F(x)$ is the probability $P(X \le x)$ and hence $0 \le F(x) \le 1$ for all x. If $x < x_1$, then

$$\{X \le x\} = \{s \mid s \in S, \ X(s) \le x\}.$$

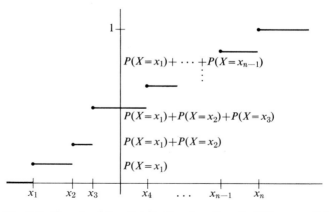

Fig. 8.3. Graph of the distribution function F of Theorem 8.2.

But this last set is the empty set $\emptyset$, since for every $s \in S$, $X(s) \geq x_1 > x$. Thus $P(X \leq x) = F(x) = 0$ for $x < x_1$. If $x \geq x_n$, then $\{X \leq x\} = S$, since $X(s) \leq x_n$ for every point s in S. Thus $F(x) = P(X \leq x) = P(S) = 1$ for $x \geq x_n$.

To show that (b) is true, note that $\{X \leq x\} \subset \{X \leq y\}$, since if $X(s) \leq x$ and $x \leq y$, then $X(s) \leq y$. Thus by part (5) of Theorem 5.1,

$$F(x) = P(X \leq x) \leq P(X \leq y) = F(y).$$

Part (c) follows from the fact that $\{x < X \leq y\} = \{X \leq y\} - \{X \leq x\}$, and hence, by part (4) of Theorem 5.1,

$$P(x < X \leq y) = P(\{X \leq y\} - \{X \leq x\}) = P(X \leq y) - P(X \leq x)$$
$$= F(y) - F(x).$$

Let us consider part (d). The set $\{x_{k-1} < X \leq x_k\} = \{X = x_k\}$, since X does not assume a value between x_{k-1} and x_k. Thus by part (c),

$$F(x_k) - F(x_{k-1}) = P(x_{k-1} < X \leq x_k) = P(X = x_k).$$

Hence

$$F(x_k) = P(X = x_k) + F(x_{k-1}). \blacktriangle$$

The function F has value zero for $x < x_1$. On the interval $x_1 \leq x < x_2$, F has the value $P(X = x_1)$, on the interval $x_2 \leq x < x_3$, F has the value $P(X = x_1) + P(X = x_2)$, and so on until on the interval $x_{n-1} \leq x < x_n$, F has the value $P(X = x_1) + P(X = x_2) + \cdots + P(X = x_{n-1})$. Finally, on the interval $x \geq x_n$, F has the value $P(X = x_1) + P(X = x_2) + \cdots + P(X = x_n) = 1$. These facts are shown in the graph in Fig. 8.3.

There is an interesting and useful corollary to part (c) of the above theorem.

Corollary 8.1. Let X be a random variable defined on the sample space S of a probability space (S, P) and let F be the distribution function of X. Then

$$P(X > x) = 1 - F(x). \tag{2}$$

The proof of this corollary is left to the reader (see Exercise 10). This corollary is especially useful when the values of $F(x)$ are tabulated. By subtracting the tabulated value from 1 we get the probability that X is greater than x.

EXAMPLE 1. A production line produces rivets. An average of two rivets per 1000 are improperly made. If a box contains 100 rivets, what is the probability that the box will contain more than one bad rivet?

Let X denote the number of bad rivets in a box of 100. We assume that X is a binomial random variable with $n = 100$, and $p = \frac{2}{1000}$. Then

$$F(1) = \sum_{k=0}^{1} \binom{100}{k} \left(\frac{2}{1000}\right)^k \left(\frac{998}{1000}\right)^{100-k}$$

is the probability of one or less bad rivets in a box, and $1 - F(1)$ is the probability of more than one bad rivet. Now

$$F(1) = \left(\frac{998}{1000}\right)^{100} + 100 \left(\frac{2}{1000}\right)\left(\frac{998}{1000}\right)^{99} = \frac{(998)^{99}}{(1000)^{100}} \cdot 1198 = 0.983.$$

Thus $P(X > 1) = 1 - 0.983 = 0.017$.

EXAMPLE 2. In Section 6.3 we discussed a probability which was called the "seller's risk." In Eq. (9) of that section:

$$P(X > c) = \sum_{k=c+1}^{n} P(X = k) = \sum_{k=c+1}^{n} \frac{\binom{Np}{k}\binom{N - Np}{n - k}}{\binom{N}{n}},$$

where X is a hypergeometric random variable. If F_X is the distribution function of this hypergeometric random variable X, then the seller's risk is

$$1 - F_X(c).$$

Observe that F_X here is the function that was denoted by f in Section 6.3.

Closely connected with the distribution function is the *probability function* of a random variable. We have frequently encountered the probability $P(X = x)$.

This value is frequently denoted by $f(x)$ or $f_X(x)$ and is called the *value at x* of the probability function of X.

Definition 8.6. Let X be a random variable defined on the sample space S of a probability space (S, P). The function f defined on the set of real numbers R^1 by the equation

$$f(x) = P(X = x), \qquad x \in R^1,$$

is called the *probability function* of X.

It should be observed that $f(x) = 0$ for all x which are *not* in the range of X, since, for such x, $\{s \mid s \in S, X(s) = x\} = \emptyset$. If $\{x_1, x_2, \ldots, x_n\}$ is the range of X, then $f(x_i) = P(X = x_i)$ and

$$f(x_1) + f(x_2) + \cdots + f(x_n) = 1.$$

That is, all of the probability is associated with the points $x_1, x_2, \ldots, x_n$ on the real axis. The connections between the distribution function F and the probability function f of a random variable X are given by the following theorem.

Theorem 8.3. Let F and f be the distribution function and the probability function, respectively, for a random variable X, and let $x_1 < x_2 < \cdots < x_n$ be the ordered range of X. Then

(a) $F(x) = \sum\limits_{x_k \le x} f(x_k)$, and

(b) $f(x_k) = F(x_k) - F(x_{k-1})$ for $k = 2, 3, \ldots, n$,

$\quad\ f(x_1) = F(x_1)$.

Proof. Part (a) follows from the comments following the proof of Theorem 8.2. An alternative proof can be given by using part (d) of Theorem 8.2 and induction to show that

$$F(x_k) = P(X = x_1) + \cdots + P(X = x_k) = f(x_1) + \cdots + f(x_k).$$

Part (b) of this theorem follows from part (d) of Theorem 8.2:

$$F(x_k) = F(x_{k-1}) + P(X = x_k), \qquad \text{for} \quad k = 2, 3, \ldots.$$

Thus

$$F(x_k) - F(x_{k-1}) = P(X = x_k) = f(x_k), \qquad \text{for} \quad k = 2, 3, \ldots, n.$$

For $k = 1$,

$$f(x_1) = P(X = x_1) = F(x_1)$$

and hence the theorem is proved. ▲

EXAMPLE 3. As a simple example, consider the function b whose value at k, $0 \leq k \leq n$, is $b(k; n, p)$. Here p and n are fixed, $0 < p < 1$, and $b(k; n, p)$ is as given in Section 7.5. According to Definition 8.6 this function is a probability function since

$$b(k; n, p) = P(X = k) = \binom{n}{k} p^k(1 - p)^{n-k},$$

where X is a binomial random variable. Observe that we must define b for every real number by requiring its value to be zero except for $k = 0, 1, 2, \ldots, n$. Figure 8.4 shows the graph of the probability function b for $n = 3$, $p = \frac{1}{2}$, Fig. 8.5 contains the graph of b for $n = 4$, $p = \frac{1}{2}$, and Fig. 8.6 contains the graph of b for $n = 4$, $p = \frac{1}{3}$. The reader should observe that in Figs. 8.4 through 8.6 we have given the graphs only for nonzero values of the corresponding function b. There is no need to graph the other values, since they are all zero and have no effect on any probabilities.

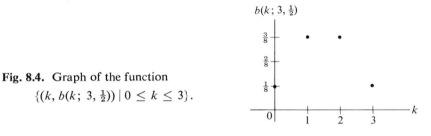

Fig. 8.4. Graph of the function

$$\{(k, b(k; 3, \tfrac{1}{2})) \mid 0 \leq k \leq 3\}.$$

In general, the function $b = \{(k, b(k; n, p)) \mid k \in R^1\}$ is called a binomial probability function. It should be observed that n and p are fixed with $n \geq 1$ and $0 < p < 1$. For different values of n and p, we obtain different binomial probability functions. Often it is said that a random variable X has a binomial distribution. This statement means that X is a binomial random variable, or, equivalently, that its probability function is a binomial probability function. More generally, if we say that a random variable has a certain type of distribution, we mean that the random variable is that type of random variable, or, equivalently, has that type of probability function.

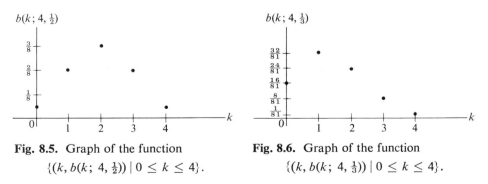

Fig. 8.5. Graph of the function

$$\{(k, b(k; 4, \tfrac{1}{2})) \mid 0 \leq k \leq 4\}.$$

Fig. 8.6. Graph of the function

$$\{(k, b(k; 4, \tfrac{1}{3})) \mid 0 \leq k \leq 4\}.$$

EXERCISES

1. Graph the probability function and the distribution function of the number of spots which will appear on a toss of an unbiased die.

2. An urn contains five white and ten black balls. A ball is drawn at random, and its color is noted. Let X denote the number of black balls drawn in the single draw. Graph the probability function and the distribution function of the random variable X.

3. Repeat Exercise 2 in case the urn contains ten white and five black balls.

4. Repeat Exercise 2 in case the urn contains equal numbers of white and black balls.

5. Let X be a Bernoulli random variable and let p be the probability of success. Graph the probability function and the distribution function of X.

6. Draw the graph of the distribution function F which corresponds to the binomial random variable whose probabilities are graphed in Fig. 8.6.

7. Find the values of the probability function which corresponds to a binomial random variable with $n = 10$ and $p = \frac{1}{3}$.

8. Let X be the random variable whose distribution function is graphed in Fig. 8.1. Determine the following from the graph.
   (a) $P(X < \frac{1}{2})$ (b) $P(X > \frac{1}{2})$ (c) $P(X < 3)$
   (d) $P(2 \leq X \leq 3)$ (e) $P(-2 < X \leq 2)$ (f) $P(|X - 2| > 1)$

9. Determine the same probabilities as in Exercise 8 if X is the random variable whose probability function is graphed in Fig. 8.6.

10. Prove Corollary 8.1.

11. In Exercise 6 of Section 8.2, express the quantity $g(p)$ in terms of the distribution function F of a binomial random variable.

12. For fixed n, M, N set
$$h(k; n, M, N) = \frac{\binom{M}{k}\binom{N - M}{n - k}}{\binom{N}{n}},$$

for $k = 0, 1, 2, \ldots$, minimum (M, n), and define h to have the value zero for other values of k [see Eq. (3) of Section 6.3]. Show that h is a probability function. The function h is called the *hypergeometric probability function*.

13. In Exercise 1, find the set of numbers x such that
   (a) $P(X \leq x) = \frac{1}{2}$,   (b) $P(X \leq x) \geq \frac{1}{2}$,   (c) $P(X \geq x) \geq \frac{1}{2}$.
   (d) Find the intersection M of the sets in parts (b) and (c). (The *median* of a distribution is any number in the set M.)

14. Repeat Exercise 13 for the random variable in Exercise 2.

15. Repeat Exercise 13 for the random variable in Exercise 3.

16. Repeat Exercise 13 for the random variable X whose distribution function is given in Fig. 8.2.

8.5 THE MEAN OF A RANDOM VARIABLE

The concept of average is familiar in everyday life. For example, a student takes three examinations and makes grades x_1, x_2, and x_3 on them. The instructor forms the average

$$\frac{x_1 + x_2 + x_3}{3} = x_1(\tfrac{1}{3}) + x_2(\tfrac{1}{3}) + x_3(\tfrac{1}{3}) \tag{1}$$

of the three grades and uses it to determine the student's grade. Sometimes an unequally weighted average is used. For instance, if the third grade counts twice as much as the first two, then the instructor computes

$$\frac{x_1 + x_2 + 2x_3}{4} = x_1(\tfrac{1}{4}) + x_2(\tfrac{1}{4}) + x_3(\tfrac{2}{4}). \tag{2}$$

Generalizations of these averages are employed in the study of probability spaces (S, P). If the values x_1, x_2, x_3 are taken on by a random variable X with corresponding probabilities p_1, p_2, p_3, then

$$x_1 p_1 + x_2 p_2 + x_3 p_3 \tag{3}$$

is the weighted average, each value being weighted with its probability, of the values x_1, x_2, x_3. These simple examples suggest the following general definition.

Definition 8.7. Let (S, P) be a probability space, and let X be a random variable defined on S. Then the *mean* or *expected value* $E[X]$ of the random variable X is

$$E[X] = \sum_{i=1}^{n} x_i P(X = x_i), \tag{4}$$

where $x_1, x_2, \ldots, x_n$ are the values assumed by the random variable X.

If we let $f(x_i) = P(X = x_i)$, $1 \leq i \leq n$, be the probability function of X, then (4) becomes

$$E[X] = \sum_{i=1}^{n} x_i f(x_i). \tag{5}$$

Furthermore, if we let $p_i = f(x_i)$, $1 \leq i \leq n$, then (5) becomes

$$E[X] = \sum_{i=1}^{n} x_i p_i, \tag{6}$$

and this formula is the generalization of formula (3). Equations (4), (5), and (6) all say the same thing: the mean (expected value or *expectation*) is a weighted average of the values of X, each value being weighted by the probability of the occurrence of this value.

The name "expectation" arose in connection with games of chance. For example, in a coin tossing game in which a penny is won or lost depending on whether a head or a tail appears, a player's expectation is

$$1 \cdot p + (-1) \cdot q = p - q = 2p - 1,$$

where p is the probability that a head will appear and q is the probability that a tail will appear. If the coin is unbiased, that is, if $p = q = \frac{1}{2}$, then the expected value is zero. Such a game is called a fair game. However, if a player plays a single game, he will certainly win or lose. The result of several games may also be a gain or loss. Experience, however, has shown that if the expected value is zero, then the average gain (or loss) which results from a large number of games is approximately zero.

EXAMPLE 1. An unbiased die is tossed once. A sample space S for this experiment is $\{1, 2, 3, 4, 5, 6\}$. Define X as follows: $X(k) = k$ for k in S, that is, the random variable X is the identity function on S. Then $f(k) = P(X = k) = \frac{1}{6}$ for k in S and

$$E[X] = \sum_{k=1}^{6} k(\tfrac{1}{6}) = \frac{1}{6} \sum_{k=1}^{6} k = \frac{7}{2}.$$

EXAMPLE 2. In a roulette game the wheel has 37 numbers, 0, 1, 2, ... , 36, marked on equally spaced slots. A player bets \$1 on a number of his choice, that is, he plays \$1 to play the game. He receives \$36 if the ball comes to rest in his slot; otherwise, he receives nothing. If X denotes the player's net gain, what is his expected gain? Is the game a "fair" game?

The sample space S for this experiment is $\{0, 1, 2, \ldots, 36\}$, and the probability of each elementary event in S is $\frac{1}{37}$. If r is the number selected by the player, then $X(r) = 35$ (if the ball stops in the chosen slot, the player receives \$36, but he has already paid \$1 for the privilege of playing; hence his net gain is \$35). If $k \neq r$, then $X(k) = -1$, since the payer pays \$1 for the privilege of playing. Furthermore, $f(35) = P(X = 35) = \frac{1}{37}$ and $f(-1) = P(X = -1) = \frac{36}{37}$. Hence

$$E[X] = 35(\tfrac{1}{37}) + (-1)(\tfrac{36}{37}) = -\tfrac{1}{37}.$$

Thus roulette is not a "fair" game, since $E[X] < 0$. A casino may pay out large sums in single games, but in the long run the casino is a consistent money maker and the players lose on the average.

EXAMPLE 3. Consider an acceptance sampling experiment in which a lot L of five items contains three good items and two defective ones. A random sample of three items is drawn from the lot. Find the mean number of defectives in samples drawn in this manner.

The reader should refer to Example 1 of Section 7.2. A sample space for this experiment is shown in Fig. 7.1. Let X be the number of defectives in a sample. Then the possible values of X are 0, 1, 2, and Fig. 7.1 shows that $f(0) = P(X = 0) = \frac{1}{10}$, $f(1) = P(X = 1) = \frac{6}{10}$, and $f(2) = P(X = 2) = \frac{3}{10}$. Then

$$E[X] = 0(\tfrac{1}{10}) + 1(\tfrac{6}{10}) + 2(\tfrac{3}{10}) = \tfrac{6}{5}. \tag{7}$$

Thus in a single sample the number of defectives varies from zero to two; in a large number of samples the number of defectives on the average is about $\frac{6}{5}$.

In connection with this example it should be noted that X is a hypergeometric random variable whose range is usually taken to be 0, 1, 2, 3 (since the sample size is 3). But in this example $\{X = 3\}$ is empty, since there are only two defectives in the entire lot. Thus $f(3) = P(X = 3) = 0$ and the term $3 \cdot 0$ which could have been added to the middle of Eq. (7) does not change the value of $E[X]$.

As we observed above, the random variable X of Example 3 is a hypergeometric random variable. It will be useful and a saving of labor to calculate once and for all times the expectation of this random variable, and two other ones, namely, the Bernoulli random variable, and the binomial random variable. It is the purpose of the next three theorems to give the expectations of these three common random variables.

Theorem 8.4. If X is a Bernoulli random variable with parameter p, then $E[X] = p$.

Proof. A Bernoulli random variable with parameter p is a random variable X whose range is $\{0, 1\}$, and such that $P(X = 1) = p$ and $P(X = 0) = 1 - p$. Thus $f(1) = p$ and $f(0) = 1 - p$. Hence

$$E[X] = 0(1 - p) + 1(p) = p. \blacktriangle$$

Theorem 8.5. If X is a binomial random variable with parameters n and p, then $E[X] = np$.

Before proving this theorem let us give a purely heuristic argument as to why it should be true. A binomial random variable arises from Bernoulli random variables as the number of successes in n Bernoulli trials. Theorem 8.4 says that the expected (average) number of successes in one Bernoulli trial is p; thus, if we have n Bernoulli trials, it seems reasonable that the expected number of successes should be np. The following proof does not approach the problem in this manner. However, after we deal with sums of random variables in Section 8.7, we shall be able to prove Theorem 8.5 in essentially the manner indicated above.

Proof of Theorem 8.5. If X is a binomial random variable with parameters n and p, then the range of X is $\{0, 1, 2, \ldots, n\}$ and

$$f(k) = P(X = k) = \binom{n}{k} p^k q^{n-k}, \qquad 0 \le k \le n, \qquad q = 1 - p.$$

Then by Eq. (4),

$$E[X] = \sum_{k=0}^{n} kP(X = k) = \sum_{k=0}^{n} k \binom{n}{k} p^k q^{n-k}$$

$$= \sum_{k=1}^{n} \frac{n!}{(k-1)!(n-k)!} p^k q^{n-k},$$

since the first term of the original sum is zero, and since a factor k can be canceled in the remaining terms of the second expression on the right. Therefore

$$E[X] = np^1 q^{n-1} + n(n-1)p^2 q^{n-2} + \cdots + n \binom{n-1}{k-1} p^k q^{n-k}$$
$$+ \cdots + np^n q^0$$
$$= np \left[p^0 q^{n-1} + (n-1)p^1 q^{n-2} + \cdots + \binom{n-1}{k-1} p^{k-1} q^{n-k} \right.$$
$$\left. + \cdots + p^{n-1} q^0 \right], \qquad (8)$$

since

$$\frac{n!}{(k-1)!(n-k)!} = n \cdot \frac{(n-1)!}{(k-1)!(n-k)!}$$
$$= n \cdot \frac{(n-1)!}{(k-1)![(n-1)-(k-1)]!} = n \binom{n-1}{k-1}.$$

By the binomial theorem (see Theorem 4.7) the terms inside the square brackets on the right-hand side of Eq. (8) are $(p+q)^{n-1} = 1^{n-1} = 1$. Hence $E[X] = np[1] = np.$▲

Theorem 8.6. If X is a hypergeometric random variable with parameters N, M, and n, then $E[X] = n(M/N)$.

If we let $p = M/N$ be the lot fraction defective in the terminology of Section 6.3, then Theorem 8.6 states that $E[X] = np$, the product of the sample size n and the fraction of the lot that is defective. This again seems reasonable since, if M/N is the ratio of defective items to total items and if we select randomly n items, we should get $n(M/N)$ defective items. These heuristic statements do not constitute a proof; a proof is given below.

Proof of Theorem 8.6. If X is a hypergeometric random variable with parameters N, M, and n, then the range of X is $\{0, 1, 2, \ldots, n\}$ and

$$f(k) = P(X = k) = \frac{\binom{M}{k} \binom{N-M}{n-k}}{\binom{N}{n}}, \qquad 0 \le k \le n.$$

By Eq. (4),

$$E[X] = \sum_{k=0}^{n} k \frac{\binom{M}{k}\binom{N-M}{n-k}}{\binom{N}{n}} = \frac{1}{\binom{N}{n}} \sum_{k=1}^{n} k \binom{M}{k}\binom{N-M}{n-k}$$

$$= \frac{1}{\binom{N}{n}} \sum_{k=1}^{n} \frac{M!}{(k-1)!(n-k)!} \binom{N-M}{n-k}$$

$$= \frac{M}{\binom{N}{n}} \sum_{k=1}^{n} \binom{M-1}{k-1}\binom{[(N-1)-(M-1)]}{[(n-1)-(k-1)]}, \tag{9}$$

since (1) $1/\binom{N}{n}$ is a constant, (2) the first term in the second expression on the right is zero and hence a factor of k can be canceled in the remaining terms, (3) $M! = M(M-1)!$, and (4) $x - y = (x-1) - (y-1)$, so that

$$\frac{(M-1)!}{(k-1)!(M-k)!} = \binom{M-1}{k-1} \quad \text{and} \quad \binom{N-M}{n-k} = \binom{[(N-1)-(M-1)]}{[(n-1)-(k-1)]}.$$

If we now let $j = k - 1$ in the right side of Eq. (9), we find that

$$E[X] = \frac{M}{\binom{N}{n}} \sum_{j=0}^{n-1} \binom{M-1}{j}\binom{[(N-1)-(M-1)]}{[(n-1)-j]}. \tag{10}$$

The term

$$\sum_{j=0}^{n-1} \binom{M-1}{j}\binom{[(N-1)-(M-1)]}{[(n-1)-j]}$$

in Eq. (10) is the sum of the numerators of a hypergeometric random variable with parameters $N - 1$, $M - 1$, and $n - 1$. Thus

$$\sum_{j=0}^{n-1} \binom{M-1}{j}\binom{[(N-1)-(M-1)]}{[(n-1)-j]} = \binom{N-1}{n-1}, \tag{11}$$

the number of ways of selecting a sample of size $n - 1$ from a lot of $N - 1$ objects. Combining Eqs. (10) and (11) we have

$$E[X] = \frac{M}{\binom{N}{n}} \binom{N-1}{n-1} = n\frac{M}{N}, \quad \text{since} \quad \frac{\binom{N-1}{n-1}}{\binom{N}{n}} = \frac{n}{N}. \blacktriangle$$

Next we illustrate Theorems 8.5 and 8.6 with two simple examples. After that we will consider some more practical applications.

EXAMPLE 4. If an unbiased coin is tossed 100 times, how many heads should we expect?

The number X of heads in 100 independent tosses is a binomial random variable with parameters $n = 100$ and $p = \frac{1}{2}$. Thus the expected number of heads is $E[X] = np = 100(\frac{1}{2}) = 50$. On the other hand, if the coin is tossed 101 times, the expected number of heads is $101(\frac{1}{2}) = 50\frac{1}{2}$. This, of course, cannot happen, but nevertheless we expect approximately this number of heads in the 101 tosses.

EXAMPLE 5. As in Example 3, a lot L of five items contains three good items and two defective items. A random sample of three is drawn. What is the expected number of defectives?

Actually we solved this problem in Example 3, but we will do so again using Theorem 8.6. If X denotes the number of defectives in the sample, then X is a hypergeometric random variable with $N = 5$, $M = 2$, and $n = 3$. Thus $E[X] = 3(\frac{2}{5}) = \frac{6}{5}$, as is given in Eq. (7).

EXAMPLE 6. Reconsider Example 7 of Section 7.5. There were m bureaucrats each having probability p of making a correct decision. There were n independent decisions to be made and we assumed that each person made his decisions independently of the others. Thus there was probability p^n that each given person would make all n decisions correctly. Moreover, if we let X denote the number of bureaucrats making all correct decisions, then X is a binomial random variable with parameters m and p^n. Thus the expected number of men making all correct decisions is

$$E[X] = mp^n. \tag{12}$$

Note that for a given p, the quantity $E[X]$ in (12) increases as m increases. This is not at all unexpected—Eq. (12) merely states that the expected number of apparently wise men increases as the size of the bureaucracy increases.

Assume that $n = 4$ decisions are made. If we want $E[X]$ in Eq. (12) to be 1, then we need $m = 1/p^4$ bureaucrats. In particular, if all decisions are made by chance ($p = \frac{1}{2}$), $n = 4$, and $m = 2^4 = 16$, then we can expect that one of the men makes all decisions correctly.

EXAMPLE 7. In connection with Model I in Section 6.4, the number X of marked fish caught in a sample of size n from a lake containing N fish of which M are marked is a hypergeometric random variable with parameters N, M, and n. Thus the expected number of marked fish in the catch of size n is

$$E[X] = n(M/N). \tag{13}$$

In that model, n, M, and the actual number k of marked fish were assumed known while N was not known. If we replace the expected number $E[X]$ caught by the actual number k caught, Eq. (13) becomes

$$k = n(M/N). \tag{14}$$

Solving (14) for N, we find that $N = n(M/k)$. Since this number need not be an integer, we choose the largest integer equal to or less than $n(M/k)$. This result agrees with the one we derived in Section 6.4 as the maximum likelihood estimate for N. What have we really done here? Actually, what we have done is to estimate $E[X]$, the expected number of marked fish in the sample, by k, the actual number of marked fish caught. This seems reasonable. Having done this, we have solved for N to obtain an estimate $\hat{N}$ for N. That this procedure gives the same answer as the procedure in Section 6.4 is encouraging.

Actually the method of estimation illustrated in the previous example has rather widespread application. As another example, suppose that we know that a random variable is a binomial random variable with known parameter n, but unknown parameter p. To estimate p, the above procedure suggests that we estimate the expected number of successes np by the observed number of successes k. Thus we set $k = np$ and, solving for p, find $p = k/n$. Hence as an estimate of p, we would use $\hat{p} = k/n$, the relative frequency of successes in n Bernoulli trials. The above method has led us back to estimating an unknown probability p by relative frequencies.

We conclude this section with a useful theorem and two of its corollaries. The theorem is especially useful in dealing with random variables which are functions of another random variable. One of the corollaries will prove useful in the next section.

Theorem 8.7. Let X be a random variable defined on the sample space S of a probability space (S, P), and let $S' = \{x_1, \ldots, x_n\}$ be the range of X. If g is a real-valued function whose domain contains S', then $Y = g(X)$ is also a random variable defined on S, and

$$E[Y] = E[g(X)] = \sum_{i=1}^{n} g(x_i)P(X = x_i). \tag{15}$$

To realize the usefulness of this theorem, the reader should note that Eq. (15) asserts that the expected value of Y can be calculated using the probability function f_X of X rather than the probability function f_Y of Y. We do not have to calculate $P(Y = y_i) = f_Y(y_i)$ to find the expected value of $Y = g(X)$. Instead we may use the (known) probability function $f_X(x_i) = P(X = x_i)$.

Proof of Theorem 8.7. Let (S, P) be the given probability space; X is a real-valued function whose domain is S. By definition, $g(X)$ is also a real-valued function defined on S, hence $g(X)$ is a random variable.

Since the only values assumed by X are $x_1, x_2, \ldots, x_n$, the only values assumed by $g(X)$ are $g(x_1), g(x_2), \ldots, g(x_n)$. Some of these values may be equal. Let the set of distinct values be denoted by $y_1, y_2, \ldots, y_r$, where $r \leq n$. Then

$$P(g(X) = y_i) = \sum_{\{j \mid g(x_j) = y_i\}} P(X = x_j), \qquad 1 \leq i \leq r.$$

Each x_j corresponds to one and only one y_i. Hence

$$E[g(X)] = \sum_{i=1}^{r} y_i P(g(X) = y_i) = \sum_{i=1}^{r} y_i \sum_{\{j \mid g(x_j) = y_i\}} P(X = x_j)$$

$$= \sum_{i=1}^{r} \sum_{\{j \mid g(x_j) = y_i\}} y_i P(X = x_j) = \sum_{i=1}^{r} \sum_{\{j \mid g(x_j) = y_i\}} g(x_j) P(X = x_j)$$

$$= \sum_{j=1}^{n} g(x_j) P(X = x_j). \blacktriangle$$

Corollary 8.2. Let (S, P) be a probability space, and let X be a random variable, defined on S, which has expectation $E[X]$. Let a and b be any two real numbers. Then the random variable $Y = aX + b$ has expectation $E[Y] = aE[X] + b$.

Proof. Let $g(x) = ax + b$. Then $g(X) = aX + b = Y$, and by Eq. (15),

$$E[Y] = \sum_{i=1}^{n} (ax_i + b) P(X = x_i) = a \sum_{i=1}^{n} x_i P(X = x_i) + b \sum_{i=1}^{n} P(X = x_i)$$

$$= aE[X] + b \cdot 1 = aE[X] + b. \blacktriangle$$

By setting $a = 0$ in Corollary 8.2, we find that the expectation of a constant b is $E[b] = b$. For a direct proof of this statement, see Exercise 11.

Corollary 8.3. Let (S, P) be a probability space, and let X be a random variable, defined on S, which has expectation $E[X]$. If c is any real number, then

$$E[X^2] = \sum_{i=1}^{n} x_i^2 P(X = x_i), \qquad (16)$$

and

$$E[(X - c)^2] = \sum_{i=1}^{n} (x_i - c)^2 P(X = x_i). \qquad (17)$$

Proof. Equation (16) is obtained from Eq. (15) by setting $g(x) = x^2$. Equation (17) is obtained from Eq. (15) by setting $g(x) = (x - c)^2$. $\blacktriangle$

EXERCISES

1. Ten balls numbered with the ten numbers 1, 2, 3, 3, 4, 5, 6, 6, 6, 7 are placed in a box, and one ball is selected at random. Let X be the random variable whose value, for each ball selected, is the number of the ball. Find $E[X]$, $E[X^2]$, $E[2 - 3X]$, and $E[4X + 2X^2]$.

2. Ivan agrees to play chess until he wins one game or until he loses three games. If the probability of Ivan's winning is $\frac{1}{2}$, find the mean number of games played.

3. A die is given which is biased (loaded) in such a way that the probability of a particular face is proportional to the number on that face. Let X be a random variable which gives the number appearing on the face of the die after it has been thrown. Find $E[X]$.

4. Personnel records of a company show that the probability of more than five absences on a given day is $\frac{1}{3}$. Given that the number of absences on any given day is independent of the number on any other day, find the number of absences that can be expected in a five day week, in 30 days, in 15 days.

5. A shipment of 10,000 items, 5% of which are defective, is subjected to a sampling inspection involving the taking of a random sample of ten items from the shipment. Find the mean number of defectives in the sample. What size sample should be drawn in order that at least two defectives would be expected?

6. The green light at an intersection is on for a 45-second interval, the yellow for a five-second interval, and the red for a 25-second interval. Suppose that "making the green light" is a chance event. Find the expected number of successes in 25 independent trials.

7. A cattleman buys 100 head of Hereford calves in the fall. The calves that survive the winter can be sold in the spring for a profit of $50 per head. Each calf that dies, however, represents a loss of $500. What is the expected profit if the probability that a calf survives the winter is 0.95?

8. Assume that all the calves in Exercise 7 can be expected to survive the winter, but that the profit per head is a random variable which depends on market conditions. Assume that the possible profits and their probabilities are those given in the following table. What is the expected profit on the lot of 100 calves?

Possible profits	40	30	20	10	0	−10	−20
Probabilities	$\frac{1}{10}$	$\frac{1}{10}$	$\frac{1}{10}$	$\frac{3}{10}$	$\frac{2}{10}$	$\frac{1}{10}$	$\frac{1}{10}$

9. Repeat Exercise 8 with the possible profits and probabilities shown in the following table.

Possible profits	32	16	0	−8
Probabilities	$\frac{1}{10}$	$\frac{7}{10}$	$\frac{1}{10}$	$\frac{1}{10}$

10. A random variable X is said to be a *uniform random variable* if its range is $\{j + 1, j + 2, \ldots, j + n\}$ for some integers j and $n, n \geq 1$, and if $P(X = j + k) = 1/n$ for $k = 1, 2, \ldots, n$. Show that

$$E[X] = \frac{2j + n + 1}{2} = j + \frac{n + 1}{2}.$$

11. Let (S, P) be a probability space, and let X be a random variable defined on S such that $X(s) = b$ for all s in S. Find the induced probability space (S', P') (see Section 8.3). Show that $E[X] = b$.

12. A lot contains two defective and three nondefective items. If these items are inspected at random, one after another, what is the expected number of items that must be inspected in order to remove all the defective ones? [*Hint:* Define X as stated, and complete the following table.]

$$X = \text{number of trial on which the second defective is found}$$
$$P(X = 2) =$$
$$P(X = 3) =$$
$$P(X = 4) =$$
$$P(X = 5) =$$

13. In Model II of Section 6.4 let X be the number of fish in the second catch, given that the second catch contains k marked fish as stated. Compute $E[X]$.

8.6 THE VARIANCE OF A RANDOM VARIABLE

Equation (17) of Section 8.5 gives a formula for $E[(X - c)^2]$, where c is a number and X is a random variable. When $c = E[X]$, the number $E[(X - c)^2]$ plays an important role in probability and statistics. The quantity $E[(X - E[X])^2]$ is called the variance of X.

Definition 8.8. Let (S, P) be a probability space, and let X be a random variable defined on S. The *variance* of the random variable X is defined to be

$$E[(X - E[X])^2].$$

By Eq. (17) of Section 8.5,

$$E[(X - E[X])^2] = \sum_{i=1}^{n} (x_i - E[X])^2 P(X = x_i).$$

It is possible to give an intuitive physical meaning to the mean and variance of a random variable as follows. Consider that mass particles with mass $P(X = x_i)$ are placed at the points x_i on the x-axis. The x-axis is to be considered a weightless rod with n particles attached at the points $x_1, x_2, \ldots, x_n$. The mean $E[X]$ can be pictured as a point on this x-axis. To be precise, $E[X]$ is the center of gravity of the n particles at the points $x_1, x_2, \ldots, x_n$; and the sum of the moments, $x_i P(X = x_i)$, of the particles which lie to the right of $E[X]$ is equal to the sum of the moments of the particles which lie to the left.

The variance is a measure of the spread or dispersion of the mass particles at the points x_i away from the mean. The variance is small if the mass particles are clustered close to the mean $E[X]$, and the variance increases as the mass is moved further from the mean.

The variance is always greater than or equal to zero, and the positive square root of the variance is called the *standard deviation*. We usually write μ or μ_X for the mean:

$$\mu = E[X] \quad \text{or} \quad \mu_X = E[X].$$

Several notations for the variance of X are

$$\text{variance } X = \sigma_X^2 = \sigma^2 = \text{Var}(X) = \text{var}(X).$$

If it is clear from the context what the random variable is, it is customary to use μ and σ^2 rather than the more awkward μ_X and σ_X^2. The standard deviation is usually denoted by σ or σ_X.

EXAMPLE 1.   Let X be defined as in Example 1 of Section 8.5. What is the variance of X?

Applying the definition and using the fact that $E[X] = \frac{7}{2}$, we find that

$$\text{var}(X) = E[(X - \tfrac{7}{2})^2] = \sum_{k=1}^{6} (k - \tfrac{7}{2})^2(\tfrac{1}{6}) = \frac{1}{6}\sum_{k=1}^{6} (k - \tfrac{7}{2})^2.$$

The summands in the summation on the right above are successively $\frac{25}{4}, \frac{9}{4}, \frac{1}{4}, \frac{1}{4}, \frac{9}{4}, \frac{25}{4}$, and hence

$$\text{var}(X) = \tfrac{1}{6} \cdot \tfrac{70}{4} = \tfrac{35}{12}.$$

Next we give the variances for three common random variables: Bernoulli, binomial, and hypergeometric.

Theorem 8.8. Let X be a random variable defined on the sample space S of a probability space (S,P).

(a) If X is a Bernoulli random variable with parameter p, then

$$\text{var}(X) = pq, \qquad (q = 1 - p). \tag{1}$$

(b) If X is a binomial random variable with parameters n and p, then

$$\text{var}(X) = npq, \qquad (q = 1 - p). \tag{2}$$

(c) If X is a hypergeometric random variable with parameters N, M, and n, then

$$\text{var}(X) = npq\,\frac{N - M}{N - 1},$$

where $p = M/N$ and $q = 1 - p$.

Proof of (a). Since a Bernoulli random variable X assumes only the values $x_1 = 0$ and $x_2 = 1$, we have

$$\sigma^2 = \sum_{i=1}^{2} (x_i - E[X])^2 P(X = x_i) = \sum_{i=1}^{2} (x_i - p)^2 P(X = x_i)$$

$$= (0 - p)^2 (1 - p) + (1 - p)^2 p = p^2 q + q^2 p = pq.\blacktriangle$$

While it is possible to give a proof that $E[X] = npq$ for a binomial random variable along the lines of the proof of Theorem 8.5, we shall not do so. Instead we suggest that the reader try to construct such a proof (see Exercise 7). In Section 8.7 we shall give a proof along other lines which, after the proper tools are developed, is much easier (see Theorem 8.15). Also, we leave the proof of part (c) of the above theorem as an exercise (Exercise 8). The next theorem is often useful in calculating var (X). In particular, the theorem relates $E[X^2]$ and var (X).

Theorem 8.9. Let (S, P) be a probability space, and let X be a random variable whose domain is S. If X has mean μ and variance σ^2, then

$$\sigma^2 = E[X^2] - \mu^2. \tag{3}$$

Proof. From Definition 8.8 we have

$$\sigma^2 = E[(X - E[X])^2] = E[(X - \mu)^2] = E[X^2 - 2\mu X + \mu^2].$$

Let $g(x) = x^2 - 2\mu x + \mu^2$ in Theorem 8.7. Then

$$E[X^2 - 2\mu X + \mu^2] = \sum_{i=1}^{n} g(x_i)P(X = x_i) = \sum_{i=1}^{n} (x_i^2 - 2\mu x_i + \mu^2)P(X = x_i)$$

$$= \sum_{i=1}^{n} x_i^2 P(X = x_i) - 2\mu \sum_{i=1}^{n} x_i P(X = x_i) + \mu^2 \sum_{i=1}^{n} P(X = x_i)$$

$$= E[X^2] - 2\mu E[X] + \mu^2 \cdot 1.$$

Thus

$$\sigma^2 = E[X^2] - 2\mu E[X] + \mu^2 = E[X^2] - 2\mu\mu + \mu^2 = E[X^2] - \mu^2,$$

since $E[X] = \mu.\blacktriangle$

EXAMPLE 2. Calculate the variance of the random variable X in Example 1 by using Theorem 8.9.

We know that $\mu = \frac{7}{2}$. Thus

$$\sigma^2 = \text{var}(X) = E[X^2] - (\tfrac{7}{2})^2. \tag{4}$$

Next

$$E[X^2] = \sum_{k=1}^{6} k^2 (\tfrac{1}{6}) = \frac{1}{6} \sum_{k=1}^{6} k^2 = \tfrac{1}{6} \cdot 91. \tag{5}$$

Combining Eqs. (4) and (5), we find that

$$\sigma^2 = \tfrac{91}{6} - \tfrac{49}{4} = \tfrac{70}{24} = \tfrac{35}{12}.$$

The following theorem, known as Chebyshev's Inequality, is a rather useful but crude theoretical tool. The usefulness will be explained in greater detail later.

Theorem 8.10. Let (S, P) be a probability space, and let X be a random variable defined on S which has mean μ and variance σ^2. Then for any real number $\epsilon > 0$,

$$P(|X - \mu| \geq \epsilon) \leq \sigma^2/\epsilon^2. \tag{6}$$

The theorem asserts that the probability associated with points outside the interval $[\mu - \epsilon, \mu + \epsilon]$ totals less than σ^2/ϵ^2. If we take, for example,

$$\epsilon = k\sigma, \qquad k > 0,$$

then (6) becomes

$$P(|X - \mu| \geq k\sigma) \leq 1/k^2. \tag{7}$$

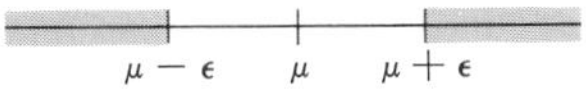

Fig. 8.7. An illustration for Eq. (6).

Thus the probability associated with values more than k standard deviations from the mean is less than $1/k^2$. (See Figs. 8.7 and 8.8.) For example, the probability of a value more than three standard deviations from the mean is less than $\tfrac{1}{9}$ for any random variable X. The strength of the theorem is that it applies to any random variable having a mean and a variance, but this is also its weakness. Since the theorem is so general, the result is not very precise in most cases.

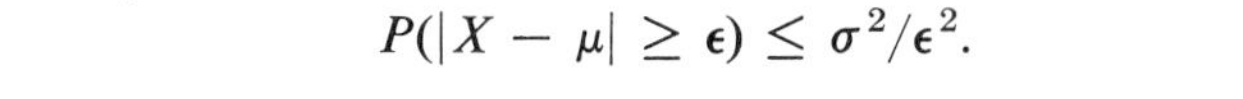

Fig. 8.8. An illustration for Eq. (7).

Proof of Theorem 8.10. The proof consists of looking at the definition of σ^2 and making a few simple observations. Now

$$\sigma^2 = \sum_{i=1}^{n} (x_i - \mu)^2 P(X = x_i)$$

$$= \sum_{\{x_i \mid |x_i - \mu| < \epsilon\}} (x_i - \mu)^2 P(X = x_i) + \sum_{\{x_i \mid |x_i - \mu| \geq \epsilon\}} (x_i - \mu)^2 P(X = x_i)$$

$$\geq 0 + \sum_{\{x_i \mid |x_i - \mu| \geq \epsilon\}} (x_i - \mu)^2 P(X = x_i)$$

$$\geq \epsilon^2 \sum_{\{x_i \mid |x_i - \mu| \geq \epsilon\}} P(X = x_i) = \epsilon^2 P(|X - \mu|^2 \geq \epsilon),$$

since on the set $\{x_i \mid |x_i - \mu| \geq \epsilon\}$ we have $|x_i - \mu|^2 \geq \epsilon^2$, and since

$$P(|X - \mu| \geq \epsilon) = \sum_{\{x_i \mid |x_i - \mu| \geq \epsilon\}} P(X = x_i).$$

Thus, we have shown that

$$\sigma^2 \geq \epsilon^2 P(|X - \mu|^2 \geq \epsilon),$$

and hence by dividing by ϵ^2 we have Eq. (6).▲

Observe that Chebyshev's Inequality must contain less information than the fact that var $(X) = \sigma^2$, since it is derived from the definition of the variance. Observe also that by taking complements, we obtain

$$P(|X - \mu| < \epsilon) > 1 - \sigma^2/\epsilon^2, \tag{8}$$

a fact that is sometimes useful.

EXAMPLE 3. A manufacturer of a new product for housewives has retained an advertising agency to conduct a television campaign for its product. The company feels that if the product can win no more than 5% of the market (of television viewers), it should be withdrawn. In analyzing the effectiveness of its television advertising, the advertising agency wishes to make a large enough survey of television viewers so that the probability is no more than 0.01 that 5% or less of the viewers sampled buy the product when, in fact, the true proportion of television viewing housewives who buy the product is 6%.

Let n be the number of housewives to be surveyed and let X be the number of those surveyed who buy the product. We assume that the housewives surveyed make their decision to buy or not buy the product independently, and hence we assume X is a binomial random variable with parameters n and $p = 0.06$. (Each housewife constitutes an independent trial.) Now $(0.05)n$ is greater than or equal to the number of housewives sampled who buy the product if no more than 5% of those sampled purchase it. Thus we are interested in the event $\{X \leq (0.05)n\}$ and its probability $P(\{X \leq (0.05)n\})$. In particular, the problem is to choose n so large that

$$P(\{X \leq (0.05)n\}) \leq 0.01. \tag{9}$$

Note that $E[X] = (0.06)n$ and hence we are interested in

$$P(\{X \leq (0.05)n\}) = P(\{X - (0.06)n \leq (0.05)n - (0.06)n\})$$
$$= P(\{X - (0.06)n \leq (-0.01)n\}). \tag{10}$$

Next observe (see Fig. 8.9) that

$$P(\{X - (0.06)n \leq (-0.01)n\}) \leq P(\{X - (0.06)n \leq (-0.01)n$$
$$\cup \{X - (0.06)n \geq (0.01)n\}) \tag{11}$$

and that

$$\{X - (0.06)n \leq (-0.01)n\} \cup \{X - (0.06)n \geq (0.01)n\}$$
$$= \{|X - (0.06)n| \geq (0.01)n\}. \tag{12}$$

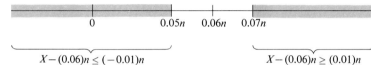

Fig. 8.9. An illustration for Eqs. (11) and (12).

Combining Eqs. (10), (11), and (12), and using Chebyshev's Inequality, we have

$$P(X \leq (0.05)n) \leq P(|X - (0.06)n| \geq (0.01)n) \leq \sigma_X^2/(0.01)^2n^2.$$

But, for a binomial random variable, $\sigma_X^2 = npq$. Furthermore, in this example, $p = 0.06$ and hence, $\sigma_X^2 = n(0.06)(0.94)$. Thus

$$P(X \leq (0.05)n) \leq \frac{(0.06)(0.94)}{(0.01)^2n}. \tag{13}$$

To complete the problem, we choose n so that

$$\frac{(0.06)(0.94)}{(0.01)^2n} \leq 0.01. \tag{14}$$

From (14) we see that any

$$n \geq \frac{(0.06)(0.94)}{(0.01)^3} = 56,400$$

will suffice to make (14) true. Then taking $n = 56,400$ and using (13), we have

$$P(X \leq (0.05)n) \leq 0.01.$$

The number n found in this example is, in fact, much too large. Better techniques for estimating probabilities yield a much smaller value of n; unfortunately these techniques are beyond the scope of this book.

Next we apply the Chebyshev Inequality to show an interesting relation between the relative frequency of successes in n Bernoulli trials and the probability p of success on each trial.

EXAMPLE 4. Let X denote the number of successes in n Bernoulli trials and let p be the probability of success at each trial. The random variable X/n is called the average number (relative frequency) of successes. Choose any number $\epsilon > 0$ and consider $P(|X/n - p| \geq \epsilon)$. Now

$$\left\{ \left| \frac{X}{n} - p \right| \geq \epsilon \right\} = \{|X - np| \geq n\epsilon\};$$

hence,

$$P\left(\left| \frac{X}{n} - p \right| \geq \epsilon \right) = P(|X - np| \geq n\epsilon). \tag{15}$$

Since X is a binomial random variable with mean np and variance npq, an application of the Chebyshev Inequality to the right-hand side of Eq. (15) gives

$$P\left(\left|\frac{X}{n} - p\right| \geq \epsilon\right) \leq \frac{npq}{n^2\epsilon^2} = \frac{pq}{n\epsilon^2}. \tag{16}$$

The quantity $pq/n\epsilon^2$ approaches zero as n becomes large; hence, for any $\epsilon > 0$, the probability $P(|X/n - p| \geq \epsilon)$ approaches zero as n becomes large.

This example is a special case of a more general theorem known as the (weak) Law of Large Numbers which will be proved in the next section (see Theorem 8.16).

EXERCISES

1. A number X is chosen at random from each of the following sets of numbers. Find the variance for the number chosen.
   (a) $S = \{-1, 0, 1, 2, 3\}$ (b) $S = \{-5, 0, 5, 10, 15\}$
   (c) $S = \{90, 100, 110, 120, 130\}$ (d) $S = \{1, 1, 1, 1, 10\}$
   (e) $S = \{1, 1, 1, 1, 1\}$

2. An unbiased coin is tossed ten times. Let X denote the number of heads that appear. Find $E[X]$ and var (X). How many times should the coin be tossed so that var $(X) \geq 25$?

3. A balanced die is thrown. If the number which appears is less than four, it is tossed again. Let X be the sum of the numbers which appear if the die is tossed twice or the number which appears on the first toss if it is thrown only once. Find $E[X]$ and var (X).

4. Assume that X is a random variable on a nonempty finite sample space S, and that $E[X^2] = (E[X])^2 = 1$. Prove that $P(|X| = 1) = 1$, and that either $P(X = 1) = 1$ or $P(X = -1) = 1$.

5. Find the variance of the random variable for the problem described in Exercise 6 of Section 8.5.

6. Find the variance for the random variable for the problem described in Exercise 7 of Section 8.5; in Exercise 8 of Section 8.5.

7. Prove part (b) of Theorem 8.8 by carrying out the following steps.
   (a) Show that $E[X^2 - X] = E[X^2] - E[X]$.
   (b) If X is a binomial random variable, show that

   $$E[X^2 - X] = \sum_{k=0}^{n} k(k-1)\binom{n}{k}p^k q^{n-k} = \sum_{k=2}^{n} k(k-1)\binom{n}{k}p^k q^{n-k}$$

   $$= p^2 n(n-1)\sum_{k=2}^{n}\binom{n-2}{k-2}p^{k-2}q^{n-k} = p^2 n(n-1).$$

   (c) Use Theorem 8.9 and the result of (b) to find var (X).

8. Prove part (c) of Theorem 8.8. The idea used in Exercise 7 might prove helpful.

9. Consider Example 3 in the case in which the actual proportion of the television viewing housewives who buy the product is 7%. Is the number of housewives needed smaller or larger than in Example 3? Can you generalize your conclusion?

10. Give a formula for the exact value of the probability $P(\{X \leq (0.05)n\})$ in Example 3 in terms of the distribution function of a binomial random variable. Explain why this formula does not aid us in our search for an n such that $P(\{X \leq (0.05)n\}) \leq 0.01$.

11. Give a careful proof of the following result [see Eq. (8)]:

$$P(|X - \mu| < \epsilon) > 1 - \sigma^2/\epsilon^2.$$

12. A drug company is testing a new drug to replace a standard drug which has proved to be 80% effective. In a clinical test, the new drug produced cures in 85 out of 100 cases.
   (a) What is an exact expression for the probability of this many or more cures if the new drug actually has the same effectiveness as the standard drug?
   (b) Estimate the probability in (a) using Chebyshev's Inequality. Does the result indicate that the new drug is really more effective?

13. Let X be a random variable and let a and b be real numbers. Let $Y = aX + b$.
   (a) Show that var $(Y) = a^2$ var (X).
   (b) Use the result (a) to compute the answers to parts (b) and (c) of Exercise 1 from part (a) of Exercise 1.

14. Use the results of Exercise 13 and Corollary 8.2 (see Section 8.5) to prove the following result. If X is a random variable with mean μ and variance σ^2, then the random variable $Y = (X - \mu)/\sigma$ has mean 0 and variance 1, that is, $E[Y] = 0$ and var $(Y) = 1$. The random variable Y is called the *standardized* (or *normalized*) random variable corresponding to X.

15. Let X be a uniform random variable with range $\{1, 2, \ldots, n\}$ (see Exercise 10 in Section 8.5). Show that var $(X) = (n + 1)(n - 1)/12$. [*Hint:* Use Theorem 8.9 and Eq. (9) in Section 3.6.]

16. Let $Y = X + j$, where j is an integer and X is the random variable of Exercise 15.
   (a) Show that Y is a uniform random variable whose range is

$$\{j + 1, j + 2, \ldots, j + n\}.$$

   (b) Use the results in Exercises 13 and 15 to find the variance of Y.

8.7 SUMS OF RANDOM VARIABLES

We have encountered Bernoulli and binomial random variables in earlier sections of this book. In fact, we have shown that the number of successes in n Bernoulli trials is a binomial random variable. One of the purposes of this section is to show that the sum of certain types of Bernoulli random variables is a binomial random variable. This result is quite useful. More generally, we wish to consider the sums and products of random variables and to derive some formulas for the expectation and variance of sums and products of random variables.

Let us begin by recalling that the sum $f + g$ and the product $f \cdot g$ of two functions were defined in Chapter 2. It was required there that f and g have the same domain (if they do not, it is necessary to restrict the two functions to the intersection of their two domains). Since random variables are functions, it follows that the sum $X + Y$ and the product XY of two random variables X and Y defined on the same sample space S of a probability space (S, P) are again random variables. Eventually we shall be interested in such events as

$$\{X + Y = z\} = \{s \mid s \in S, \; X(s) + Y(s) = z\},$$
$$\{X + Y \leq z\} = \{s \mid s \in S, \; X(s) + Y(s) \leq z\},$$
$$\{XY = z\} = \{s \mid s \in S, \; X(s)Y(s) = z\},$$

and

$$\{XY \leq z\} = \{s \mid s \in S, \; X(s)Y(s) \leq z\}.$$

Also of interest will be such events as

$$\{X = x\} \cap \{Y = y\} = \{s \mid s \in S, \; X(s) = x\} \cap \{s \mid s \in S, \; Y(s) = y\}.$$

We shall always abbreviate this event as follows:

$$\{X = x, \; Y = y\} = \{X = x\} \cap \{Y = y\}. \tag{1}$$

This notation agrees with our earlier notation.

Next, let us investigate the range of $X + Y$ and XY. If the range of X is $R_X = \{x_1, x_2, \ldots, x_n\}$ and the range of Y is $R_Y = \{y_1, y_2, \ldots, y_m\}$, then the range R_{X+Y} of $X + Y$ satisfies

$$R_{X+Y} \subset \{x_i + y_j \mid x_i \in R_X, \; y_j \in R_Y\}. \tag{2}$$

Likewise, the range R_{XY} of XY satisfies

$$R_{XY} \subset \{x_i y_j \mid x_i \in R_X, \; y_j \in R_Y\}. \tag{3}$$

A word of explanation may be needed in Eqs. (2) and (3). If $X + Y = z$, then there must be an $s \in S$ such that $X(s) + Y(s) = z$. But the only possible values of $X(s)$ are those in R_X, and the only possible values for $Y(s)$ are those in R_Y. Thus $X(s) = x_i$ for some i, and $Y(s) = y_j$ for some j, and hence $z = x_i + y_j$ for some i and some j. We have thus shown that if $z \in R_{X+Y}$, then z is an element of the set on the right in Eq. (2). Thus Eq. (2) is true. On the other hand, it is conceivable that a particular value, $x_i + y_j$, is not assumed by $X + Y$. The following example illustrates this point.

EXAMPLE 1. Let X and Y be defined on $\{0, 1\}$ with $X(0) = 1$, $X(1) = 2$, $Y(0) = 4$, $Y(1) = -1$. Then Eq. (2) asserts that

$$R_{X+Y} \subset \{1 + 4, 1 - 1, 2 + 4, -1 + 2\} = \{0, 1, 5, 6\}.$$

Actually,

$$R_{X+Y} = \{X(0) + Y(0), X(1) + Y(1)\} = \{5, 1\}.$$

Similarly, Eq. (3) asserts that

$$R_{XY} \subset \{-1, -2, 4, 8\}$$

when, in fact,

$$R_{XY} = \{-2, 4\}.$$

Next we state and prove a theorem which asserts that the expectation of a sum of two random variables is the sum of the expectations of the individual random variables.

Theorem 8.11. Let (S, P) be a probability space and let X and Y be random variables whose domains are S. Then

$$E[X + Y] = E[X] + E[Y]. \tag{4}$$

Proof. We begin by observing that, by definition,

$$E[X] = \sum_{i=1}^{n} x_i P(X = x_i),$$

$$E[Y] = \sum_{j=1}^{m} y_j P(Y = y_j).$$

For each fixed i, $1 \leq i \leq n$, we have

$$\{X = x_i\} = \{X = x_i\} \cap S = \{X = x_i\} \cap \bigcup_{j=1}^{m} \{Y = y_j\}$$

$$= \bigcup_{j=1}^{m} (\{X = x_i\} \cap \{Y = y_j\}) = \bigcup_{j=1}^{m} \{X = x_i, Y = y_j\}.$$

Also, for $j \neq k$, we see that

$$\{X = x_i, Y = y_j\} \cap \{X = x_i, Y = y_k\} = \emptyset.$$

Therefore, by the additivity of P,

$$P(X = x_i) = \sum_{j=1}^{m} P(X = x_i, Y = y_j).$$

Then from the expression for $E[X]$ given above we see that

$$E[X] = \sum_{i=1}^{n} x_i \sum_{j=1}^{m} P(X = x_i, Y = y_j) = \sum_{i=1}^{n} \sum_{j=1}^{m} x_i P(X = x_i, Y = y_j).$$

In the same way we can show that

$$P(Y = y_j) = \sum_{i=1}^{n} P(X = x_i, \ Y = y_j),$$

and that

$$E[Y] = \sum_{j=1}^{m} \sum_{i=1}^{n} y_j P(X = x_i, \ Y = y_j) = \sum_{i=1}^{n} \sum_{j=1}^{m} y_j P(X = x_i, \ Y = y_j).$$

Therefore

$$E[X] + E[Y] = \sum_{i=1}^{n} \sum_{j=1}^{m} (x_i + y_j) P(X = x_i, \ Y = y_j). \tag{5}$$

Let $z_1, z_2, \ldots, z_r$ be the set of different values of $x_i + y_j$ for $i = 1, 2, \ldots, n$ and $j = 1, 2, \ldots, m$. Then

$$\sum_{i=1}^{n} \sum_{j=1}^{m} (x_i + y_j) P(X = x_i, \ Y = y_j) = \sum_{k=1}^{r} \sum_{\{(i,j)\,|\,x_i+y_j=z_k\}} z_k P(X = x_i, \ Y = y_j)$$

$$= \sum_{k=1}^{r} z_k \sum_{\{(i,j)\,|\,x_i+y_j=z_k\}} P(X = x_i, \ Y = y_j)$$

$$= \sum_{k=1}^{r} z_k P(X + Y = z_k) = E[X + Y].$$

This last equation and Eq. (5) together show that

$$E[X + Y] = E[X] + E[Y]. \blacktriangle$$

A formula for $E[X_1 + X_2 + \cdots + X_n]$ can be obtained by applying mathematical induction to the results in Theorem 8.11; the result is stated in the next theorem.

Theorem 8.12. Let (S, P) be a probability space and let $X_1, X_2, \ldots, X_n$ be random variables defined on S. Then

$$E[X_1 + X_2 + \cdots + X_n] = E[X_1] + E[X_2] + \cdots + E[X_n]. \tag{6}$$

EXAMPLE 2. A single die is thrown twice. What is the expected value of the sum of the dots which appear?

Let X be the number of the dots which appear on the first toss and let Y be the number of dots which appear on the second toss. Then $X + Y$ is the sum of the dots and

$$E[X + Y] = E[X] + E[Y]$$

is the expected number of dots. Now $E[X] = E[Y] = \frac{7}{2}$; hence, $E[X + Y] = 7$.

The quantity $E[X + Y]$ can also be computed by noting that the range of $X + Y$ is $\{2, 3, \ldots, 12\}$, and that $P(X + Y = 2) = \frac{1}{36}$, $P(X + Y = 3) = \frac{2}{36}$, $P(X + Y = 4) = \frac{3}{36}, \ldots, P(X + Y = 12) = \frac{1}{36}$. Then by definition, the expected value of $X + Y$ is

$$2 \cdot \tfrac{1}{36} + 3 \cdot \tfrac{2}{36} + \cdots + 12 \cdot \tfrac{1}{36} = 7.$$

The previous calculation is much easier.

It should be noted that the common sample space for the random variables X and Y is $S = \{(i, j) \mid 1 \le i \le 6, \ 1 \le j \le 6\}$, that is, the product sample space $S = \{1, \ldots, 6\} \times \{1, \ldots, 6\}$. An element (i, j) of S corresponds to the appearance of i dots on the first throw and j dots on the second throw. Thus

$$X((i, j)) = i \quad \text{and} \quad Y((i, j)) = j, \quad 1 \le i \le 6, 1 \le j \le 6.$$

Next we show that a binomial random variable X can be considered as a sum of Bernoulli random variables which correspond to Bernoulli trials. Assume that X is a binomial random variable with parameters n and p. We have shown (see Example 2 in Section 8.2 and Theorem 7.6 in Section 7.5) that the number X of successes in n Bernoulli trials is a binomial random variable with parameters n and p, where p is the probability of success on each trial. The sample space is $S = S_1 \times S_1 \times \cdots \times S_1$ (n factors), where $S_1 = \{s, f\}$. Define n Bernoulli random variables X_i, $i = 1, 2, \ldots, n$, by setting

$$X_i = \begin{cases} 1 & \text{if the outcome of the } i\text{th trial is } s, \\ 0 & \text{if the outcome of the } i\text{th trial is } f. \end{cases}$$

Thus, if $(x_1, \ldots, x_{i-1}, x_i, x_{i+1}, \ldots, x_n)$ is an element of S, then

$$X_i((x_1, \ldots, x_{i-1}, x_i, x_{i+1}, \ldots, x_n)) = \begin{cases} 1 & \text{if } x_i = s, \\ 0 & \text{if } x_i = f. \end{cases}$$

The sum $X_1 + X_2 + \cdots + X_n$ is the number of x_i which are s (success); hence

$$X = X_1 + X_2 + \cdots + X_n.$$

Using the result obtained above, we can easily calculate the mean of a binomial random variable. Each of the random variables X_i above is a Bernoulli random variable, and $P(X_i = 1) = p$, $P(X_i = 0) = 1 - p$. Therefore $E[X_i] = p$ for $1 \le i \le n$, and

$$E[X] = E[X_1 + X_2 + \cdots + X_n] = E[X_1] + E[X_2] + \cdots + E[X_n]$$
$$= p + p + \cdots + p = np,$$

by Theorem 8.12. This result agrees, as it should, with the conclusion of Theorem 8.5. The computation involved here is much simpler than that encountered in proving Theorem 8.5, which is based on first principles only. In addition to giving a simpler proof of an earlier result, we have shown that a binomial random variable is the sum of n Bernoulli random variables.

It is natural to inquire whether the results of Theorem 8.11 and 8.12 are true for variances as well as for means. Unfortunately, it is not true in general that var $(X_1 + \cdots + X_n) = $ var $(X_1) + \cdots +$ var (X_n), but there is an important special case in which the result is true. Before we can state the theorem, it is necessary to define independent random variables.

Definition 8.9. Let (S, P) be a probability space and let X and Y be two random variables whose domain is S. Then X and Y are *independent* if for each pair x, y of real numbers, the events $A = \{s \mid s \in S,\ X(s) = x\}$ and $B = \{s \mid s \in S,\ Y(s) = y\}$ are independent events. That is, X and Y are independent random variables if and only if

$$P(X = x, Y = y) = P(X = x)P(Y = y). \tag{7}$$

This definition can be extended in an obvious manner to any finite number of random variables.

EXAMPLE 3. Let X and Y be the random variables of Example 2. Then X and Y are independent.

Recall that in Example 2 we were considering the product probability space (S, P) where

$$S = \{1, 2, \ldots, 6\} \times \{1, 2, \ldots, 6\} = \{(i, j) \mid 1 \leq i \leq 6,\ 1 \leq j \leq 6\}.$$

Consider the event

$$
\begin{aligned}
A = \{s \mid s \in S,\ X(s) = i\} &= \{(k, j) \mid (k, j) \in S,\ X((k, j)) = i\} \\
&= \{(i, j) \mid 1 \leq j \leq 6\} = \{i\} \times \{1, 2, \ldots, 6\}.
\end{aligned}
$$

Similarly

$$B = \{s \mid s \in S,\ Y(s) = j\} = \{1, 2, \ldots, 6\} \times \{j\}.$$

We have thus shown that A and B are events determined by the first and second trials, respectively. Since we are working in the product probability space, these events are independent; this statement is the content of Theorem 7.5 in Section 7.5. Thus X and Y are independent random variables. Actually, we have considered only numbers $x = i$ and $y = j$. If we consider other values of x with $x \notin \{1, 2, \ldots, 6\}$, then the event $\{X = x\} = \emptyset$, and hence it is independent of any other event B. Similarly if $y \notin \{1, 2, \ldots, 6\}$, then $\{Y = y\} = \emptyset$. Thus we need, as we did, only to check that Eq. (7) holds for x in the range of X and y in the range of Y.

The above example can be generalized considerably. If (S, P) is a product probability space, where $S = S_1 \times S_2 \times \cdots \times S_n$, and if $X_1, X_2, \ldots, X_n$ are random variables defined on S such that the value of X_i depends only on the ith component of points in S, $1 \leq i \leq n$, then $X_1, X_2, \ldots, X_n$ are independent random variables. This statement follows by the same considerations as in Example 3 and, of course, the natural generalization of Theorem 7.5 is needed to prove it. Thus, in particular, the Bernoulli random variables X_i, which were used to show that a binomial random variable X can be written as $X_1 + \cdots + X_n$, are independent random variables.

Theorem 8.13. Let (S, P) be a probability space and let X and Y be independent random variables defined on S. Then

$$\text{var } (X + Y) = \text{var } (X) + \text{var } (Y). \tag{8}$$

The proof of this theorem requires the result of the next theorem. It should be observed, however, that the next theorem contains a result which is important for its own sake.

Theorem 8.14. Let (S, P) be a probability space and let X and Y be independent random variables defined on S. Then

$$E[XY] = E[X]E[Y]. \tag{9}$$

Proof. We observed earlier that the product XY is a random variable defined on S whether or not X and Y are independent. The proof consists of calculating $E[X]E[Y]$. By definition

$$E[X]E[Y] = \left[\sum_{i=1}^{n} x_i P(X = x_i) \right] \left[\sum_{j=1}^{m} y_j P(Y = y_j) \right]$$

$$= \sum_{i=1}^{n} \sum_{j=1}^{m} x_i y_j P(X = x_i) P(Y = y_j).$$

But since X and Y are independent random variables by hypothesis,

$$P(X = x_i) P(Y = y_j) = P(X = x_i, Y = y_j),$$

and

$$E[X]E[Y] = \sum_{i=1}^{n} \sum_{j=1}^{m} x_i y_j P(X = x_i, Y = y_j).$$

Let $z_1, z_2, \ldots, z_r$ be the set of different values of $x_i y_j$ for $i = 1, 2, \ldots, n$ and $j = 1, 2, \ldots, m$. Then

$$E[X]E[Y] = \sum_{k=1}^{r} \sum_{\{(i,j) \mid x_i y_j = z_k\}} x_i y_j P(X = x_i, Y = y_j)$$

$$= \sum_{k=1}^{r} z_k \sum_{\{(i,j) \mid x_i y_j = z_k\}} P(X = x_i, Y = y_j)$$

$$= \sum_{k=1}^{r} z_k P(XY = z_k) = E[XY]. \blacktriangle$$

Proof of Theorem 8.13. By Theorem 8.11, $E[X + Y] = E[X] + E[Y]$. Then by definition of the variance,

$$
\begin{aligned}
\text{var } (X + Y) &= E[\{(X + Y) - (E[X] + E[Y])\}^2] \\
&= E[\{(X - E[X]) + (Y - E[Y])\}^2] \\
&= E[(X - E[X])^2 + (Y - E[Y])^2 + 2(X - E[X])(Y - E[Y])] \\
&= \text{var } (X) + \text{var } (Y) + 2E[(X - E[X])(Y - E[Y])]. \quad (10)
\end{aligned}
$$

Theorem 8.11 was used to obtain the last equation from the preceding one. Using Theorem 8.11 again, and also Corollary 8.2 in Section 8.5, we find that

$$
\begin{aligned}
E[(X - E[X])(Y - E[Y])] &= E[XY - XE[Y] - YE[X] + E[X]E[Y]] \\
&= E[XY] - E[Y]E[X] - E[X]E[Y] + E[X]E[Y] \\
&= E[XY] - E[X]E[Y].
\end{aligned}
$$

But, by Theorem 8.14, $E[XY] = E[X]E[Y]$. This fact and the last equation above show that

$$
E[(X - E[X])(Y - E[Y])] = 0 \quad (11)
$$

for independent random variables X and Y. This result and Eq. (10) established earlier show that var $(X + Y) = $ var $(X) + $ var (Y).▲

Theorem 8.13 has an extension which applies to the sum of two or more independent random variables. If $X_1, X_2, \ldots, X_n$ are independent random variables defined on a common sample space, then

$$
\text{var } (X_1 + X_2 + \cdots + X_n) = \text{var } (X_1) + \text{var } (X_2) + \cdots + \text{var } (X_n). \quad (12)
$$

Next, as we pointed out following Example 2, a binomial random variable can be expressed as a sum of n independent Bernoulli random variables. From this fact and Eq. (12) we obtain the following theorem, which was stated without proof in part (b) of Theorem 8.8 in Section 8.6.

Theorem 8.15. Let (S, P) be a probability space and let X be a binomial random variable, with parameters n and p, which is defined on S. Then $\sigma^2 = $ var $(X) = npq$.

Proof. We have shown that $X = X_1 + X_2 + \cdots + X_n$, where $X_1, X_2, \ldots, X_n$ are independent Bernoulli random variables defined on S. By part (a) of Theorem 8.8, the variance of a Bernoulli random variable, with parameter p, is pq; hence var $(X_i) = pq$ for $1 \leq i \leq n$. Since the X_i are independent, by (12) we have

$$
\begin{aligned}
\text{var } (X) &= \text{var } (X_1) + \text{var } (X_2) + \cdots + \text{var } (X_n) \\
&= pq + pq + \cdots + pq = npq.▲
\end{aligned}
$$

We conclude this section with a theorem which is known as the (weak) Law of Large Numbers. This result is a simple generalization of the result in Example 4 of Section 8.6.

Theorem 8.16 (*Law of Large Numbers*). Let (S, P) be a probability space and let $X_1, X_2, \ldots, X_n$ be n independent random variables defined on S such that $E[X_i] = \mu$, var $(X_i) = \sigma^2$ for $1 \leq i \leq n$. That is, all the random variables have the same mean and variance. Then, for any real number $\epsilon > 0$,

$$P\left(\left|\frac{X_1 + \cdots + X_n}{n} - \mu\right| \geq \epsilon\right) \to 0 \quad \text{as} \quad n \to \infty. \tag{13}$$

Stated another way,

$$P\left(\left|\frac{X_1 + \cdots + X_n}{n} - \mu\right| < \epsilon\right) \to 1 \quad \text{as} \quad n \to \infty. \tag{14}$$

Proof. Let $Y = (X_1 + \cdots + X_n)/n$. Then

$$E[Y] = (1/n)E[X_1 + \cdots + X_n] = (1/n)(E[X_1] + \cdots + E[X_n])$$
$$= (1/n)(\mu + \cdots + \mu) = (1/n)n\mu = \mu.$$

Also, by Exercise 13 of Section 8.6 and Eq. (12) above,

var $(Y) = (1/n^2)$ var $(X_1 + \cdots + X_n) = (1/n^2)(\text{var } (X_1) + \cdots + \text{var } (X_n))$
$= (1/n^2)n\sigma^2 = \sigma^2/n.$

Thus, applying Chebyshev's Inequality to Y, we have

$$P\left(\left|\frac{X_1 + \cdots + X_n}{n} - \mu\right| \geq \epsilon\right) = P(|Y - E[Y]| \geq \epsilon) \leq \frac{\text{var } (Y)}{\epsilon^2} = \frac{\sigma^2}{n\epsilon^2}.$$

But $\dfrac{\sigma^2}{\epsilon^2} \cdot \dfrac{1}{n} \to 0$ as $n \to \infty$, and hence we have (13).

To establish (14), use Eq. (8) of Section 8.6 instead of Chebyshev's Inequality; we have

$$P\left(\left|\frac{X_1 + \cdots + X_n}{n} - \mu\right| < \epsilon\right) = P(|Y - E[Y]| < \epsilon)$$
$$> 1 - \frac{\text{var } (Y)}{\epsilon^2}$$
$$= 1 - \frac{1}{n} \cdot \frac{\sigma^2}{\epsilon^2}$$
$$\to 1 \quad \text{as} \quad n \to \infty. \blacktriangle$$

An important special case is that in which the random variables $X_1, X_2, \ldots,$ X_n are independent and *identically distributed*, that is, each random variable X_i has the same probability function. Then the random variables $X_1, X_2, \ldots, X_n$ have the same mean and variance. For example, any collection $X_1, \ldots, X_n$ of Bernoulli random variables having the same parameter p are identically distributed. Since a binomial random variable with parameters n and p is a sum of n independent identically distributed Bernoulli random variables, we see that the result of Example 4 of Section 8.6 is a special case of Theorem 8.16.

EXERCISES

1. A fair coin is to be tossed twice. You bet a dollar on a head's appearing on the first toss. If you win, you bet another dollar on a head's appearing on the second toss; if you lose on the first toss, you bet two dollars on the appearance of a head on the second toss. Let X be your gain on the first toss and Y be your gain on the second toss.
   (a) What does $X + Y$ represent? What sample space is $X + Y$ defined on?
   (b) Find the range of $X + Y$.
   (c) Calculate

   $$P(X = 1, Y = 1), P(X = 1, Y = -1), P(X = -1, Y = 1),$$
   $$P(X = -1, Y = 2), P(X = -1, Y = -2), P(X = 1, Y = 2).$$

   (d) Calculate $P(X + Y = 2), P(X + Y = 0), P(X + Y = 1), P(X + Y = -3)$.
   (e) Calculate $E[X + Y]$ in two ways.
   (f) Show that X and Y are not independent random variables.

2. A balanced coin is tossed. The random variable X is defined to have the value zero if a tail appears on the coin and to have the value one if a head appears. A balanced die is thrown independently, and the value of the random variable Y is the number which appears on the face of the die. Compute the quantities named in parts (a) to (k) of this exercise.
   (a) $E[X]$ (b) $E[Y]$ (c) $E[X + Y]$ (d) range $X + Y$
   (e) probabilities $P(X + Y = k)$ for each k in the range of $X + Y$
   (f) $E[X + Y]$ (Use the definition.)   (g) $E[(X + Y)/2]$
   (h) var (X) (i) var (Y)
   (j) var $(X + Y)$ (Give two solutions.)   (k) var $(3Y + 5)$
   (l) Find $E[XY]$ and show that $E[XY] = E[X]E[Y]$.

3. Given that Madison wrote the essay, explain why the random variables X and Y in Example 3 of Section 8.3 are independent.

4. A man's suit has two pairs of trousers. The expected life of the first pair is 1500 days and the expected life of the second pair is 750 days. Assuming that the coat will outwear the two pairs of trousers, what is the expected life of the suit?

5. It is estimated that a component of a space system will last k days with probability $\binom{10}{k}(0.8)^k(0.2)^{10-k}$, $0 < k < 10$, and that a backup component, which is independent of the first, will last k days with probability $\binom{5}{k}(0.8)^k(0.2)^{5-k}$, $0 \le k \le 5$.

Let X denote the number of days the first component lasts and let Y denote the number of days the second component lasts.
(a) What kind of random variables are X and Y?
(b) Give an interpretation of $X + Y$. Are X and Y independent?
(c) Find $E[X + Y]$ and find var $(X + Y)$.
(d) Use Chebyshev's Inequality to estimate the probability $P(9 < X + Y < 15)$.
(e) What kind of random variable is $X + Y$?

6. Let X and Y be independent binomial random variables with parameters n, p, and m, p, respectively. (We assume X and Y are defined on the same sample space.)
(a) Show that $E[X + Y] = (n + m)p$.
(b) Show that var $(X + Y) = (n + m)pq$.
(c) Show that $X + Y$ is a binomial random variable with parameters $n + m$ and p. This problem generalizes Exercise 5. [*Hint:* Consider X and Y on $S \times T$, where $S = S_1 \times S_1 \times \cdots \times S_1$ (n factors) and $T = T_1 \times T_1 \times \cdots \times T_1$ (m factors), and define $n + m$ independent Bernoulli random variables $X_1, X_2, \ldots,$ $X_n, Y_1, Y_2, \ldots, Y_m$ on $S \times T$. Then show that $X + Y = X_1 + \cdots + X_n + Y_1 + \cdots + Y_m$.]

7. Use mathematical induction to prove that the formula in Eq. (12) is true, where $X_1, X_2, \ldots, X_n$ are n independent random variables defined on a common sample space.

8. If X and Y are two random variables defined on a sample space S, we define the *covariance* of X and Y to be

$$\text{cov } (X, Y) = E[(X - E[X])(Y - E[Y])].$$

(a) Prove that

$$\text{var } (X + Y) = \text{var } (X) + \text{var } (Y) - 2 \text{ cov } (X, Y).$$

(b) Prove that cov $(X, Y) = 0$ if and only if var $(X + Y) = \text{var } (X) + \text{var } (Y)$.
(c) Prove that if X and Y are independent, then cov $(X, Y) = 0$.

9. Give an example of a pair of random variables X and Y such that cov $(X, Y) = 0$, but X and Y are *not* independent.

10. Prove that if (S, P) is a product probability space, where $S = S_1 \times S_2 \times \cdots \times S_n$, and if $X_1, X_2, \ldots, X_n$ are random variables defined on S such that the values X_i depend only on S_i, $1 \leq i \leq n$, then $X_1, X_2, \ldots, X_n$ are independent random variables.

8.8 SOME FURTHER APPLICATIONS

In Sections 8.5 and 8.6 we introduced the ideas of the mean and the variance of a random variable. In this section we shall give three applications where such ideas are useful. The first application is to an inventory problem; the second and third are related problems dealing with maximizing profits. A fourth application deals with a learning model developed by W. K. Estes. This model uses a combination of probability theory and matrices.

APPLICATION 1 (A Simple Inventory Problem).   A store has a certain quantity I of brand Q product on hand at the close of a business day.   Assume that the demand D for the product during the next day is a random variable with a known distribution (perhaps binomial with known parameters).   Further, assume that it is possible to order an amount δ so as to have delivery before the opening of the store, but that orders made after the opening of the store cannot be filled until the next business day (and hence they will not be made until the end of the day).   What quantity δ should be ordered if we wish to minimize the expected loss where both the loss due to carrying an inventory larger than the demand and the loss due to excess of demand over supply are proportional (with the same constant of proportionality) to the square of the excess stock and excess demand, respectively?

To formalize the problem, let

I = inventory on hand at the close of the previous business day,
δ = amount to be ordered,
D = demand, a random variable,
L = loss due to demand D with order δ and inventory I,
α = positive constant of proportionality.

Then $I + \delta$ is the stock available for sale during a given business day while D represents the demand.   The quantity $I + \delta - D$ is the difference between the stock and the demand.   If $I + \delta - D > 0$, then there is a loss due to excess stock and the loss L is given by

$$L = \alpha[I + \delta - D]^2, \qquad I + \delta - D > 0. \qquad (1)$$

If $I + \delta - D < 0$, then the demand D exceeds the stock $I + \delta$ available, and the loss L is given by

$$L = \alpha[D - (I + \delta)]^2, \qquad I + \delta - D < 0. \qquad (2)$$

Finally, if $I + \delta - D = 0$, then there is no loss and

$$L = 0, \qquad I + \delta - D = 0. \qquad (3)$$

Thus

$$L = \begin{cases} \alpha[I + \delta - D]^2, & \text{if } I + \delta - D > 0, \\ \alpha[D - (I + \delta)]^2, & \text{if } I + \delta - D < 0, \\ 0, & \text{if } I + \delta - D = 0. \end{cases} \qquad (4)$$

Note that L is a random variable, since it is a function of a random variable D, and that our problem is to choose δ so as to minimize $E[L]$, the expected loss. Also note that, since $[I + \delta - D]^2 = [D - (I + \delta)]^2$,

$$L = \alpha[I + \delta - D]^2. \qquad (5)$$

It is Eq. (5) that we shall use in calculating $E[L]$:

$$
\begin{aligned}
E[L] &= E[\alpha\{I + \delta - D\}^2] \\
&= \alpha E[\{(I + \delta) - D\}^2] \\
&= \alpha E[(I + \delta)^2 - 2(I + \delta)D + D^2] \\
&= \alpha\{(I + \delta)^2 - 2(I + \delta)E[D] + E[D^2]\}.
\end{aligned}
$$

Letting $\mu_D = E[D]$ and using the fact that $E[D^2] = \text{var}(D) + \mu_D^2$, we have

$$
E[L] = \alpha\{(I + \delta)^2 - 2(I + \delta)\mu_D + \text{var}(D) + \mu_D^2\}.
$$

If we let $a = I + \delta$, then we see that $E[L]$ is a quadratic function of a and that

$$
\begin{aligned}
E[L] &= \alpha\{a^2 - 2a\mu_D + \text{var}(D) + \mu_D^2\} \\
&= \alpha\{(a - \mu_D)^2 + \text{var}(D)\}.
\end{aligned}
$$

Since both $(a - \mu_D)^2$ and $\text{var}(D)$ are nonnegative, we see that $E[L]$ is minimized (made as small as possible) by making $(a - \mu_D)^2$ as close to zero as possible. Thus it appears that we should choose $a = \mu_D$ or

$$
\delta = \mu_D - I; \tag{6}
$$

that is, choose δ to be the difference between the expected demand μ_D and the previous day's closing inventory. Unfortunately, it may happen that $\mu_D - I$ is negative and we cannot (for obvious reasons) choose such a value for δ. In fact, if $\mu_D - I < 0$, we should choose $\delta = 0$ (we already have too much inventory on hand—the expected demand is less than the inventory). If $\mu_D - I \geq 0$, we choose $\delta = \mu_D - I$. See Figs. 8.10 and 8.11 (note that for physical reasons we always have $a \geq I$, since $\delta \geq 0$).

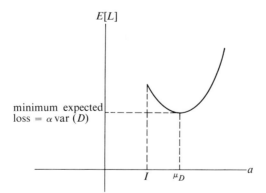

Fig. 8.10. Graph of $E[L]$, as a function of a for $\mu_D \geq I$, showing the minimum value of $E[L]$.

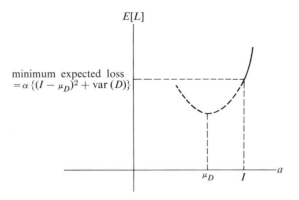

Fig. 8.11. Graph of $E[L]$, as a function of a for $\mu_D < I$, showing the minimum value of $E[L]$.

We may summarize the above discussion as follows:

(a) If the expected demand μ_D is greater than the inventory I on hand, order an amount δ so that $I + \delta = \mu_D$; that is, bring the inventory up to the expected demand.

(b) If the expected demand is less than the inventory, do not order any more; let the inventory decrease.

If rules (a) and (b) are followed, then the expected loss is minimized. In case (a) the minimum value of the expected loss is $\alpha \operatorname{var}(D)$, while in case (b) the minimum value of the expected loss is $\alpha\{(I - \mu_D)^2 + \operatorname{var}(D)\}$.

Of course, this model is too simple; it does not take into account the cost of reordering or the possibility that different constants of proportionality could (and probably should) be assigned to the two types of losses. A loss function which would take this last point into account could be given by replacing Eq. (2) by

$$L = \beta[D - (I + \delta)]^2, \qquad I + \delta - D < 0. \tag{7}$$

Then Eq. (4) becomes

$$L = \begin{cases} \alpha[I + \delta - D]^2, & \text{if } I + \delta - D > 0, \\ \beta[D - (I + \delta)]^2, & \text{if } I + \delta - D < 0, \\ 0, & \text{if } I + \delta - D = 0. \end{cases} \tag{8}$$

Equation (5) is no longer true, and the subsequent calculations are more involved. We will leave it to the reader to work out the answer in this case.

Another variation of the above problem is the following. Assume that the loss due to excess demand or overstocking is proportional to the magnitude of the shortage or oversupply. Then the loss L is given by

$$L = \alpha|(I + \delta) - D|, \tag{9}$$

since $|(I + \delta) - D|$ gives the magnitude of the difference between the actual supply $I + \delta$ and the demand D. As before, α is a positive constant of proportionality. Again, if we wish to minimize the expected loss $E[L]$, how should we choose δ?

The answer to the above question is supplied by the following lemma.

Lemma 1. Let a be a real number and let X be a random variable. The value of a which minimizes $E[|X - a|]$ is $a = m_X$, the median of X. [Recall from Exercise 13 of Section 8.4 that m_X is defined to be any number m such that $P(X \leq m) \geq \frac{1}{2}$ and $P(X \geq m) \geq \frac{1}{2}$.]

To prove Lemma 1 we need another result; this result is stated in Lemma 2.

Lemma 2. Let X and Y be random variables defined on the same sample space S of a probability space (S, P) and assume that $X(s) \leq Y(s)$ for each $s \in S$. Then $E[X] \leq E[Y]$.

Proof. Let $Z = Y - X$. Then Z is a random variable which assumes only positive values since $Z(s) = Y(s) - X(s) \geq 0$. Thus

$$E[Z] = \sum_{i=1}^{n} z_i P(Z = z_i) \geq 0,$$

since $z_i \geq 0$ and $P(Z = z_i) \geq 0$ for each z_i in the range of Z. Thus

$$E[Z] = E[Y - X] = E[Y] - E[X] \geq 0$$

and

$$E[Y] \geq E[X]. \blacktriangle$$

Proof of Lemma 1. Let $a = m_X + c$, where $c > 0$ (see Fig. 8.12). Then $a > m_X$, and

$$
\begin{aligned}
|X - a| - |X - m_X| &= c, &&\text{if } X \leq m_X; \\
-c \leq |X - a| - |X - m_X| &\leq c, &&\text{if } m_X < X < m_X + c; \\
|X - a| - |X - m_X| &= -c, &&\text{if } X \geq m_X + c.
\end{aligned}
$$

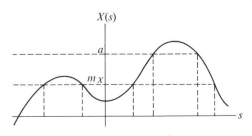

Fig. 8.12. Graph of X.

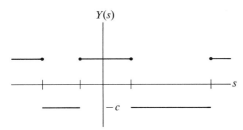

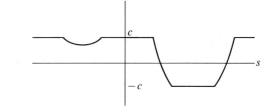

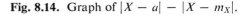

Fig. 8.13. Graph of Y.   **Fig. 8.14.** Graph of $|X - a| - |X - m_X|$.

Define a random variable Y by

$$Y = \begin{cases} c & \text{if } X \le m_X, \\ -c & \text{if } X > m_X. \end{cases}$$

It is readily seen that (see Figs. 8.13 and 8.14)

$$Y \le |X - a| - |X - m_X|,$$

and hence, by Lemma 2,

$$E[Y] \le E[|X - a|] - E[|X - m_X|].$$

Now

$$E[Y] = cP(Y = c) - cP(Y = -c) = cP(X \le m_X) - cP(X > m_X)$$
$$= c\{P(X \le m_X) - P(X > m_X)\} = c[2P(X \le m_X) - 1],$$

and

$$P(X \le m_X) \ge \tfrac{1}{2},$$

so that

$$E[Y] \ge 0.$$

Therefore

$$E[|X - a|] \ge E[|X - m_X|], \qquad \text{for all } a > m_X. \tag{10}$$

A similar argument [using the fact that $P(X \ge m_X) \ge \tfrac{1}{2}$] shows that (10) holds for all $a < m_X$ and hence that m_X minimizes $E[|X - a|]$.▲

If we let $a = I + \delta$ in Eq. (9), then we see by Lemma 1 that

$$E[L] = \alpha E[|D - a|]$$

is minimized by choosing $a = m_D$, the median of D. Unfortunately, it may not be possible to choose δ so that

$$I + \delta = m_D. \tag{11}$$

This occurs when $I > m_D$; in this case we can only choose $\delta = 0$ and make $I + \delta$ as close to m_D as possible.

We may summarize our results as follows:

(a) If the median m_D is greater than the inventory I on hand, order an amount δ so that $I + \delta = m_D$; that is, bring the inventory up to the median of the demand.
(b) If the median of the demand is less than the inventory, do not order any more; let the inventory decrease.

It should be noted that there may be more than one choice for the median m_D of D; any value of m_D leads to the same expected loss. Therefore any one of these values may be used.

The loss function L in Eq. (9) can be replaced by a slightly more general loss function:

$$L = \begin{cases} \alpha[(I + \delta) - D], & \text{if } I + \delta - D \geq 0, \\ \beta[D - (I + \delta)], & \text{if } I + \delta - D < 0, \end{cases} \quad (12)$$

where α and β are positive constants. This loss function would be appropriate if it were judged more costly to incur one type of possible loss than the other. For example, if $\beta > \alpha$, then it would be more costly to run out of stock than to carry too much stock. In Exercise 17 the reader is asked to show that if L is given by Eq. (12), $E[L]$, the expected loss, is minimized by choosing δ so that $I + \delta$ is as close to $m_D(\alpha, \beta)$ as possible, where $m_D(\alpha, \beta)$ is the $\beta/(\alpha + \beta)$ percentile of D and is defined as any number m such that

$$P(X \leq m) \geq \frac{\beta}{\alpha + \beta} \quad \text{and} \quad P(X \geq m) \geq \frac{\alpha}{\alpha + \beta}$$

or equivalently,

$$P(X \leq m) \geq \frac{\beta}{\alpha + \beta} \quad \text{and} \quad P(X < m) \leq \frac{\beta}{\alpha + \beta}.$$

APPLICATION 2 (*The Bakery Chain Problem*). A bakery chain has n outlets (retail stores); each of these outlets has a demand for a certain number of loaves of bread each day. Let D_i denote the number of loaves demanded at the ith outlet; we assume that D_i is a random variable. Let p_i be the probability function of D_i. The graph of a typical p_i might be as shown in Fig. 8.15. Let c_i be the number of loaves of bread delivered to the ith outlet. We assume that

$$c_1 + c_2 + \cdots + c_n = c, \quad (13)$$

where c is the total number of loaves baked each day. Let X_i be the actual number of loaves sold by the ith outlet. Then X_i is a random variable which may assume only the values $0, 1, \ldots, c_i$. Actually,

$$X_i = \min\{D_i, c_i\}, \quad (14)$$

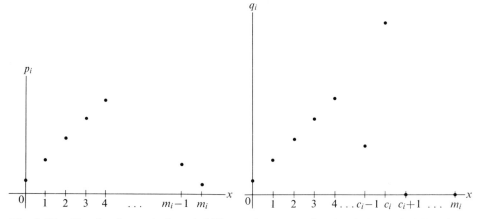

Fig. 8.15. Graph of a typical probability function p_i for the demand D_i; $p_i(x) = P(D_i = x)$.

Fig. 8.16. Graph of the probability function q_i of X_i; $q_i(x) = P(X_i = x)$.

where $\min\{x, y\}$ denotes the smaller of the two numbers x and y. In terms of the underlying sample space S, the value $X_i(s)$ is given by

$$X_i(s) = \min\{D_i(s), c_i\}, \qquad \text{for each } s \in S. \tag{15}$$

Of course Eq. (15) is just what is meant by (14). Letting q_i denote the probability function of X_i, we have

$$
\begin{aligned}
q_i(0) &= p_i(0), \\
q_i(1) &= p_i(1), \\
&\vdots \\
q_i(c_i - 1) &= p_i(c_i - 1), \\
q_i(c_i) &= p_i(c_i) + p_i(c_i + 1) + p_i(c_i + 2) + \cdots,
\end{aligned}
$$

since $P(X_i = k) = P(D_i = k)$ for $0 \le k < c_i$ and

$$P(X_i = c_i) = P(D_i \ge c_i) = p_i(c_i) + p_i(c_i + 1) + \cdots.$$

A typical graph of a probability function q_i for the random variable X_i defined by Eq. (14) is given in Fig. 8.16.

Suppose that each loaf of bread costs a cents to produce and sells for b cents, where $b > a$. Ignoring transportation and handling costs, we see that the (net) profit N on a day's sales is

$$N = \sum_{i=1}^{n} bX_i - ca. \tag{16}$$

Since each X_i is a random variable, so is N. Also, since X_i depends on c_i, N is a function of $c_1, c_2, \ldots, c_n$.

We can now formulate the first problem. Later we shall study a more general version of this problem.

Problem 1. Given that the total number of loaves baked c is fixed, that all the probability functions p_i are the same, and that the company decides to operate the business (choose $c_1, c_2, \ldots, c_n$) in such a way that the expected profit $E[N]$ is a maximum, determine how $c_1, c_2, \ldots, c_n$ should be chosen.

Thus we are given that the random variables $D_1, \ldots, D_n$ are identically distributed and that

$$c_1 + c_2 + \cdots + c_n = c,$$

where c is a fixed constant. We are to choose $c_1, \ldots, c_n$ such that

$$E[N] = \sum_{i=1}^{n} bE[X_i] - ca \qquad (17)$$

is a maximum. A little reflection will quickly convince the reader that there is an obvious solution to this problem. Since the D_i's are identically distributed, there is no point in sending more bread to one store than another. Thus we should send the same amount to each store and the obvious solution is to choose

$$c_1 = c_2 = \cdots = c_n = c/n. \qquad (18)$$

We now proceed to give a mathematical justification of the choices given in (18). Much of what we do is more elaborate than necessary to solve Problem 1, but the techniques are useful in solving similar problems.

We wish to choose $c_1, c_2, \ldots, c_n$ so that

$$E[N] = \sum_{i=1}^{n} bE[X_i] - ca \qquad (17)$$

is as large as possible. Since b is a constant and ca is the constant cost of producing the c loaves, $E[N]$ will be a maximum when

$$\sum_{i=1}^{n} E[X_i] \qquad (19)$$

is a maximum. Let us examine each term $E[X_i]$ in expression (19). Since $X_i = \min\{D_i, c_i\}$, X_i depends on c_i; hence $E[X_i] = E[\min\{D_i, c_i\}]$ depends on c_i. We can indicate this dependence by writing

$$d_i(c_i) = E[X_i].$$

What we have done here is define a function d_i by setting

$$d_i(t) = E[\min\{D_i, t\}],$$

for each real number $t \geq 0$. In attempting to maximize the expression (19) we are attempting to maximize

$$d_1(c_1) + d_2(c_2) + \cdots + d_n(c_n) \tag{20}$$

subject to the conditions

$$c_1 + c_2 + \cdots + c_n = c, \qquad c_1 \geq 0, c_2 \geq 0, \ldots, c_n \geq 0. \tag{21}$$

Since each D_i has the same probability function in Problem 1, we see that

$$d_1(t) = d_2(t) = \cdots = d_n(t),$$

for each real number t, and hence we can call this common value $d(t)$. Expression (20) becomes

$$d(c_1) + d(c_2) + \cdots + d(c_n). \tag{22}$$

The problem of maximizing (22) subject to conditions (21) is a special case of the following problem.

Problem 2. Let $d_1, d_2, \ldots, d_n$ be given functions. Maximize

$$d_1(c_1) + d_2(c_2) + \cdots + d_n(c_n) \tag{20}$$

by appropriately choosing $c_1, c_2, \ldots, c_n$, where $c_1, c_2, \ldots, c_n$ must satisfy

$$c_1 + c_2 + \cdots + c_n = c, \qquad c_1 \geq 0, c_2 \geq 0, \ldots, c_n \geq 0, \tag{21}$$

and where c is a given positive number.

The maximum value of expression (20) subject to the conditions (21) can be denoted by

$$\max_{\substack{\Sigma c_i = c \\ c_i \geq 0}} \{d_1(c_1) + \cdots + d_n(c_n)\}.$$

This makes clear that the maximum value depends on the number n of functions (and on the functions $d_1, \ldots, d_n$, of course) and on the value c. To indicate this we shall write

$$f_n(c) = \max_{\substack{\Sigma c_i = c \\ c_i \geq 0}} \{d_1(c_1) + \cdots + d_n(c_n)\}. \tag{23}$$

The following lemma is useful in dealing with Problem 2.

Lemma 3. Let $f_n(c)$ be as given in Eq. (23). (We always assume that this maximum exists for each n and each c.) Then

$$f_n(c) = \max_{0 \leq c_n \leq c} \{f_{n-1}(c - c_n) + d_n(c_n)\}, \qquad n \geq 2. \tag{24}$$

In the above lemma

$$f_{n-1}(c - c_n) = \max_{\substack{\Sigma_1^{n-1} c_i = c - c_n \\ c_i \geq 0}} \{d_1(c_1) + \cdots + d_{n-1}(c_{n-1})\};$$

that is, $f_{n-1}(c - c_n)$ is the result of maximizing the sum of the first $n - 1$ functions $d_1, \ldots, d_{n-1}$ subject to the condition that the sum of c_i values used add to $c - c_n$. Let us examine some special cases:

$$f_1(c) = \max_{\substack{c_1 = c \\ c_1 \geq 0}} \{d_1(c_1)\} = d_1(c);$$

$$f_2(c) = \max_{\substack{c_1 + c_2 = c \\ c_1, c_2 \geq 0}} \{d_1(c_1) + d_2(c_2)\} = \max_{0 \leq c_2 \leq c} \{d_1(c - c_2) + d_2(c_2)\}$$

$$= \max_{0 \leq c_2 \leq c} \{f_1(c - c_2) + d_2(c_2)\},$$

since $c_1 = c - c_2$ and $d_1(c - c_2) = f_1(c - c_2)$. Thus Lemma 3 is valid for $n = 2$. We now show that Eq. (24) is valid in general. When the quantity

$$d_1(c_1) + \cdots + d_n(c_n)$$

is maximized, some particular value of c_n, $0 \leq c_n \leq c$, will have been chosen; there will remain out of the total available, c, an amount $c - c_n$. This will have been distributed among the first $n - 1$ d's. Thus we have a value for

$$d_1(c_1) + \cdots + d_{n-1}(c_{n-1}), \qquad c_1 + \cdots + c_{n-1} = c - c_n.$$

This value is always less than or equal to

$$f_{n-1}(c - c_n) = \max_{\substack{\Sigma c_i = c - c_n \\ c_i \geq 0}} \{d_1(c_1) + \cdots + d_{n-1}(c_{n-1})\}.$$

Thus we can always do as well by choosing values of $c_1, \ldots, c_{n-1}$ which give the maximum value $f_{n-1}(c - c_n)$. Hence

$$f_n(c) = f_{n-1}(c - c_n) + d_n(c_n),$$

where c_n is a maximizing value. Thus

$$f_n(c) = \max_{0 \leq c_n \leq c} \{f_{n-1}(c - c_n) + d_n(c_n)\}.\blacktriangle$$

We wish to apply this basic lemma to the problem we have been studying, Problem 1. There all d_i's were the same, that is,

$$d(t) = d_1(t) = d_2(t) = \cdots = d_n(t) \qquad \text{for all } t.$$

We are attempting to maximize

$$d(c_1) + d(c_2) + \cdots + d(c_n). \tag{22}$$

By Lemma 3,

$$f_n(c) = \max_{\substack{\Sigma c_i = c \\ c_i \geq 0}} \{d(c_1) + \cdots + d(c_n)\}$$

$$= \max_{0 \leq c_n \leq c} \{f_{n-1}(c - c_n) + d(c_n)\}.$$

We wish to find this maximum (assuming, of course, that it exists) and the values of $c_1, c_2, \ldots, c_n$ which give this value. To do this we need the following definition.

Definition 8.10. A real-valued function d defined on an interval I (usually R^1 or the nonnegative real numbers) is said to be concave if, for each real number λ, $0 \leq \lambda \leq 1$, and each pair of points $x, y \in I$,

$$d(\lambda x + (1 - \lambda)y) \geq \lambda d(x) + (1 - \lambda) d(y).$$

Geometrically, this says that the graph of d on any interval $J = [x, y]$ lies on or above the set of points lying on the line segment joining the points $(x, d(x))$ and $(y, d(y))$; see Figs. 8.17 and 8.18.

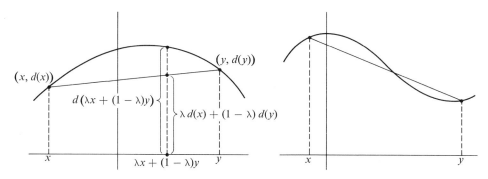

Fig. 8.17. The graph of a concave function.   **Fig. 8.18.** The graph of a nonconcave function.

The next lemma shows that, for concave functions d, the problem of finding $f_n(c)$ is readily solved.

Lemma 4. Let d be a concave function defined for the nonnegative real numbers and let

$$f_n(c) = \max_{\substack{\Sigma c_i = c \\ c_i \geq 0}} \{d(c_1) + \cdots + d(c_n)\}.$$

Then $f_n(c) = n \, d(c/n)$ and the choice

$$c_1 = c_2 = \cdots = c_n = c/n$$

maximizes the sum $d(c_1) + \cdots + d(c_n)$ for $c_i \geq 0$, $1 \leq i \leq n$, and $\sum_{i=1}^{n} c_i = c$.

Proof. The proof proceeds by induction on n. For $n = 1$,

$$f_1(c) = d(c).$$

For $n = 2$,

$$d(c_1) + d(c_2) = 2[\tfrac{1}{2} \, d(c_1) + \tfrac{1}{2} \, d(c_2)] \leq 2 \, d\!\left(\frac{c_1 + c_2}{2}\right) = 2 \, d(c/2),$$

by the concavity of d (using $\lambda = \tfrac{1}{2}$) and the fact that $c_1 + c_2 = c$. Thus we see that

$$f_2(c) \leq 2 \, d(c/2),$$

but this value is obviously achieved by taking $c_1 = c_2 = c/2$. Therefore

$$f_2(c) = 2 \, d(c/2).$$

We next assume that

$$f_{n-1}(t) = (n - 1) \, d\!\left(\frac{t}{n - 1}\right), \qquad \text{for all } t \geq 0,$$

and show that

$$f_n(c) = n \, d(c/n).$$

By Lemma 3,

$$f_n(c) = \max_{0 \leq c_n \leq c} \{ f_{n-1}(c - c_n) + d(c_n) \};$$

also, by our induction hypothesis,

$$f_{n-1}(c - c_n) = (n - 1) \, d\!\left(\frac{c - c_n}{n - 1}\right).$$

Therefore

$$f_n(c) = \max_{0 \leq c_n \leq c} \left\{ (n - 1) \, d\!\left(\frac{c - c_n}{n - 1}\right) + d(c_n) \right\}.$$

Now let $\lambda = (n - 1)/n$ in the definition of concavity; we get

$$n \left\{ \frac{n - 1}{n} \, d\!\left(\frac{c - c_n}{n - 1}\right) + \frac{1}{n} \, d(c_n) \right\} \leq n \, d\!\left(\frac{n - 1}{n} \left(\frac{c - c_n}{n - 1}\right) + \frac{1}{n} \, c_n\right) = n \, d\!\left(\frac{c}{n}\right).$$

Therefore

$$f_n(c) \leq n \, d(c/n),$$

but this value is actually achieved for f_n if we choose $c_1 = c_2 = \cdots = c_n = c/n$, since

$$\underbrace{d(c/n) + \cdots + d(c/n)}_{n \text{ terms}} = n\, d(c/n).$$

Therefore

$$f_n(c) = n\, d(c/n),$$

and by induction the lemma is proved.▲

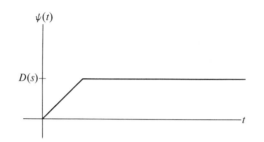

Fig. 8.19. The graph of $\psi(t) = \min\{D(s), t\}$ for fixed $s \in S$.

To apply the results of Lemma 4 to the bakery chain problem, Problem 1, we need to show that the function d of that problem is concave. Recall that

$$d(t) = E[\min\{D, t\}], \qquad t \ge 0,$$

where D is any random variable having the common probability function p_i of the D_i's. The random variable $\min\{D, t\}$ has for each $s \in S$, the sample space on which D is defined, the value $\min\{D(s), i\}$. For a fixed $s \in S$, let us denote this value by $\psi(t)$, that is, $\psi(t) = \min\{D(s), t\}$. The graph of ψ appears in Fig. 8.19. (Of course, we are assuming that $D(s) \ge 0$, since it represents the demand for a product.) From the graph of ψ in Fig. 8.19 we see that ψ is a concave function of t:

$$\psi(\lambda t_1 + (1 - \lambda)t_2) \ge \lambda\psi(t_1) + (1 - \lambda)\psi(t_2).$$

Therefore

$$\min\{D, \lambda t_1 + (1 - \lambda)t_2\} \ge \lambda \min\{D, t_1\} + (1 - \lambda)\min\{D, t_2\}.$$

Using the previously established fact (Lemma 2) that $E[X] \ge E[Y]$ if $X \ge Y$, we have

$$E[\min\{D, \lambda t_1 + (1 - \lambda)t_2\}] \ge \lambda E[\min\{D, t_1\}] + (1 - \lambda)E[\min\{D, t_2\}].$$

In terms of the function d, this asserts that

$$d(\lambda t_1 + (1 - \lambda)t_2) \ge \lambda\, d(t_1) + (1 - \lambda)\, d(t_2),$$

and hence that d is a concave function of t, $t \ge 0$.

Having established that the function d in the bakery chain problem is a concave function, we may apply Lemma 4. Lemma 4 asserts that the maximum of $\sum_{i=1}^{n} E[X_i]$ is $n\, d(c/n) = nE[\min\{D, c/n\}]$ and that this value is achieved by sending the same amount c/n to each outlet. Thus the maximum expected profit is

$$\max E[N] = nb\, d(c/n) - ca. \tag{25}$$

The reader might find it helpful to note that

$$d(c/n) = E[\min\{D, (c/n)\}] = \sum_{x < c/n} xP(D = x) + (c/n)P(D \geq c/n)$$

$$= \sum_{x < c/n} xp(x) + (c/n)P(D \geq c/n), \tag{26}$$

where p is the common probability function for the demands D_i.

Combining (25) and (26), we have

$$\max E[N] = nb \sum_{x < c/n} xp(x) + bcP(D \geq c/n) - ca$$

$$= c[bP(D \geq c/n) - a] + nb \sum_{x < c/n} xp(x). \tag{27}$$

APPLICATION 3 [The Bakery Chain Problem (continued)]. We now consider the following generalization of Problem 1.

Problem 3. Let us assume that the total number c of loaves baked is fixed and that the bakery chain decides to operate the business (choose $c_1, c_2, \ldots, c_n$) in such a way that the expected profit $E[N]$ is a maximum. How should $c_1, c_2, \ldots, c_n$ be chosen?

Problem 3 differs from Problem 1 in that each of the demands D_i may have a distinct probability function p_i. Thus the functions d_i defined by

$$d_i(c_i) = E[X_i], \tag{28}$$

where $X_i = \min\{D_i, c_i\}$, may be different. If we define the functions d_i by Eq. (28), then Problem 3 is exactly equivalent to Problem 2: we are attempting to maximize

$$d_1(c_1) + d_2(c_2) + \cdots + d_n(c_n) \tag{20}$$

by choosing $c_1, c_2, \ldots, c_n$ subject to the conditions

$$c_1 + c_2 + \cdots + c_n = c, \qquad c_1 \geq 0, c_2 \geq 0, \ldots, c_n \geq 0, \tag{21}$$

since

$$E[N] = b \sum_{i=1}^{n} d_i(c_i) - ca$$

will be maximized whenever $\sum_{i=1}^{n} d_i(c_i)$ is maximized.

Let us note that

$$d_i(c_i) = E[X_i] = E[\min \{D_i, c_i\}] = \sum_{x \le c_i} x p_i(x) + c_i \sum_{x > c_i} p_i(x)$$
$$= \sum_{x \le c_i} x p_i(x) + c_i P(D_i > c_i), \tag{29}$$

where p_i is the probability function for D_i. Equation (29) expresses $d_i(c_i)$ in terms of the probability function of D_i.

The prcblem we are studying is resolved by the following lemma.

Lemma 5. If it is possible to choose $c_1, c_2, \ldots, c_n$ satisfying (21) so that

$$P(D_1 > c_1) = P(D_2 > c_2) = \cdots = P(D_n > c_n),$$

then this choice of $c_1, c_2, \ldots, c_n$ will maximize $d_1(c_1) + \cdots + d_n(c_n)$, where $d_i(c_i) = E[X_i]$.

Before proceeding to the proof of Lemma 5, let us note that it can be specialized to the solution of Problem 1 when the D_i's are identically distributed. In that case, if we choose $c_1 = c_2 = \cdots = c_n = c/n$, then

$$P(D_1 > c_1) = P(D_1 > c/n), \ldots, P(D_n > c_n) = P(D_n > c/n)$$

and

$$P(D_1 > c/n) = P(D_2 > c/n) = \cdots = P(D_n > c/n).$$

Also, it should be pointed out that Lemma 5 solves Problem 3, but not, in general, Problem 2, since the functions d_i in Problem 2 do not necessarily arise in the manner indicated in Lemma 5.

Proof of Lemma 5. The proof consists of calculating the value of

$$d_1(c_1) + d_2(c_2) + \cdots + d_n(c_n),$$

when the c_i's are chosen so that the probabilities $P(D_i > c_i)$ are all equal, and showing that the value obtained by any other choice of the c_i's is less than or equal to the former value. To this end, let

$$\bar{\beta} = d_1(\bar{c}_1) + \cdots + d_n(\bar{c}_n) = \sum_{i=1}^{n} d_i(\bar{c}_i),$$

where $\bar{c}_1 + \bar{c}_2 + \cdots + \bar{c}_n = c$ and

$$P(D_1 > \bar{c}_1) = P(D_2 > \bar{c}_2) = \cdots = P(D_n > \bar{c}_n) = \alpha.$$

Suppose now that $\tilde{c}_1, \tilde{c}_2, \ldots, \tilde{c}_n$ are values for $c_1, c_2, \ldots, c_n$ for which

$$c_1 + c_2 + \cdots + c_n = c, \qquad c_1 \ge 0, c_2 \ge 0, \ldots, c_n \ge 0,$$

and let

$$\tilde{\beta} = d_1(\tilde{c}_1) + \cdots + d_n(\tilde{c}_n) = \sum_{i=1}^{n} d_i(\tilde{c}_i).$$

We now show that $\tilde{\beta}$ is equal to $\bar{\beta}$ plus a term which is less than or equal to zero and hence $\tilde{\beta} \leq \bar{\beta}$.

$$\tilde{\beta} = \sum_{i=1}^{n} d_i(\tilde{c}_i) = \sum_{i=1}^{n} d_i(\bar{c}_i) + \sum_{i=1}^{n} [d_i(\tilde{c}_i) - d_i(\bar{c}_i)]$$

$$= \bar{\beta} + \sum_{i=1}^{n} [d_i(\tilde{c}_i) - d_i(\bar{c}_i)]. \tag{30}$$

Each of the terms $d_i(\tilde{c}_i) - d_i(\bar{c}_i)$ will now be shown to be less than or equal to $(\tilde{c}_i - \bar{c}_i)\alpha$. To do this, we divide the integers $1, 2, \ldots, n$ into three sets A, B, and C shown below:

$$A = \{i \mid 1 \leq i \leq n \quad \text{and} \quad \bar{c}_i = \tilde{c}_i\},$$
$$B = \{i \mid 1 \leq i \leq n \quad \text{and} \quad \bar{c}_i > \tilde{c}_i\},$$
$$C = \{i \mid 1 \leq i \leq n \quad \text{and} \quad \bar{c}_i < \tilde{c}_i\}.$$

For $i \in A$, $\tilde{c}_i = \bar{c}_i$ and hence $d_i(\tilde{c}_i) = d_i(\bar{c}_i)$. Thus

$$d_i(\tilde{c}_i) - d_i(\bar{c}_i) = (\tilde{c}_i - \bar{c}_i)\alpha, \qquad i \in A.$$

For $i \in B$, $\tilde{c}_i < \bar{c}_i$ and hence by (29),

$$d_i(\tilde{c}_i) - d_i(\bar{c}_i) = \sum_{x \leq \tilde{c}_i} x p_i(x) - \sum_{x \leq \bar{c}_i} x p_i(x) + \tilde{c}_i P(D_i > \tilde{c}_i) - \bar{c}_i P(D_i > \bar{c}_i)$$

$$= -\sum_{\tilde{c}_i < x \leq \bar{c}_i} x p_i(x) + \tilde{c}_i P(D_i > \tilde{c}_i) - \bar{c}_i P(D_i > \bar{c}_i)$$

$$\quad + \tilde{c}_i P(D_i > \bar{c}_i) - \tilde{c}_i P(D_i > \bar{c}_i)$$

$$= -\sum_{\tilde{c}_i < x \leq \bar{c}_i} x p_i(x) + \tilde{c}_i P(\tilde{c}_i < D_i \leq \bar{c}_i) + (\tilde{c}_i - \bar{c}_i)\alpha$$

$$\leq -\tilde{c}_i P(\tilde{c}_i < D_i \leq \bar{c}_i) + \tilde{c}_i P(\tilde{c}_i < D_i \leq \bar{c}_i) + (\tilde{c}_i - \bar{c}_i)\alpha$$

$$= (\tilde{c}_i - \bar{c}_i)\alpha.$$

For $i \in C$, $\bar{c}_i < \tilde{c}_i$ and hence by (29),

$$d_i(\tilde{c}_i) - d_i(\bar{c}_i) = \sum_{x \leq \tilde{c}_i} x p_i(x) - \sum_{x \leq \bar{c}_i} x p_i(x) + \tilde{c}_i P(D_i > \tilde{c}_i) - \bar{c}_i P(D_i > \bar{c}_i)$$

$$= \sum_{\bar{c}_i < x \leq \tilde{c}_i} x p_i(x) + \tilde{c}_i P(D_i > \tilde{c}_i) - \bar{c}_i P(D_i > \bar{c}_i)$$

$$\quad + \tilde{c}_i P(D_i > \bar{c}_i) - \tilde{c}_i P(D_i > \bar{c}_i)$$

$$= \sum_{\bar{c}_i < x \leq \tilde{c}_i} x p_i(x) - \tilde{c}_i P(\bar{c}_i < D_i \leq \tilde{c}_i) + (\tilde{c}_i - \bar{c}_i)P(D_i > \bar{c}_i)$$

$$\leq \tilde{c}_i P(\bar{c}_i < D_i \leq \tilde{c}_i) - \tilde{c}_i P(\bar{c}_i < D_i \leq \tilde{c}_i) + (\tilde{c}_i - \bar{c}_i)\alpha$$

$$= (\tilde{c}_i - \bar{c}_i)\alpha.$$

Therefore we have shown that

$$d_i(\tilde{c}_i) - d_i(\bar{c}_i) \le (\tilde{c}_i - \bar{c}_i)\alpha, \qquad \text{for } 1 \le i \le n. \tag{31}$$

Combining (30) and (31), we have

$$\tilde{\beta} \le \bar{\beta} + \sum_{i=1}^{n} (\tilde{c}_i - \bar{c}_i)\alpha = \bar{\beta} + \alpha\left[\sum_{i=1}^{n} \tilde{c}_i - \sum_{i=1}^{n} \bar{c}_i\right] = \bar{\beta} + \alpha(c - c) = \bar{\beta}.$$

Thus we have shown that $\tilde{\beta} \le \bar{\beta}$ for any sum $\tilde{\beta}$ and therefore $\bar{\beta}$ must be the maximum value.▲

Let us now consider a related problem.

Problem 4. If the manager of the ith store is free to choose c_i, the number of loaves delivered to his store, how should he select c_i to maximize his expected profit (ignoring all other stores)?

It is clear that the (net) profit from the ith store is

$$b \min\{D_i, c_i\} - ac_i, \tag{32}$$

when the demand is D_i and the number of loaves supplied is c_i. This quantity is a random variable and its expectation for a given value of c_i is

$$bE\left[\min\{D_i, c_i\}\right] - ac_i. \tag{33}$$

Since $\min\{D_i, c_i\} = X_i$ and $d_i(c_i) = E[X_i]$, the expression (33) becomes

$$bd_i(c_i) - ac_i. \tag{34}$$

Let us denote this quantity by g_i, that is,

$$g_i(c_i) = bd_i(c_i) - ac_i. \tag{35}$$

We wish to maximize g_i by appropriately choosing c_i. The following lemma indicates a solution.

Lemma 6. If it is possible to choose $c_i \ge 0$ so that $P(D_i > c_i) = a/b$, then this choice of c_i will maximize

$$bE[\min\{D_i, c_i\}] - ac_i. \tag{33}$$

In this case the maximum value is

$$b \sum_{x \le c_i} x p_i(x). \tag{36}$$

Proof. Let $\bar{c}_i$ be a number so that $P(D_i > \bar{c}_i) = a/b$ and suppose $\tilde{c}_i$ is a choice of c_i for which $P(D_i > \tilde{c}_i) \neq a/b$, say $P(D_i > \tilde{c}_i) > a/b$. Then $\tilde{c}_i < \bar{c}_i$, and we wish to show that

$$g_i(\tilde{c}_i) \leq g_i(\bar{c}_i).$$

An easy calculation, using (29), shows that

$$g_i(\bar{c}_i) = b\Big[\sum_{x \leq \bar{c}_i} xp_i(x) + \bar{c}_i P(D_i > \bar{c}_i)\Big] - a\bar{c}_i = b\sum_{x \leq \bar{c}_i} xp_i(x).$$

Again using (29), we find, for $\tilde{c}_i < \bar{c}_i$, that

$$
\begin{aligned}
g_i(\tilde{c}_i) &= g_i(\bar{c}_i) + [g_i(\tilde{c}_i) - g_i(\bar{c}_i)] \\
&= g_i(\bar{c}_i) + b\Big[\sum_{x \leq \tilde{c}_i} xp_i(x) + \tilde{c}_i P(D_i > \tilde{c}_i)\Big] - a\tilde{c}_i - b\sum_{x \leq \bar{c}_i} xp_i(x) \\
&= g_i(\bar{c}_i) + b\Big[- \sum_{\tilde{c}_i < x \leq \bar{c}_i} xp_i(x) + \tilde{c}_i P(D_i > \tilde{c}_i)\Big] - a\tilde{c}_i \\
&\leq g_i(\bar{c}_i) + b[-\tilde{c}_i P(\tilde{c}_i < D_i \leq \bar{c}_i) + \tilde{c}_i P(D_i > \tilde{c}_i)] - a\tilde{c}_i \\
&= g_i(\bar{c}_i) + b[\tilde{c}_i P(D_i > \bar{c}_i)] - a\tilde{c}_i \\
&= g_i(\bar{c}_i) + b\tilde{c}_i(a/b) - a\tilde{c}_i \\
&= g_i(\bar{c}_i).
\end{aligned}
$$

Therefore

$$g_i(\bar{c}_i) = b\sum_{x \leq \bar{c}_i} xp_i(x)$$

is the maximum value.▲

Another problem of interest is the following in which we discard the assumption from Problem 3 that c, the total number of loaves baked, is fixed.

Problem 5. If the manufacturer can fulfill any demand, how much should be produced and how should it be distributed to maximize the manufacturer's expected profit?

It is clear that the expected profit $E[N]$, when c_i loaves are sent to the ith outlet, is

$$E[N] = \sum_{i=1}^{n} \{bE[\min\{D_i, c_i\}] - ac_i\} = \sum_{i=1}^{n} g_i(c_i).$$

Hence, if there are no restrictions on the amount that can be produced, then the amount manufactured should be such that each of the terms $g_i(c_i)$ is maximized. Thus, by Lemma 6, an amount

$$c = \bar{c}_1 + \bar{c}_2 + \cdots + \bar{c}_n,$$

where $\bar{c}_i$ is such that

$$P(D_i > \bar{c}_i) = a/b, \qquad 1 \leq i \leq n, \tag{37}$$

should be manufactured. This assumes, of course, that it is possible to select $\bar{c}_i$ such that $P(D_i > \bar{c}_i) = a/b$, for $1 \le i \le n$. Also, from Lemma 6, it is apparent that the maximum value for $E[N]$ is

$$b \sum_{i=1}^{n} \sum_{x \le \bar{c}_i} x p_i(x). \tag{38}$$

It should be pointed out that most of Applications 2 and 3 were motivated by consideration of so-called "continuous" random variables. In particular, in the "continuous" case, simple facts from calculus show that the values given for c_i in Lemmas 5 and 6 are the obvious choices. In our treatment, it is unfortunately not apparent that these are the obvious choices.

APPLICATION 4 (Estes' Learning Model). A rat is sent down a narrow passageway which at some point branches into two passageways, A and B, as shown in Fig. 8.20. Food is put at the end of passage A with probability $1 - a$, and at the end of passage B with probability $1 - b$. Assume that the rat goes through the maze many times and that no "learning" takes place, that is, if the rat finds food at the previous trial, he selects the same passage; if no food is found, he selects the opposite passage. [We assume that the rat cannot remember back more than one trial; if he could, he would use this information to estimate which one of the probabilities $1 - a$ and $1 - b$ is larger and then always go to that side.] We wish to calculate the probabilities of going to the different sides and to find what the limiting behavior is if the experiment is repeated indefinitely. These values can then be compared with the actual observed proportions of the time that a rat chooses the sides to see if "learning" does actually take place.

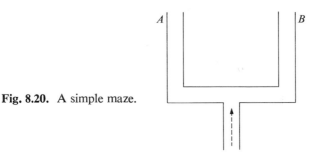

Fig. 8.20. A simple maze.

To be more precise, we make the following assumptions:

(i) At the first trial the rat is just as likely to select passage A as passage B.

(ii) If at the nth trial the rat finds food, he will select the same passage on the $(n + 1)$ trial.

(iii) If at the nth trial the rat does not find food, he selects the other passage on the $(n + 1)$ trial.

(iv) Food is placed in the two passages with given probabilities: $1 - a$ is the probability of placing food in passage A and $1 - b$ is the probability of placing food in passage B, where $0 \leq a \leq 1, 0 \leq b \leq 1$.

If we let p_n be the probability that the rat chooses passage A on the nth trial and q_n be the probability that the rat chooses passage B on the nth trial, then we wish to find p_n and q_n and to study their behavior as $n \to \infty$. To achieve this end we introduce the following notation:

$$A_n = \text{the event that the rat chooses channel } A \text{ on the } n\text{th trial,}$$
$$B_n = \text{the event that the rat chooses channel } B \text{ on the } n\text{th trial,}$$
$$F_n = \text{the event that the rat gets food on the } n\text{th trial.}$$

Then
$$p_n = P(A_n) \quad \text{and} \quad q_n = P(B_n).$$

In order to calculate these quantities, observe that the rat chooses channel A on the nth trial in the cases (and only in these cases) that he chose channel A on the previous trial and found food on that trial, or that he chose channel B on the previous trial and did not find food on that trial. Thus

$$A_n = (A_{n-1} \cap F_{n-1}) \cup (B_{n-1} \cap F_{n-1}^c). \tag{39}$$

Similarly,

$$B_n = (B_{n-1} \cap F_{n-1}) \cup (A_{n-1} \cap F_{n-1}^c). \tag{40}$$

Using the fact that A_{n-1} and B_{n-1} are disjoint and using conditional probabilities, we find from (39) that

$$\begin{aligned} P(A_n) &= P(A_{n-1} \cap F_{n-1}) + P(B_{n-1} \cap F_{n-1}^c) \\ &= P(F_{n-1} \mid A_{n-1})P(A_{n-1}) + P(F_{n-1}^c \mid B_{n-1})P(B_{n-1}) \\ &= (1 - a)P(A_{n-1}) + bP(B_{n-1}), \end{aligned}$$

since
$$P(F_{n-1} \mid A_{n-1}) = 1 - a$$

and
$$P(F_{n-1}^c \mid B_{n-1}) = 1 - P(F_{n-1} \mid B_{n-1}) = 1 - (1 - b) = b$$

by assumption (iv). Thus we have

$$p_n = (1 - a)p_{n-1} + bq_{n-1}, \quad \text{for } n \geq 2. \tag{41}$$

In the same manner, using (40) instead of (39), we find that

$$q_n = ap_{n-1} + (1 - b)q_{n-1}, \quad \text{for } n \geq 2. \tag{42}$$

Also, by assumption (i), we know that

$$p_1 = q_1 = \tfrac{1}{2}. \tag{43}$$

Equations (41) and (42) are a pair of simultaneous difference equations which we wish to solve with the initial probabilities given by equations (43). To solve these equations, it is convenient to introduce matrices. Let

$$v(n) = \left\| \begin{matrix} p_n \\ q_n \end{matrix} \right\|$$

be the column vector of the probabilities of the two responses on the nth trial and let

$$A = \left\| \begin{matrix} 1 - a & b \\ a & 1 - b \end{matrix} \right\|.$$

Then Eqs. (41) and (42) become

$$v(n) = A * v(n - 1), \qquad n \geq 2, \tag{44}$$

and equations (43) become

$$v(1) = \left\| \begin{matrix} \frac{1}{2} \\ \frac{1}{2} \end{matrix} \right\|. \tag{45}$$

Using Eq. (45) we can easily solve Eq. (44) as follows:

$$v(2) = A * v(1),$$
$$v(3) = A * v(2) = A * (A * v(1)) = A^2 * v(1),$$
$$\vdots$$
$$v(n) = A^{n-1} * v(1).$$

Thus

$$v(n) = A^{n-1} * \left\| \begin{matrix} \frac{1}{2} \\ \frac{1}{2} \end{matrix} \right\|. \tag{46}$$

Unfortunately, Eq. (46) is not very useful, since we do not explicitly know A^{n-1}. To calculate A^{n-1}, we observe that

$$A = \left\| \begin{matrix} 1 - a & b \\ a & 1 - b \end{matrix} \right\|$$

$$= 1 \cdot \left\| \begin{matrix} \dfrac{b}{b + a} & \dfrac{b}{b + a} \\ \dfrac{a}{b + a} & \dfrac{a}{b + a} \end{matrix} \right\| + (1 - a - b) \left\| \begin{matrix} \dfrac{a}{b + a} & -\dfrac{b}{b + a} \\ -\dfrac{a}{b + a} & \dfrac{b}{b + a} \end{matrix} \right\|$$

$$= 1 \cdot B + (1 - a - b) \cdot C,$$

where

$$B = \left\| \begin{matrix} \dfrac{b}{b + a} & \dfrac{b}{b + a} \\ \dfrac{a}{b + a} & \dfrac{a}{b + a} \end{matrix} \right\|, \qquad C = \left\| \begin{matrix} \dfrac{a}{b + a} & -\dfrac{b}{b + a} \\ -\dfrac{a}{b + a} & \dfrac{b}{b + a} \end{matrix} \right\|.$$

A systematic discussion of why the matrices B and C are introduced may be found in S. Goldberg, *Introduction to Difference Equations* (New York: Wiley, 1958, pp. 226–232). Observe that

$$B * C = \begin{Vmatrix} 0 & 0 \\ 0 & 0 \end{Vmatrix} = 0_{2 \times 2}, \tag{47}$$

$$B * B = B, \tag{48}$$

$$C * C = C. \tag{49}$$

Using (47), (48), and (49), we see that

$$A^2 = [1 \cdot B + (1 - a - b)C] * [1 \cdot B + (1 - a - b)C]$$
$$= 1^2 \cdot B * B + (1 - a - b)^2 C * C$$
$$= 1^2 \cdot B + (1 - a - b)^2 C,$$

and, more generally, that

$$A^{n-1} = 1^{n-1}B + (1 - a - b)^{n-1}C. \tag{50}$$

Equation (50) now affords us with a convenient method for calculating $v(n)$:

$$v(n) = A^{n-1} * v(1) = [B + (1 - a - b)^{n-1}C] * v(1)$$
$$= B * v(1) + (1 - a - b)^{n-1}C * v(1)$$
$$= \begin{Vmatrix} \dfrac{b}{b + a} \\ \dfrac{a}{b + a} \end{Vmatrix} + (1 - a - b)^{n-1} \begin{Vmatrix} \dfrac{a - b}{2(b + a)} \\ \dfrac{b - a}{2(b + a)} \end{Vmatrix}.$$

Therefore

$$
\begin{aligned}
p_n &= \frac{b}{b + a} + (1 - a - b)^{n-1} \frac{a - b}{2(b + a)}, \\
q_n &= \frac{a}{b + a} + (1 - a - b)^{n-1} \frac{b - a}{2(b + a)}.
\end{aligned}
\tag{51}
$$

From (51) it is apparent that, for $0 < a + b < 2$,

$$
\begin{aligned}
p_n &\to \frac{b}{b + a}, \qquad \text{as} \quad n \to \infty, \\
q_n &\to \frac{a}{b + a}, \qquad \text{as} \quad n \to \infty.
\end{aligned}
\tag{52}
$$

If $a + b = 0$, then $a = b = 0$ and $1 - a = 1 - b = 1$, so that the rat will always repeat his initial decision. Thus

$$p_n = \tfrac{1}{2}, \qquad q_n = \tfrac{1}{2}$$

in this case. This can be readily verified from Eq. (46). If $a + b = 2$, then $a = b = 1$ and $1 - a = 1 - b = 0$. In this case the rat will alternate from one side to the other. Equations (51) assert that

$$p_n = q_n = \tfrac{1}{2}.$$

EXERCISES

1. A large bookstore has 10 copies of a best-selling book in stock. The manager knows that the demand for the book the next day will have a binomial distribution with parameters $p = \tfrac{3}{5}$ and $n = 20$. Given the following conditions, how many copies should he order for delivery the next morning?
   (a) The loss function is given by Eq. (5) with $\alpha = 2$. What is the resulting expected loss?
   (b) The loss function is given by Eq. (9) with $\alpha = 2$.

2. Repeat Exercise 1 when the parameters of the binomial distribution are $p = \tfrac{2}{5}$ and $n = 20$.

3. Compute the expected loss in part (b) of Exercise 1.

4. Suppose that D is a random variable having a binomial distribution with $p = \tfrac{1}{2}$ and $n = 10$. Let $X = \min\{D, c\}$, where c is a real number. Find the probability function for the random variable X when
   (a) $c = 2$,   (b) $c = 5$,   (c) $c = 8$,   (d) $c \geq 10$.

5. Let D and X be random variables as defined in Exercise 4. Find $E[X]$ when
   (a) $c = 2$,   (b) $c = 5$,   (c) $c = 8$,   (d) $c \geq 10$.

6. In Problem 1 assume that there are 10 outlets, that the bakery produces 100 loaves of rye bread, and that the demand for rye bread at each outlet is given by a binomial random variable D_i with parameters $p = \tfrac{1}{2}$ and $n = 20$ (the same for each outlet). Find the maximum expected profit, max $E[N]$, if $b = 25$ and $a = 10$. What is the most advantageous way of distributing the bread among the 10 outlets?

7. Repeat Exercise 6 with $b = 30$ and $a = 10$. With $b = 30$ and $a = 15$.

8. Suppose that D is a random variable having a binomial distribution with $p = \tfrac{1}{2}$ and $n = 4$, and let $X = \min\{D, c\}$, where c is an integer, $0 \leq c \leq 4$. Find the maximum value of $16E[X] - 5c$ by
   (a) computing $16E[X] - 5c$ for $c = 0, 1, 2, 3, 4$;
   (b) applying Lemma 6.

9. Let D, X, and c be as in Exercise 6. Find the maximum value of $5E[X] - 2c$. What is the relation of your answer to Lemma 6?

10. Suppose that the bakery chain in Problem 5 has 20 outlets, each having a demand for chocolate cakes which is a binomial random variable with parameters $p = \tfrac{1}{2}$ and $n = 4$ as in Exercise 8. Suppose that $b = 16$ and $a = 5$. If it is possible to meet any demand, how many chocolate cakes should the bakery send to each outlet and how many should it bake in all to maximize its expected profits from the sale of chocolate cakes?

11. Repeat Exercise 10 when $b = 5$ and $a = 2$.

12. Suppose that the bakery chain in Problem 3 has four outlets, each having a demand for chocolate cakes which is a binomial random variable but with different parameters. Assume that the first demand has parameters $p = \frac{1}{2}$, $n = 5$, that the second has parameters $p = \frac{1}{2}$, $n = 7$, that the third has parameters $p = \frac{1}{2}$, $n = 9$, and that the fourth has parameters $p = \frac{1}{2}$, $n = 3$. If there are 10 cakes to be distributed among these four outlets, decide how to allot them so as to maximize the expected profit $E[N]$. What is the expected profit if $b = 78$ and $a = 35$?

13. Find the probability that a rat selects passage A on the 100th trial in the Estes' Learning Model if:
    (a) $a = b = \frac{1}{2}$,   (b) $a = \frac{1}{3}$, $b = \frac{2}{3}$,   (c) $a = \frac{1}{3}$, $b = \frac{5}{6}$,   (d) $a = \frac{2}{3}$, $b = \frac{1}{2}$.

14. Find the limiting values of p_n and q_n in the Estes' Learning Model for the various values of a and b given in Exercise 13.

15. A moody baseball player gets hits depending on his "confidence factor." If at any time at bat he gets a hit, then his probability of getting a hit the next time at bat is p. If at any time at bat he does not get a hit, then his probability of getting a hit the next time at bat is p'. Assume that he does not remember past his last time at bat. Find this player's batting average, that is, the probability that after a large number of times at bat, he will get a hit at any given time at bat. Does his average depend on the result of his initial time at bat?

*16. A man has $n(= 20)$ years to live. He has an initial capital of c dollars which he can invest at a rate of $p(= \frac{5}{100})$. Each year some of his money will be spent for necessary goods and some will be spent for enjoyment. There is a measure of value, namely "utility," associated with money spent. Assume that the utility of spending s dollars in a year is $d(s)$, where $d(s) \geq d(t)$, if $s \geq t$ and $d(s) \geq 0$ for $s \geq 0$. The problem facing the man is: What fraction of his capital should he invest and what fraction should he spend each year to maximize

$$d(s_1) + d(s_2) + \cdots + d(s_{20}),$$

where s_i is the amount spent in the ith year?

   Assume that d is a concave function and carry out the following steps to solve the man's problem.
   Let $a = 1 + p$ and let

$$f_n(c) = \max [d(s_1) + d(s_2) + \cdots + d(s_n)]$$

for each value of n, the number of years the man lives.
   (a) Show that

$$f_1(c) = d(c),$$

that is, if he were to live one year, he should spend all of his capital.
   (b) Show that

$$f_n(c) = \max_{0 \leq s \leq c} [f_{n-1}(a(c - s)) + d(s)], \qquad n \geq 2.$$

---

* Starred number indicates a particularly difficult exercise.

(c) Let a_{19} be the fraction of his capital he should spend the first year, a_{18} the fraction of his new capital he should spend the second year, etc., a_0 the fraction he should spend the 20th year. Show that

$$a_0 = 1, a_1 = \frac{a}{1+a}, \ldots, a_{n+1} = \frac{aa_n}{1+aa_n}, \qquad 1 \leq n \leq 20,$$

that

$$f_n(c) = n\, d(a_{n-1}c), \qquad 1 \leq n \leq 20,$$

and that

$$\max_{0 \leq s \leq c}\, [f_{n-1}(a(c-s)) + d(s)]$$

is attained for $s = a_{n-1}c$.

*17. Show that if the loss L in an inventory problem is given by Eq. (12), then the expected loss is minimized by choosing δ so that $I + \delta$ is as close to $m_D(\alpha, \beta)$ as possible.

*18. Work out how to choose δ if the loss function L in an inventory problem is a quadratic loss function as given in Eq. (18).

Answers to Selected Problems

CHAPTER 1

Section 1.2

1. $\{0\}$, $\{n \mid n = 0\}$
2. $\{\frac{2}{3}\}$
3. (a) $\{1, -1\}$
   (b) $\{-1\}$
   (c) $\{x \mid -1 \le x \le 5\}$
   (d) $\{-1, 0, 1, 2, 3, 4, 5\}$
4. (a) {Dole, Mize, Shriver, Skubitz, Winn}   (b) {Carlson, Pearson}
6. $\{1, 2, 3, 4, 5, 6\}$
7. $\{x \mid x \in A\} = A$

Section 1.3

1. (b) no, yes, yes
2. no

Section 1.4

1. antireflexive, antisymmetric, antitransitive
2. antireflexive, symmetric, transitive
3. antireflexive, nonsymmetric, nontransitive
4. antireflexive, antisymmetric, nontransitive
5. antireflexive, symmetric, nontransitive

Section 1.5

1. (a) $\{2, 8\}$
   (b) $\{0, 1, 4, 9, 16\}$
   (c) $\{x \mid x \in R^1, -1 \le x < 1\}$
   (d) $\{x \mid x \in R^1, -1 \le x < 1\}$
   (e) $\{(2, -1)\}$
   (f) $\emptyset$
2. (a) $\emptyset$ (b) A (c) A (d) $A \subset B$
4. (a) $\{-1, 0, 2, 4, 5, 8, 11, 12, 14, 16\}$ (b) $\{x \mid x \in R^1, -5 < x \le 5\}$
   (c) $\{x \mid x \in R^1, -5 < x \le 5\}$ (d) B
6. (a) A (b) A (c) B (d) $A \subset B$ 9. $\emptyset$

341

Section 1.6

1. (a) $\emptyset$ (b) $\{6, 9\}$ (c) $\{2n - 1 \mid n \in J^+\}$ (d) $\{x \mid x \in R^1, 0 < x \le 1\}$
   (e) $A - B$ is the set of people who will buy a television set in 1967 which is not a color television set.

3. (a) $\emptyset$ (b) A (c) $\emptyset$ (d) $\emptyset$ (e) A (f) $A \cup B$ (g) A (h) $\emptyset$
   (i) $(A - B) \cup (A - C)$ (j) $(A - B) \cap (A - C)$

4. (a) $A - B \subset A$ (b) $(A - B) \cup B \supset A$
   (c) $B - A \subset C - A$ (d) $A - B \supset A - C$

6. 2^n

7. $\emptyset, \{\emptyset\}, \{\{0\}\}, \{\{1\}\}, \{\{0,1\}\}, \{\emptyset, \{0\}\}, \{\emptyset, \{1\}\}, \{\emptyset, \{0, 1\}\}, \{\{0\}, \{1\}\},$
   $\{\{0\}, \{0, 1\}\}, \{\{1\}, \{0, 1\}\}, \{\emptyset, \{0\}, \{1\}\}, \{\emptyset, \{0\}, \{0, 1\}\}, \{\emptyset, \{1\}, \{0, 1\}\},$
   $\{\{0\}, \{1\}, \{0, 1\}\}, \{\emptyset, \{0\}, \{1\}, \{0, 1\}\}$

16. $\{\emptyset\}$

19. (a) $(A \cap B^c \cap Rh) \cup (A^c \cap B^c \cap Rh) \cup (A \cap B^c \cap Rh^c) \cup (A^c \cap B^c \cap Rh^c)$,
    $A^c \cap B^c \cap Rh^c$,
    $(A \cap B \cap Rh^c) \cup (A^c \cap B \cap Rh^c) \cup (A \cap B^c \cap Rh^c) \cup (A^c \cap B^c \cap Rh^c)$
    (b) $(A \cap B^c \cap Rh) \cup (A \cap B \cap Rh)$ (c) $A^c \cap B^c \cap Rh^c$ (d) $A \cap B \cap Rh$

20. (a) 107,700   (b) 10,330,000   (c) 10,437,700   (d) 42,700
    (e) 47,000   (f) 65,000   (g) 60,700   (h) 0
    (i) 0   (j) 2,030,000   (k) 190,000   (l) 4,338,500

21. (a) 3110, 4341, 2867, 4584, 7003, 448, 2043, 7046
    (b) against increased taxes, against aid to education, and for a balanced budget; 3485

CHAPTER 2

Section 2.1

1. (a) $\{\{\text{father}\}, \{\text{father, son}\}\}$ (b) $\{\{\text{pitcher}\}, \{\text{pitcher, catcher}\}\}$
   (c) $\{\{1\}, \{1, 2\}\}$ (d) $\{\{2\}, \{1, 2\}\}$
   (e) $\{\{1\}, \{1, 1\}\}$ (f) $\{\{\text{employer}\}, \{\text{employer, employee}\}\}$

2. (a) (mother, daughter)   (b) (coach, player)   (c) (player, coach)
   (d) (player, coach)   (e) $(\emptyset, A)$ (f) $(1, 2)$ (g) $(1, 1)$
   (h) $(1, 1)$ (i) $(A, \emptyset)$ (j) $(\emptyset, \{\emptyset\})$

Section 2.2

1. (a) $C = A \times B = \begin{Bmatrix} (1, 2) & (1, 3) & (1, 5) \\ (2, 2) & (2, 3) & (2, 5) \end{Bmatrix}$

2. (a) $C = A \times B = \begin{Bmatrix} (-1, -1) & (-1, 1) \\ (1, -1) & (1, 1) \end{Bmatrix}$

3. (a) $C = A \times B$, where $A = \{1\}$ and $B = \{0\}$
   (b) not a Cartesian product   (c) not a Cartesian product
   (d) $C = A \times B$, where $A = \{0, 1\}$ and $B = \{0, 1\}$

(e) $C = A \times B$, where $A = \{-1, 0, 1\}$ and $B = \{2\}$

(f) $C = A \times B$, where $A = \{7, 8, 11\}$ and $B = \{-1, 1\}$

(g) not a Cartesian product

4. (a) $B = \begin{cases} \text{(yes, yes, yes)} & \text{(yes, yes, no)} & \text{(yes, no, yes)} & \text{(yes, no, no)} \\ \text{(no, yes, yes)} & \text{(no, yes, no)} & \text{(no, no, yes)} & \text{(no, no, no)} \end{cases}$

(b) B is the set of all possible ways of making three decisions.

5. The graph consists of the following set:

$$\{(x, y) \mid x \in R^1, y \in R^1, 0 \le x \le 1, 0 \le y \le 1\}.$$

6. The set $A \times B$ is empty.

Section 2.3

1. $C = A \times B = \begin{cases} (1, 2) & (1, 3) & (1, 5) \\ (2, 2) & (2, 3) & (2, 5) \end{cases}$

(a) Every subset of C is a relation R such that $R \subset C$. The set C has 2^6 subsets. One relation R is $\{(1, 2), (1, 3), (2, 2), (2, 5)\}$.

(b) The graph of the sample relation R in (a) is the set of points whose coordinates are (1, 2), (1, 3), (2, 2), and (2, 5).

(c) If R is the sample relation in (a), then dom $R = \{1, 2\}$ and ran $R = \{2, 3, 5\}$.

(d) If R is the sample relation in (a), then R is not a Cartesian product.

2. One relation R with the property specified is $\{(1, 3), (2, 5)\}$.

3. (a) If $(x, y) \in \hat{R}$, then x and y may or may not be married to each other. Also, x and y may both be men or both be women.

(b) dom $\hat{R} = $ ran $\hat{R} = $ set of all living people who are married

4. The graph is a straight line which bisects the first and third quadrants. This relation has the property stated in Exercise 2.

Section 2.4

1. (a) $f(0) = 1$ (b) $f(1) = 2$ (c) $f(-1) = 0$

2. (a) The graph of g is identical with that part of the graph of f in Exercise 1 which lies above the interval $0 \le x \le 2$.

(b) The function g is obtained from the function f in Exercise 1 by restricting the domain of f to the interval $0 \le x \le 2$.

3. (a) Since $2x + 3y = 6$, there is exactly one y for each real number x.

(b) $L(x) = (-2x + 6)/3$ (c) $L = \{(x, (-2x + 6)/3) \mid x \in R^1\}$

4. The graph of f is the part of the parabola $y^2 = x$ which lies on and above the x axis.

dom $f = $ ran $f = \{x \mid x \in R^1, x \ge 0\}$,

$f = \{(x, y) \mid x \in R^1, x \ge 0, y = \sqrt{x}\}$

5. (b) yes

6. The domain of f is a restriction of the domain of g; hence, $f \ne g$.

7. Yes, $h = g$. The sets of ordered pairs h and g are equal.

8. (a) H is a function.   (b) dom $H = P$

(c) $H(p)$ denotes the height of p to the nearest inch.

9. (a) $N(\emptyset) = 0, \quad N(S) = n$

10. (a) $P(\emptyset) = 0$, $P(S) = 1$

(b) $\operatorname{dom} P = \Pi(S)$, $\operatorname{ran} P = \left\{0, \dfrac{1}{n}, \dfrac{2}{n}, \ldots, \dfrac{n-1}{n}, 1\right\}$

11. V is not a function. The graph of V is the vertical line $x = 1$.

13. The following subsets of $A \times A$ are functions. $\{(a, a)\}$, $\{(a, b)\}$, $\{(b, a)\}$, $\{(b, b)\}$, $\{(a, a), (b, a)\}$, $\{(a, a), (b, b)\}$, $\{(a, b), (b, a)\}$, $\{(a, b), (b, b)\}$

14. $\binom{3}{1}3 + \binom{3}{2}3^2 + \binom{3}{3}3^3 = 63$ (See Sections 4.1 through 4.3.)

15. (c) no; $f(1) = f(2) = 1$ and $f(3) = f(4) = 2$

16. (b) $\operatorname{ran} f = \{y \mid 0 \le y < 1\}$

Section 2.5

1. $g \circ f = \{(0, 0), (1, 0), (2, 5)\}$

2. (a) $u \circ h = \{(x, \sqrt{x^2 + 1}) \mid x \in R^1\}$, $(u \circ h)(1) = \sqrt{2}$

(b) $h \circ u = \{(x, (\sqrt{x})^2 + 1) \mid x \in R^1, x \ge 0\}$,

$\operatorname{dom} h \circ u = \{x \mid x \in R^1, x \ge 0\}$, $\operatorname{ran} h \circ u = \{y \mid y \in R^1, y \ge 1\}$

3. (a) $u \circ v = \{(x, \sqrt{1 - x^2}) \mid x \in R^1, -1 \le x \le 1\}$

(b) $u(v(x)) = \sqrt{1 - x^2}$ for $-1 \le x \le 1$

(d) $(u \circ v)(\tfrac{1}{2}) = \dfrac{\sqrt{3}}{2}$, $(u \circ v)(-1) = 0$, $(u \circ v)(0) = 1$

6. $S \circ R = \{(3, 0), (4, 11), (5, 1)\}$

7. (a) $f^{-1} = \{(2, 0), (2, 1), (3, 2)\}$, $g^{-1} = \{(0, 2), (5, 3), (7, 6)\}$

f^{-1} is not a function, but g^{-1} is a function.

(b) $f \circ f^{-1} = \{(2, 2), (3, 3)\}$, $g \circ g^{-1} = \{(0, 0), (5, 5), (7, 7)\}$

(c) $f^{-1} \circ f = \{(0, 0), (0, 1), (1, 0), (1, 1), (2, 2)\}$, $g^{-1} \circ g = \{(2, 2), (3, 3), (6, 6)\}$

(d) $f \circ f^{-1}$, $g \circ g^{-1}$, and $g^{-1} \circ g$ are functions.

Section 2.6

1. (a) $f + g = \{(1, 3), (2, 1), (3, 4)\}$ (b) $f + g = \{(1, 3), (2, 1), (3, 4)\}$

(c) $f + g = \{(x, 2x) \mid x \in R^1, 0 < x \le 1\}$ (d) $f + g = \{(x, x) \mid x \in R^1\}$

(e) $(f + g)(x) = x + 1/x + 3/(x - 1)$, $x \ne 0$ and $x \ne 1$

(f) $(f + g)(x) = 0$, $x \in \operatorname{dom} f$ (g) $(f + g)(x) = f(x)$, $x \in \operatorname{dom} f$

(h) $(f + g)(x) = f(x) + 1$, $x \in \operatorname{dom} f$

2. (a) $f \cdot g = \{(1, 2), (2, 0), (3, 3)\}$ (b) $f \cdot g = \{(1, 2), (2, 0), (3, 3)\}$

(c) $f \cdot g = \{(x, x^2) \mid x \in R^1, 0 < x \le 1\}$ (d) $f \cdot g = \{(x, 0) \mid x \in R^1\}$

(e) $(f \cdot g)(x) = \dfrac{(2x^2 + 1)(-x^2 + x + 3)}{x(x - 1)}$, $x \ne 0$ and $x \ne 1$

(f) $(f \cdot g)(x) = -[f(x)]^2$, $x \in \operatorname{dom} f$ (g) $(f \cdot g)(x) = 0$, $x \in \operatorname{dom} f$

(h) $(f \cdot g)(x) = f(x)$, $x \in \operatorname{dom} f$

3. (a) $\operatorname{dom}(f + g) = \operatorname{dom}(f \cdot g) = \{1, 2, 3\}$

(b) $\operatorname{dom}(f + g) = \operatorname{dom}(f \cdot g) = \{1, 2, 3\}$

(c) $\operatorname{dom}(f + g) = \operatorname{dom}(f \cdot g) = \{x \mid x \in R^1, 0 < x \le 1\}$

(d) $\operatorname{dom}(f + g) = \operatorname{dom}(f \cdot g) = R^1$

(e) $\mathrm{dom}(f + g) = \mathrm{dom}(f \cdot g) = \{x \mid x \in R^1, x \neq 0, x \neq 1\}$

(f) $\mathrm{dom}(f + g) = \mathrm{dom}(f \cdot g) = \mathrm{dom}\, f$ (g) $\mathrm{dom}(f + g) = \mathrm{dom}(f \cdot g) = \mathrm{dom}\, f$

(h) $\mathrm{dom}(f + g) = \mathrm{dom}(f \cdot g) = \mathrm{dom}\, f$

4. Quotients f/g and domains of f/g for Exercise 1 are:

(a) $f/g = \{(1, \frac{1}{2}), (2, 0), (3, \frac{1}{3})\}$, $\mathrm{dom}\, f/g = \{1, 2, 3\}$

(b) $f/g = \{(1, \frac{1}{2}), (2, 0), (3, \frac{1}{3})\}$, $\mathrm{dom}\, f/g = \{1, 2, 3\}$

(c) $f/g = \{(x, 1) \mid x \in R^1, 0 < x \leq 1\}$, $\mathrm{dom}\, f/g = \{x \mid x \in R^1, 0 < x \leq 1\}$

(d) f/g is not defined.

(e) $(f/g)(x) = \dfrac{(2x^2 + 1)(x - 1)}{x(-x^2 + x + 3)}$, $x \neq 0, \quad x \neq 1, \quad x \neq \dfrac{(1 \pm \sqrt{13})}{2}$;

$\mathrm{dom}\, f/g = \left\{x \mid x \in R^1, x \neq 0, x \neq 1, x \neq \dfrac{1 \pm \sqrt{13}}{2}\right\}$

(f) $(f/g)(x) = -1$, $f(x) \neq 0$; $\mathrm{dom}\, f/g = \mathrm{dom}\, f - \{x \mid f(x) = 0\}$

(g) f/g is not defined

(h) $(f/g)(x) = f(x)$, $x \in \mathrm{dom}\, f$; $\mathrm{dom}\, f/g = \mathrm{dom}\, f$

5. The functions $2g$ and $-3g$ for Exercise 1 are the following.

(a) $2g = \{(1, 4), (2, 2), (3, 6)\}$, $-3g = \{(1, -6), (2, -3), (3, -9)\}$

(b) $2g = \{(1, 4), (2, 2), (3, 6), (4, -2)\}$,

$-3g = \{(1, -6), (2, -3), (3, -9), (4, 3)\}$

(c) $(2g)(x) = 2x$, $0 < x$; $(-3g)(x) = -3x$, $0 < x$

(d) $(2g)(x) = 0$, $x \in R^1$; $(-3g)(x) = 0$, $x \in R^1$

(e) $(2g)(x) = \dfrac{2(-x^2 + x + 3)}{x - 1}$, $x \neq 1$;

$(-3g)(x) = \dfrac{3(x^2 - x - 3)}{x - 1}$, $x \neq 1$

(f) $(2g)(x) = -2f(x)$, $x \in \mathrm{dom}\, f$; $(-3g)(x) = 3f(x)$, $x \in \mathrm{dom}\, f$;

(g) $(2g)(x) = 0$, $x \in \mathrm{dom}\, f$; $(-3g)(x) = 0$, $x \in \mathrm{dom}\, f$

(h) $(2g)(x) = 2$, $x \in \mathrm{dom}\, f$; $(-3g)(x) = -3$, $x \in \mathrm{dom}\, f$

Section 2.7

1. (a) f is not a polynomial.   (b) f is a polynomial of degree 3.

(c) f is a polynomial of degree 0.   (d) f is not a polynomial $(f(x) = |x|!)$.

(e) f is a polynomial of degree 3.   (f) f is not a polynomial.

2. Parts (a), (c), (d), (f), and (g) define rational functions.

3. (a) $\mathrm{dom}\, f = R^1 - \{0\}$ (c) $\mathrm{dom}\, f = R^1 - \{1\}$

(d) $\mathrm{dom}\, f = R^1$ (f) $\mathrm{dom}\, f = R^1$

(g) $\mathrm{dom}\, f = R^1 - \{0, -\frac{4}{3}\}$

4. (a) If $g(x) = x^2$ and $h(x) = |x|$ for $x \in R^1$, then $f = g \circ h$. Also, if $g(x) = |x|$ and $h(x) = x^2$ for $x \in R^1$, then

$$(g \circ h)(x) = g(h(x)) = |x^2| = |x|^2 = f(x).$$

5. (a) If $h(x) = x^3$ and $u(x) = |x|$ for $x \in R^1$, then $g = h \circ u$. Also, if $h(x) = |x|$ and $u(x) = x^3$, then $g = h \circ u$.

(b) No, because $g(x) = |x|^3 \neq x^3$ if $x < 0$.

7. Let f, g, and h be the functions defined by Eqs. (8), (9), and (10), respectively. Then, since $\operatorname{dom} p = \operatorname{dom} q = R^1$, we have

$$\operatorname{dom} f = \{x \mid x \in R^1, x \geq 0\},$$

$$\operatorname{dom} g = \left\{x \mid x \in R^1, q(x) \neq 0, \frac{p(x)}{q(x)} \geq 0\right\},$$

$$\operatorname{dom} h = \{x \mid x \in R^1, x \geq 0, q(\sqrt{x}) \neq 0\}.$$

CHAPTER 3

Section 3.2

1. (a) 20, 110   (b) 4, -5 (c) 0, 45   (d) 50, 275   (e) 7, 160   (f) $-27, -135$
2. (a) $u(k) = u(k-1) + 2$, $k = 1, 2, \ldots$, $u(0) = 2$
   (b) $u(k) = u(k-1) + 1$, $k = 1, 2, \ldots$, $u(0) = -5$
   (c) $u(k) = u(k-1) - 1$, $k = 1, 2, \ldots$, $u(0) = 9$
   (d) $u(k) = u(k-1) + 5$, $k = 1, 2, \ldots$, $u(0) = 5$
   (e) $u(k) = u(k-1) - 2$, $k = 1, 2, \ldots$, $u(0) = 25$
   (f) $u(k) = u(k-1) - 3$, $k = 1, 2, \ldots$, $u(0) = 0$
4. 156   5. \$15,500; \$123,500   6. 14, 11, 8, 5, 2   7. $-1, 3, 7, 11, 15, 19, 23$
8. 46, 49, 52, $\ldots$, 415, 418; $u(n) = 43 + 3n$, $n = 1, 2, \ldots, 125$
9. 32   14. 36   15. \$27,200   16. $3\frac{1}{3}\%$ 17. \$300

Section 3.3

1. (a) 39,366, 59,048   (b) 59,049, 88,572   (c) $\dfrac{-1}{512}, \dfrac{341}{512}$

   (d) $-2, 0$ (e) $-39,366$, $-29,524$ (f) $\dfrac{512}{19,683}, \dfrac{58,025}{19,683}$

3. (a) 32, 63   (b) $-32, -21$ (c) 96, 189   (d) $-96, -63$
   (e) 96, 63   (f) $\frac{1}{8}, \frac{63}{8}$ (g) $-\frac{1}{8}, \frac{21}{8}$
5. (a) 2   (b) 2   (c) $\frac{1}{3}$ (d) Sum does not exist.
   (e) Sum does not exist.   (f) 10
6. $\frac{7}{9}$ 7. 6, 12, 24, 48, 96   8. 8
11. The amount which remains at time t is $10(\frac{9}{10})^t$. The amounts which remain at times $t = 1, 2, \ldots, 10$ are approximately 9.0, 8.1, 7.3, 6.6, 5.9, 5.3, 4.8, 4.3, 3.9, 3.5. The total amount of the substance which has disintegrated up to time t is $10[1 - (\frac{9}{10})^t]$. The amounts which have disintegrated up to times $t = 1, 2, \ldots, 10$ are approximately 1.0, 1.9, 2.7, 3.4, 4.1, 4.7, 5.2, 5.7, 6.1, and 6.5. The half-life of the substance is approximately 7.
12. The value of the automobile at the end of t years is $4000(\frac{9}{10})^t$. The values at times $t = 1, 2, \ldots, 10$ are approximately \$3600, \$3240, \$2916, \$2624, \$2362, \$2126, \$1913, \$1722, \$1550, \$1395. The total depreciation in value of the automobile up to the end of t years is $4000[1 - (\frac{9}{10})^t]$. The total depreciation up to time $t = 1, 2, \ldots, 10$ is approximately \$400, \$760, \$1084, \$1376, \$1638, \$1874, \$2087, \$2287, \$2450, \$2605, respectively. The automobile is approximately seven years old when its value is one-half of the original purchase price.

13. The total value of all payments at the beginning of year k $(k = 1, 2, \ldots, 10)$ is

$$500 + 500(1.05) + 500(1.05)^2 + \cdots + 500(1.05)^{k-1} = 10,000[(1.05)^k - 1].$$

14. The population of the city in the year $1950 + k$ is $10,000(1.05)^k$, $k = 0, 1, 2, \ldots$

15. 1.25×10^5

Section 3.4

1. (a) 530.00, 561.80, 595.51, 631.24, 669.11. The difference equation is a compound interest equation; $i = 0.06$ and $P = 500$ [see Eqs. (6) and (7)].
   (b) 530.00, 560.00, 590.00, 620.00, 650.00. The difference equation is a simple interest equation; $i = 0.06$ and $P = 500$ [see Eqs. (3) and (4)].
   (c) 470.00, 441.80, 415.29, 390.37, 366.95. The difference equation is an exponential decay equation; $i = 0.06$ and $a = 500$ [see Eqs. (9) and (10)].
   (d) 1030.00, 1591.80, 2187.31, 2818.55, 3487.66. The difference equation is an annuity equation; $i = 0.06$ and $P = 500$ [see Eqs. (12) and (13)].
   (e) 500.00, 500.00, 500.00, 500.00, 500.00. The difference equation is a harvest equation; $i = 0.06$, $P = 500$, and $W = 30 = iP$ [see Eqs. (15) and (16)].
   (f) 480.00, 458.80, 436.33, 412.51, 387.26. The difference equation is a harvest equation; $i = 0.06$, $P = 500$, and $W = 50 > iP$ [see Eqs. (15) and (16)].
   (g) 520.00, 541.20, 563.67, 587.49, 612.74. The difference equation is a harvest equation; $i = 0.06$, $P = 500$, and $W = 10 < iP$ [see Eqs. (15) and (16)].

2. (a) 125,000, 175,000, 275,000, 475,000, 875,000
   (b) 75,000, 25,000, $-75,000$ (c) $N = 100,000$

3. $u(k) = 2^k N$, $\displaystyle\sum_{k=0}^{99} u(k) = (2^{100} - 1)N$

4. $u(k) = 4 \cdot 4^k$, $\displaystyle\sum_{k=0}^{49} u(k) = \tfrac{4}{3}(4^{50} - 1)$

The total number of letters is greater than the number of people on the earth.

Section 3.7

2. $\dfrac{n^2(n + 1)^2(2n^2 + 2n - 1)}{12}$

CHAPTER 4

Section 4.1

1. (a) 6,227,020,800   (b) 28   (c) 90   (d) 1326   (e) 10,100   (f) 1320

2. $P_6(1) + P_6(2) + P_6(3) + P_6(4) + P_6(5) + P_6(6)$
   $= 1!C_6(1) + 2!C_6(2) + 3!C_6(3) + 4!C_6(4) + 5!C_6(5) + 6!C_6(6)$
   $= 1956$

4. $7! = 5{,}040$; $7!C_{10}(7) = P_{10}(7) = 10 \cdot 9 \cdot 8 \cdot \ldots \cdot 4 = 604{,}800$

5. 24 if arrangements are counted in terms of positions at the table; 6 if arrangements are counted in terms of seating order; 3 if arrangements are counted in terms of sets of neighbors

6. $n!$ if arrangements are counted in terms of positions at the table; $(n - 1)!$ if arrangements are counted in terms of seating order; $(n - 1)!/2$ if arrangements are counted in terms of sets of neighbors

7. $3!C_4(3) = P_4(3) = 4 \cdot 3 \cdot 2 = 24$

8. $P_5(4) = 5 \cdot 4 \cdot 3 \cdot 2 = 120$, $4!C_5(4) = \dfrac{5!}{1!} = 120$.   The two methods are the same since $4!C_5(4) = P_5(4)$.

9. There are $C_{100}(4)$ sets of officers, but the four offices (president, vice-president, secretary, treasurer) can be filled in $4!C_{100}(4)$ different ways.

10. $2P_4(2) = 24$

11. $P_4(2) + P_4(3) = 36$. The principle of sequential counting cannot be used because the number of ways in which the second act can be performed depends on the outcome of the first act.

Section 4.2

1. 6^6

2. $6^3 + 6^4 + 6^5 + 6^6$

3. $6 + 6^2 + 6^3 + 6^4 + 6^5 + 6^6$

4. 10^7

5. 10^4

6. 10^4. The value of a number is not changed by placing one or more zeros on its left.

7. $n^2 - n = n(n - 1)$

8. (a) $2^{11} - 1$ (b) $2^{11} - 11 - 1$

9. (a) $2^{10} - 1$ (b) $2^{10} - 10 - 1$
   (c) $2^{10} - C_{10}(4) - C_{10}(3) - C_{10}(2) - C_{10}(1) - C_{10}(0)$

11. $n^n > n!$ for $n \geq 2$ 12. $N(\emptyset) = 0$ 15. $N(S) = 2^n$

16. There are 36 possible outcomes.   17. There are 6^n n-tuples.

Section 4.3

1. (a) 21 (b) 28 (c) 5050

2. $\dbinom{490}{20}$, $\dbinom{10}{1}\dbinom{490}{19}$

3. $2^9 = 512, \dbinom{9}{3} + \dbinom{9}{4} + \dbinom{9}{5} + \dbinom{9}{6} = 420$ 4. $\dbinom{98}{50}$

5. $\dbinom{3}{2}\dbinom{3}{1} + \dbinom{3}{1}\dbinom{3}{2} + \dbinom{3}{0}\dbinom{3}{3} = 19$, $\dbinom{6}{3} - \dbinom{3}{3} = 19$

9. (a) $\dbinom{3}{2} = 3$ (b) $\dbinom{3}{1}\dbinom{3}{1} = 9$

   (c) $\dbinom{3}{1}\dbinom{3}{2} = 9$ (d) $\dbinom{3}{2} + \dbinom{3}{2} + \dbinom{3}{1}\dbinom{3}{1} = 15$

Section 4.4

1. (a) $(x + y)^5 = \sum_{r=0}^{5} \binom{5}{r} x^{5-r} y^r = x^5 + 5x^4 y + 10x^3 y^2 + 10x^2 y^3 + 5xy^4 + y^5$

   (b) $(x - y)^5 = \sum_{r=0}^{5} \binom{5}{r} x^{5-r} (-y)^r$

   $= x^5 - 5x^4 y + 10x^3 y^2 - 10x^2 y^3 + 5xy^4 - y^5$

   (c) $(a + b)^6 = \sum_{r=0}^{6} \binom{6}{r} a^{6-r} b^r$

   (d) $(x + y)^{10} = \sum_{r=0}^{10} \binom{10}{r} x^{10-r} y^r$

   (e) $(1 + x)^8 = \sum_{r=0}^{8} \binom{8}{r} x^r$

   (f) $(1 - x)^6 = \sum_{r=0}^{6} \binom{6}{r} (-x)^r$

   (g) $(x + 2y)^4 = \sum_{r=0}^{4} \binom{4}{r} x^{4-r} (2y)^r = x^4 + 8x^3 y + 24x^2 y^2 + 32xy^3 + 16y^4$

   (h) $(2x - 3y)^4 = \sum_{r=0}^{4} \binom{4}{r} (2x)^{4-r} (-3y)^r$

   $= 16x^4 - 96x^3 y + 216x^2 y^2 - 216xy^3 + 81y^4$

   (i) $(1 - 2x)^7 = \sum_{r=0}^{7} \binom{7}{r} (-2x)^r$

2. 1792

Section 4.5

1. (a) $(x + y + z)^4 = \sum \binom{4}{r_1, r_2, r_3} x^{r_1} y^{r_2} z^{r_3}$, where the summation is extended over all ordered 3-tuples (r_1, r_2, r_3) of nonnegative integers r_1, r_2, r_3 such that $r_1 + r_2 + r_3 = 4$.

   (b) $(x + y + z + w)^3 = \sum \binom{3}{r_1, r_2, r_3, r_4} x^{r_1} y^{r_2} z^{r_3} w^{r_4}$, where $0 \le r_i \le 3$ for $i = 1, 2, 3, 4$, and $r_1 + r_2 + r_3 + r_4 = 3$.

   (c) $(1 - x - y)^4 = \sum \binom{4}{r_1, r_2, r_3} (-x)^{r_2} (-y)^{r_3}$, where $0 \le r_i \le 4$ for $i = 1, 2, 3$, and $r_1 + r_2 + r_3 = 4$.

   (d) $(1 + 2x - 2y)^4 = \sum \binom{4}{r_1, r_2, r_3} (2x)^{r_2} (-2y)^{r_3}$, where $0 \le r_i \le 4$ for $i = 1, 2, 3$, and $r_1 + r_2 + r_3 = 4$.

   (e) $(ax + by + cz)^n = \sum \binom{n}{r_1, r_2, r_3} (ax)^{r_1} (by)^{r_2} (cz)^{r_3}$, where $0 \le r_i \le n$ for $i = 1, 2, 3$, and $r_1 + r_2 + r_3 = n$.

   (f) $(x + y + z + w)^5 = \sum \binom{5}{r_1, r_2, r_3, r_4} x^{r_1} y^{r_2} z^{r_3} w^{r_4}$, where $0 \le r_i \le 5$ for $i = 1, 2, 3, 4$, and $r_1 + r_2 + r_3 + r_4 = 5$.

2. (a) $\binom{10}{10, 0, 0, 0} = 1$ (b) $\binom{10}{0, 5, 5, 0} = 252$ (c) $\binom{10}{4, 2, 1, 3} = 12{,}600$

3. (a) 15　　(b) 21　　(c) 20　　(d) 35　　(e) $\dbinom{n+k-1}{n}$

4. $\dbinom{6}{3,2,1} = 60,$　　$\dbinom{5}{3,2} + \dbinom{5}{3,2} = 20$

5. $\dbinom{35}{1,1,1,1,2,2,2,2,2,2,3,3,3}$

10. $\dbinom{n}{1,1,1,\ldots,1} = P_n(n) = n!$　　11. 15

Section 4.6

1. $\dbinom{22}{5,6,4,7} = \dfrac{22!}{5!6!4!7!}$　　　　3. $\dbinom{15}{1,4,10} = \dfrac{15!}{1!4!10!}$

4. $\dbinom{102}{100} = 5151$ (The voters are indistinguishable.)

$\displaystyle\sum \dbinom{100}{r_1, r_2, r_3} = 3^{100}$ (The voters are distinguishable.)

5. (a) $\dbinom{21}{9}$　　　　　　(b) $\dbinom{13}{9,4} = 715$

6. The problem is ambiguous. *First solution:* The word "MOON" contains the three *distinct* letters M, O, N. From these letters it is possible to form $3!\binom{3}{3}$ distinct words with three letters each, $2!\binom{3}{2}$ distinct words with two letters each, and $1!\binom{3}{1}$ distinct words with one letter each. Thus the answer is

$$3!\binom{3}{3} + 2!\binom{3}{2} + 1!\binom{3}{1} = 15.$$

Second solution: The word "MOON" contains four letters and words are to be formed using each of these four letters at most once. The sets of letters are: {M, O, O, N}, {M, O, N}, {M, O, O}, {O, O, N}, {M, O}, {M, N}, {O, O}, {O, N}, {M}, {O}, {N}. The number of distinguishable words that can be formed from these sets of letters is

$$\binom{4}{1,1,2} + 3! + \binom{3}{1,2} + \binom{3}{2,1} + 2! + 2! + \binom{2}{2} + 2! + 1 + 1 + 1 = 34.$$

7. $\dbinom{25+5-1}{25} = \dbinom{29}{25} = 23{,}751$

8. $\dbinom{12}{10} = 66,$　　$\dbinom{9}{6} = 84,$　　$\dbinom{n+1}{n} = n+1$

9. $\displaystyle\sum \dbinom{100}{r_1, r_2, r_3} = 3^{100}$　　　　10. $P_4(4) = 15$

11. $P_n(4) = \dfrac{4^{n-1} + 3 \cdot 2^{n-1} + 2}{3!}$　　12. $P_n(5) = \dfrac{5^{n-1} + 6 \cdot 3^{n-1} + 8 \cdot 2^{n+1} + 9}{4!}$

CHAPTER 5

Section 5.2

1. elementary events: $\{a\}, \{b\}, \{c\}$; events: $\emptyset, \{a\}, \{b\}, \{c\}, \{a, b\}, \{a, c\}, \{b, c\}, S$

2. A or $B = A \cup B = \{(H, H, T, T, T), (H, H, H, T, T), (T, T, H, H, H)\}$, A and $B = A \cap B = \{(H, H, T, T, T)\}$

3. $N(S) = \binom{5}{3} = 10;$

   elementary events: $\{\{R_1, R_2, R_3\}\}, \{\{R_1, R_2, G_1\}\}, \{\{R_1, R_2, G_2\}\}, \{\{R_1, R_3, G_1\}\},$
   $\{\{R_1, R_3, G_2\}\}, \{\{R_1, G_1, G_2\}\}, \{\{R_2, R_3, G_1\}\}, \{\{R_2, R_3, G_2\}\}, \{\{R_2, G_1, G_2\}\},$
   $\{\{R_3, G_1, G_2\}\}; A = S, B = S - \{\{R_1, R_2, R_3\}\}; A$ or $B = A \cup B = A = S,$
   A and $B = A \cap B = B.$

4. $N(S) = P_5(3) = 60.$ The 60 elementary events can be obtained by forming the $3! = 6$ arrangements of the three letters in each of the elementary events in Exercise 3.

5. $N(S) = \binom{52}{2} = 1326$

   (a) $N(A) = \binom{4}{2} = 6$ (b) $N(B) = \binom{13}{2} = 78$

   (c) $N(C) = \binom{8}{2} = 28$ (d) $N(A \cap B) = N(\emptyset) = 0$

   (e) $N(A \cup B) = N(A) + N(B) = 84$ since $N(A \cap B) = 0$
   (f) $N(A \cap C) = N(A) = 6, N(B \cap C) = 1, N(A \cap B \cap C) = N(\emptyset) = 0$
   (g) $N(A \cup C) = 28, N(B \cup C) = 105, N(A \cup B \cup C) = N(B \cup C) = 105$

6. $N(S) = 5^{25}$

7. $N(S) = \binom{100}{10}$

   (a) $N(A_i) = \binom{95}{10 - i}\binom{5}{i}$

   (b) No sample contains both i and j defective radios if $i \neq j.$

Section 5.3

1. The functions P in parts (a) and (h) cannot possibly be probability functions.
   (a) If P is a probability function, then $P(\{a\}) \leq P(\{a, b\}).$
   (h) If P is a probability function, then
   $P(\{a, b, c\}) = P(\{a, b\}) + P(\{b, c\}) - P(\{b\}) \leq P(\{a, b\}) + P(\{b, c\}).$

2. $P(\{k\}) = 1/n$ for $k = 1, 2, \ldots, n$

4. $P(\{a, b\}) = 1,$ $P(\{a, c\}) = \frac{1}{2},$ $P(\{b, c\}) = \frac{1}{2},$ $P(\{a, b, c\}) = 1$

5. $P(C) = \dfrac{N(C)}{32},$ $P(A \cup B) = \frac{3}{32},$ $P(A \cap B) = \frac{1}{32}$

6. $P(A \cup B) = P(S) = 1,$ $P(A \cap B) = \frac{9}{10}$

7. $P(A \cup B) = P(S) = 1,$ $P(A \cap B) = \frac{9}{10}$

8. (a) $P(A) = \dfrac{\binom{4}{2}}{\binom{52}{2}},\qquad P(B) = \dfrac{\binom{13}{2}}{\binom{52}{2}},\qquad P(C) = \dfrac{\binom{8}{2}}{\binom{52}{2}}$

(b) $P(A \cup B) = \dfrac{\binom{4}{4} + \binom{13}{2}}{\binom{52}{2}},\qquad P(A \cup C) = P(C) = \dfrac{\binom{8}{2}}{\binom{52}{2}},$

$P(B \cup C) = \dfrac{\binom{13}{2} + \binom{8}{2} - 1}{\binom{52}{2}},\qquad P(A \cup B \cup C) = P(B \cup C)$

(c) $P(A \cap B) = P(\emptyset) = 0,\qquad P(A \cap C) = P(A) = \dfrac{\binom{4}{2}}{\binom{52}{2}},$

$P(B \cap C) = \dfrac{1}{\binom{52}{2}},\qquad P(A \cap B \cap C) = P(\emptyset) = 0$

9. (b) $P'(\{i\}) = 0\qquad$ for $\quad i = 6, 7, \ldots, 10$

Section 5.4

1. (a) $S = \{(i, j) \mid i \text{ and } j \text{ are integers}, 1 \le i \le 6, 1 \le j \le 6\},\qquad P(\{(i, j)\}) = \frac{1}{36}$
    (b) $A = \{(1, 6), (2, 5), (3, 4), (4, 3), (5, 2), (6, 1)\}\qquad$ (c) $P(A) = \frac{1}{6}$

2. $S = \{1, 2, 3, 4, 5, 6\},\qquad P(\{i\}) = \dfrac{i}{21}\quad$ for $\quad i = 1, 2, \ldots, 6;\qquad P(\{1, 3, 5\}) = \frac{3}{7}$

3. (a) $S = \{\text{Jones, Black, Smith}\}$
    (b) $P(\{\text{Black}\}) = \frac{1}{6},\qquad P(\{\text{Jones}\}) = \frac{1}{2},\qquad P(\{\text{Smith}\}) = \frac{1}{3}$
    (c) $P(\{\text{Jones, Black}\}) = \frac{2}{3},\qquad P(\{\text{Jones, Smith}\}) = \frac{5}{6},\qquad P(\{\text{Black, Smith}\}) = \frac{1}{2},$
    $P(S) = 1,\qquad P(\emptyset) = 0$
    (d) $P(\{\text{Black, Smith}\}) = P(\{\text{Jones}\})$

4. (a) $S = \{X, Y, Z\}$ $\qquad\qquad\qquad\qquad$ (b) $P(\{X\}) = P(\{Y\}) = \frac{2}{5},\qquad P(\{Z\}) = \frac{1}{5}$
    (c) $P(\{X\} \cup \{Y\}) = \frac{4}{5}$ $\qquad\qquad\quad$ (d) $P(\{X\} \cup \{Z\}) = \frac{3}{5}$

5. $S = \{0, 1, 2, 3, 4, 5, \text{more than } 5\}$
    (a) $P(\{1, 2\}) = \frac{135}{274}\quad$ (b) $P(\{4, 5, \text{more than } 5\}) = \frac{299}{1096}\quad$ (c) $P(\{0, 1\}) = \frac{497}{1096}$
    (d) $P(\text{more than seven mistakes}) \le \frac{1}{8}$, but the exact probability cannot be determined from the information given.

6. $\frac{1}{126}$

7. $S = \{(i, j) \mid i, j = s, \text{ or } u, \text{ or } o\}$
    (a) $P(\{(s, s), (u, s), (s, u), (s, o), (o, s)\}) = 0.64$
    (b) $P(\{(s, s)\}) = 0.12$
    (c) $P(\{(s, o), (o, s), (o, u), (u, o)\}) = 0.24$

8. One sample space consists of the ten circular arcs whose end points are the numbers $0, 1, 2, \ldots, 9$. The probability that the needle stops between 1 and 2 is $\frac{1}{10}$.

9. $S = \{(H, H), (H, T), (T, H), (T, T)\}$, and the elementary events in this sample space are equally likely. $P(\{(H, T), (T, H)\}) = \frac{1}{2} \neq \frac{1}{3}$.

10. Let A_k be the event in which the sample contains k defective radios.

(a) $P(A_1) = \dfrac{\dbinom{3}{1}\dbinom{97}{4}}{\dbinom{100}{5}}$

(b) $P(A_2) = \dfrac{\dbinom{3}{2}\dbinom{97}{3}}{\dbinom{100}{5}}$

(c) $P(A_0 \cup A_1 \cup A_2) = \displaystyle\sum_{k=0}^{2} \dfrac{\dbinom{3}{k}\dbinom{97}{5-k}}{\dbinom{100}{5}}$

12. If c represents a counterfeit coin and g represents a genuine coin, then

$$S = \{(\{c, c\}, g), (\{c, c\}, c), (\{c, g\}, g), (\{c, g\}, c)\},$$
$$P(\{(\{c, c\}, g)\}) = \tfrac{3}{15}, \qquad P(\{(\{c, c\}, c)\}) = \tfrac{2}{15}),$$
$$P(\{(\{c, g\}, g)\}) = \tfrac{8}{15}, \qquad P(\{(\{c, g\}, c)\}) = \tfrac{2}{15}.$$

The probability that the customer receives a counterfeit coin is $\frac{4}{15}$.

Section 5.5

1. $\dfrac{1}{24!}$

2. $\dfrac{21!}{24!}$

3. $P(X \le 3) = \displaystyle\sum_{k=0}^{3} \dfrac{\dbinom{10}{k}\dbinom{90}{5-k}}{\dbinom{100}{5}}$, $\qquad P(4 \le X \le 5) = \displaystyle\sum_{k=4}^{5} \dfrac{\dbinom{10}{k}\dbinom{90}{5-k}}{\dbinom{100}{5}}$

4. 0.2

5. (a) $S = \{1, 2, 3, \ldots, 10\}$, $\qquad P(\{x\}) = \frac{1}{10}$ for $x = 1, 2, 3, \ldots, 10$
   (b) $P(\{5\}) = \frac{1}{10}$ $\qquad$ (c) $P(\{8, 9, 10\}) = \frac{3}{10}$ $\qquad$ (d) $P(\{1, 3, 5, 7, 9\}) = \frac{1}{2}$

6. $1 - \dfrac{365 \cdot 364 \cdot \ldots \cdot 356}{365^{10}}$, $\qquad 1 - \dfrac{365 \cdot 364 \cdot \ldots \cdot 346}{365^{20}}$,

   $1 - \dfrac{365 \cdot 364 \cdot \ldots \cdot 336}{365^{30}}$, $\qquad 1 - \dfrac{365 \cdot 364 \cdot \ldots \cdot (365 - n + 1)}{365^n}$

7. (a) $1/7^4$
   (b) If the problem means that at least one meeting is to be held on each of Monday, Wednesday, and Friday, then the answer is $180/7^4$. If the problem means exactly one meeting is to be held on each of Monday, Wednesday, and Friday, then the answer is $144/7^4$.
   (c) If the problem means at least one meeting on a Monday, the answer is

   $$1 - (6^4/7^4).$$

   If the problem means exactly one meeting on a Monday, the answer is $4 \cdot 6^3/7^4$.
   (d) $4 \cdot 6^3/7^4$

(e) If the problem means that exactly one meeting will be scheduled on a Monday or a Wednesday (but not both), the answer is $8 \cdot 5^3/7^4$. Other interpretations can be given to the problem.

(f) $6^4/7^4$

8. (a) $P(A) = \frac{13}{16}$, $P(B) = \frac{5}{8}$, $P(D) = \frac{5}{16}$, $P(E) = \frac{3}{8}$

(b) $P(A \cup B) = P(\{C_1, C_2, C_3, C_4\}) = \frac{7}{8}$,

$P(D \cup E) = P(\{C_2, C_3, C_4, C_5\}) = \frac{11}{16}$

(c) $P(A \cap B) = P(\{C_1, C_2\}) = \frac{9}{16}$

(d) $P(A \cap D) = (\{PC_3\}) = \frac{1}{4}$

(e) $P(A \cup B \cup D \cup E) = P(\{C_1, C_2, C_3, C_4, C_5\}) = 1$

9. $\dfrac{\dbinom{10}{3}\dbinom{990}{97}}{\dbinom{1000}{100}}$, $\qquad \dfrac{\dbinom{10}{0}\dbinom{990}{100} + \dbinom{10}{1}\dbinom{990}{99}}{\dbinom{1000}{100}}$

10. $1 - \dfrac{51^2}{52^2}$

11. $1 - \dfrac{\dbinom{10}{0}\dbinom{490}{20}}{\dbinom{500}{20}}$

12. (a) $\dfrac{\dbinom{30}{2}\dbinom{20}{3}}{\dbinom{100}{5}}$

(b) $\dfrac{\dbinom{10}{5}}{\dbinom{100}{5}}$

(c) $\dfrac{\dbinom{30}{2}\dbinom{40}{1}\dbinom{20}{1}\dbinom{10}{1}}{\dbinom{100}{5}} + \dfrac{\dbinom{30}{1}\dbinom{40}{2}\dbinom{20}{1}\dbinom{10}{1}}{\dbinom{100}{5}}$

$+ \dfrac{\dbinom{30}{1}\dbinom{40}{1}\dbinom{20}{2}\dbinom{10}{1}}{\dbinom{100}{5}} + \dfrac{\dbinom{30}{1}\dbinom{40}{1}\dbinom{20}{1}\dbinom{10}{2}}{\dbinom{100}{5}}$

(d) Depending on how the problem is interpreted, the answer is

$$\dfrac{\dbinom{40}{3}\dbinom{60}{2}}{\dbinom{100}{5}}$$

or

$$\dfrac{\dbinom{40}{3}\dbinom{60}{2}}{\dbinom{100}{5}} + \dfrac{\dbinom{40}{4}\dbinom{60}{1}}{\dbinom{100}{5}} + \dfrac{\dbinom{40}{5}\dbinom{60}{0}}{\dbinom{100}{5}}.$$

14. $P(A) = \frac{9}{25}$ or $P(A) = 1$.

CHAPTER 6

Section 6.2

1. $\dfrac{1}{\binom{8}{3}}$, $\dfrac{\binom{5}{3}}{\binom{8}{3}}$, $1 - \dfrac{1}{\binom{8}{3}}$

2. $\dfrac{\binom{10}{1}\binom{90}{4}}{\binom{100}{5}}$, $1 - \dfrac{\binom{90}{5}}{\binom{100}{5}}$

3. $\dfrac{\binom{10}{1}\binom{90}{2}}{\binom{100}{3}}$, $1 - \dfrac{\binom{90}{3}}{\binom{100}{3}}$

4. $\dfrac{\binom{3}{2}\binom{11}{2}}{\binom{14}{4}}$, $\dfrac{\binom{3}{2}\binom{6}{2}}{\binom{14}{4}}$,

$\dfrac{\binom{3}{2}\binom{5}{1}\binom{6}{1}}{\binom{14}{4}} + \dfrac{\binom{3}{1}\binom{5}{2}\binom{6}{1}}{\binom{14}{4}} + \dfrac{\binom{3}{1}\binom{5}{1}\binom{6}{2}}{\binom{14}{4}} = \dfrac{495}{910}$

6. (a) $\frac{1}{4}$ (b) $\frac{1}{4}$ (c) $\frac{1}{4}$ (d) $\dfrac{1}{4!}$ (e) $\dfrac{\binom{4}{2} + 1}{4!} = \dfrac{7}{24}$

7. (a) $\dfrac{1}{2^{10}}$ (b) $\dfrac{\binom{10}{1}\binom{9}{9}}{2^{10}}$ (c) $\dfrac{\binom{10}{2}\binom{8}{8}}{2^{10}}$

8. $\binom{n}{k} \Big/ 2^n$

Section 6.3

1. (a) $P(X \leq 1) = \displaystyle\sum_{k=0}^{1} \dfrac{\binom{1000}{k}\binom{19{,}000}{100-k}}{\binom{20{,}000}{100}}$

(b) $P(X \leq 1) = \displaystyle\sum_{k=0}^{1} \dfrac{\binom{100}{k}\binom{1900}{100-k}}{\binom{2000}{100}}$

(c) $P(X \leq 1) = \displaystyle\sum_{k=0}^{1} \dfrac{\binom{10}{k}\binom{190}{100-k}}{\binom{200}{100}}$ (d) 1

2.

M	$f(M/8)$
0	1
1	1
2	$\frac{55}{70}$
3	$\frac{35}{70}$
4	$\frac{17}{70}$
5	$\frac{5}{70}$
6	0
7	0
8	0

3.

$n =$	5	6	8
M	$f(M/8)$	$f(M/8)$	$f(M/8)$
0	1	1	1
1	1	1	1
2	$\frac{36}{56}$	$\frac{13}{28}$	0
3	$\frac{16}{56}$	$\frac{3}{28}$	0
4	$\frac{4}{56}$	0	0
5	0	0	0
6	0	0	0
7	0	0	0
8	0	0	0

4. $f\left(\dfrac{5}{100}\right) = \displaystyle\sum_{k=0}^{1} \dfrac{\dbinom{5}{k}\dbinom{95}{10-k}}{\dbinom{100}{10}}$

5. $f\left(\dfrac{25}{1000}\right) = \displaystyle\sum_{k=0}^{2} \dfrac{\dbinom{25}{k}\dbinom{975}{50-k}}{\dbinom{1000}{50}}$

Section 6.4

1. $\hat{N} = \dfrac{2000 \cdot 500}{200} = 5000.$ Yes. 5000

2. yes   **3.** no

4. It is impossible to know how many rabbits there are in the preserve without counting them, but Models I and II provide an estimate of 2222 rabbits.

7. 40   **8.** 40   **9.** 33

Section 6.6

1. (a) 0, 7!, $(10)_7$ (b) $4^7, 7^7, 10^7$ **2.** (a) 0, 1, $\dbinom{10}{7}$ (b) $\dbinom{10}{7}, \dbinom{13}{7}, \dbinom{16}{7}$

3. 0, 7!, $(10)_7$ **4.** 0, 1, $\dbinom{10}{7}$

5. (a) $\dfrac{1}{120}$ (b) $\dfrac{7!}{10^7}$ **6.** (a) $\dfrac{1}{\dbinom{10}{7}} = \dfrac{1}{120}$ (b) $\dfrac{1}{\dbinom{16}{7}}$

7. (a) $\dfrac{\dbinom{6}{2,3,1}}{3^6}$ (b) $\dfrac{1}{\dbinom{8}{6}}$ (c) $\dfrac{\dbinom{10}{2,3,2,1,2}}{5^{10}}$ (d) $\dfrac{1}{\dbinom{14}{10}}$

8. $\dfrac{\dbinom{6}{2,3,1}}{3^6}$ **9.** $\dfrac{\dbinom{6}{2,3,1}}{3^6}$

10. $P(A_k) = \dfrac{(10)_{k-1}(k-1)}{10^k},$ $1 - \dfrac{(10)_{10}}{10^{10}},$ 1

18. (a) $\frac{5}{7}, \frac{4}{7}$ (b) $\frac{411}{495}, \frac{14}{33}$ 19. $\frac{5}{21}, \frac{1}{7}, \frac{1}{21}$

20. $\frac{8}{33}, \frac{7}{99}, \frac{1}{495}$ 21. (a) $\frac{24}{625}$ (b) $\frac{18}{143}$

22. $\dfrac{\dbinom{n + k - i - 2}{k - i}}{\dbinom{n + k - 1}{k}}$ 23. $\dfrac{(450)_{10}}{(450)^{10}}$ 24. $\dfrac{(300)_{50}}{(300)^{50}}$

Section 6.7

1. (a) $\frac{11}{30}, \frac{3}{8}, \frac{1}{6}, \frac{1}{12}, 0, \frac{1}{120}$ (b) 1

3. (a) $\frac{1}{2}, 0, \frac{1}{4}, \frac{1}{6}, \frac{3}{16}, \frac{11}{60}, \frac{53}{288}$ (b) $\dfrac{1}{2e}$ (c) $\dfrac{1}{k!e}$

4. Yes. See Example 3.   5. $\frac{11}{30}, \frac{3}{8}, \frac{1}{6}, \frac{1}{12}, 0, \frac{1}{120}$

6. (a) $\frac{1}{5}$ (b) $\frac{3}{5}$ (c) $\frac{1}{5}$ 9. (c) $\dfrac{\dbinom{m}{k}^2}{\dbinom{2m}{m}}$ 10. $\frac{25}{63}$

11. (b) $0, 0, \frac{1}{14}, 0, \frac{8}{21}, 0, \frac{3}{7}, 0, \frac{4}{35}, 0, \frac{1}{210}$

12. The probability of $2k + (2n - 2m)$ matches is

$$\dfrac{\dbinom{m}{k}\dbinom{2n - m}{m - k}}{\dbinom{2n}{m}} \quad \text{for} \quad k = 0, 1, 2, \ldots, m.$$

The probability of any number of matches other than $(2n - 2m), 2 + (2n - 2m), 4 + (2n - 2m), \ldots, 2(m - 1) + (2n - 2m), 2n$ is zero.

13. The possible number of matches is $2k + N - 2m$ for $k = 0, 1, 2, \ldots, m$. The number of matches is even if N is even and odd if N is odd. The probability of $2k + N - 2m$ matches is

$$\dfrac{\dbinom{m}{k}\dbinom{N - m}{m - k}}{\dbinom{N}{m}} \quad \text{for} \quad k = 0, 1, 2, \ldots, m.$$

The probability of any other number of matches is zero.

CHAPTER 7

Section 7.2

1. $\frac{1}{2}, \frac{1}{2}$

2. (a) $\dfrac{\dbinom{4}{2}\dbinom{48}{11}}{\dbinom{4}{1}\dbinom{48}{12} + \dbinom{4}{2}\dbinom{48}{11} + \dbinom{4}{3}\dbinom{48}{10} + \dbinom{4}{4}\dbinom{48}{9}}$ (b) $\dfrac{\dbinom{3}{1}\dbinom{48}{11}}{\dbinom{51}{12}}$

3. (a) $\frac{1}{3}$ (b) $\frac{1}{2}$ 4. $\frac{8}{9}$ 5. $\frac{1}{2}$

6. (a) $\dfrac{\binom{11}{3}\binom{19}{2}}{\binom{11}{2}\binom{19}{3} + \binom{11}{3}\binom{19}{2} + \binom{11}{4}\binom{19}{1} + \binom{11}{5}\binom{19}{0}}$

(b) $\dfrac{\binom{11}{3}\left[\binom{2}{1}\binom{17}{1} + \binom{2}{2}\binom{17}{0}\right]}{\binom{2}{1}\binom{28}{4} + \binom{2}{2}\binom{28}{3}}$

(c) $\dfrac{\binom{11}{3}\left[\binom{13}{1}\binom{6}{1} + \binom{13}{2}\binom{6}{0}\right]}{\left\{\binom{11}{1}\left[\binom{13}{1}\binom{6}{3} + \binom{13}{2}\binom{6}{2} + \binom{13}{3}\binom{6}{1} + \binom{13}{4}\binom{6}{0}\right]\right.}$

$\qquad + \binom{11}{2}\left[\binom{13}{1}\binom{6}{2} + \binom{13}{2}\binom{6}{1} + \binom{13}{3}\binom{6}{0}\right]$

$\qquad \left. + \binom{11}{3}\left[\binom{13}{1}\binom{6}{1} + \binom{13}{2}\binom{6}{0}\right] + \binom{11}{4}\binom{13}{1}\right\}$

7. (a) $\frac{1}{10}$ (b) $\frac{1}{16}$ (c) $\dfrac{\binom{4}{1}\binom{13}{1}}{\binom{17}{2}} = \dfrac{13}{34}$ (d) $\frac{13}{16}$

8. $\frac{1}{25}$

9. (a) $\dfrac{\binom{4}{3}}{\binom{4}{2}\binom{9}{1} + \binom{4}{3}\binom{9}{2}}$ (b) $\dfrac{\binom{4}{1}\binom{9}{2}}{\binom{9}{2}\binom{4}{1} + \binom{9}{3}\binom{4}{0}}$ (c) $\dfrac{\binom{12}{2}}{\binom{12}{2} + \binom{12}{3}} = \dfrac{3}{13}$

12. $\frac{1}{32}$

Section 7.3

1. $\frac{5}{12}$ 2. $\frac{3}{8}, \frac{2}{7}$
3. The probabilities are equal.
4. 0.3   5. $\frac{3}{4}$ 6. $\frac{1}{3}$
7. $A: \frac{4}{11}, B: \frac{6}{11}, C: \frac{1}{11}$ 8. 0.3   9. 47
10. (a) $\dfrac{999}{10,000}$ (b) $\dfrac{1009}{10,000}$ (c) $\frac{1}{10}$ (d) $\dfrac{1008}{10,000}$ (e) $\frac{1}{10}$ (f) $\dfrac{99,910}{1,000,000}$

Section 7.4

3. 0.56   4. $\frac{1}{4}$ 5. (a) $\frac{3}{100}$ (b) $\frac{1}{24}$
6. (a) S and every other event are independent.
9. (a) $\frac{4}{15}$ (b) $\frac{8}{15}$ 10. 29

Section 7.5

1. (a) $\frac{7}{128}$ (b) $(\frac{3}{4})^9 \cdot 7$ (c) $\frac{121}{128}$ (d) $1 - (\frac{3}{4})^9 \cdot 7$

2. $\frac{5}{16}$ 3. $\frac{5}{16}$

4. $\binom{10}{7} (\frac{2}{3})^7 (\frac{1}{3})^3$ 5. $\frac{7}{128}$

6. (a) $(0.95)^5$ (b) $1 - (0.95)^5$

7. (a) $\frac{3}{8}$ (b) $\frac{1}{8}$ (c) $\frac{7}{8}$

8. no, $\frac{1}{216}, \frac{1}{72}$

9. $\displaystyle\sum_{k=6}^{31} \binom{31}{k} (0.1)^k (0.9)^{31-k} = 1 - \sum_{k=0}^{5} \binom{31}{k} (0.1)^k (0.9)^{31-k}$

10. (a) $\binom{15}{5,2,8} \left(\frac{1}{3}\right)^{15}$ (b) $\binom{15}{5,6,4} \left(\frac{1}{3}\right)^{15}$ (c) $(\frac{2}{3})^{15}$

11. $\frac{5}{32}$

12. 7 (With 7, $\sum_{k=7}^{10} \binom{10}{k}(\frac{1}{2})^{10} = 0.05453$.)

13. $\hat{N} = 30$. The quality was poor.

14. $m \geq \dfrac{-\log 2}{\log (1 - p^n)}, \quad m \geq \dfrac{\log R}{\log (1 - p^n)}$

Section 7.6

3. $\frac{1}{4}, \frac{1}{2}, \frac{1}{4};$ $\frac{1}{4}, \frac{1}{2}, \frac{1}{4}$ 4. $2h = \frac{1}{2}$

5. (a) $\frac{1}{2}P(M_{Aa})$ (b) 0   (c) $\frac{1}{4}P(M_{Aa})$ 6. $\frac{1}{4}$

8. (a) $\frac{1}{2}, \frac{1}{4}$ (b) $\frac{1}{2}, \frac{1}{2}$ (c) $p = v, q = v + w$

9. (a) $p_{11} = p,$ $p_{12} = q,$ $p_{13} = 0,$
      $p_{21} = \frac{1}{2}p,$ $p_{22} = \frac{1}{2},$ $p_{23} = \frac{1}{2}q,$
      $p_{31} = 0,$ $p_{32} = p,$ $p_{33} = q$
(b) 1

CHAPTER 8

Section 8.1

1. $X(k) = k,$ $k = 1, 2, \ldots, 6$ 2. $2, 4, 6; \frac{1}{2}$

3. (a) $\{1, 2, 3, 4, 5, 6\}$ (b) $\emptyset$ (c) $\emptyset$ (d) $\{1, 2, 3, 4, 5, 6\}$ (e) $\emptyset$

4. $1, 0, 0, 1, 0$

5. $\frac{1}{36}, \frac{2}{36}, \frac{3}{36}, \frac{4}{36}, \frac{5}{36}, \frac{6}{36}, \frac{5}{36}, \frac{4}{36}, \frac{3}{36}, \frac{2}{36}, \frac{1}{36}$; yes; 1

7. dom $X = \{(a_1, a_2, \ldots, a_n) \mid a_i$ is the number of the hat the ith man receives$\}$,
ran $X = \{0, 1, 2, \ldots, n\}$

8. $P(\{s \mid s \in S, X(s) = k\}) = \dfrac{1}{k!}\left[1 - \dfrac{1}{1!} + \dfrac{1}{2!} - \dfrac{1}{3!} + \cdots + \dfrac{(-1)^{n-k}}{(n-k)!}\right].$

9. dom $X = \{(a_1, \ldots, a_{10}) \mid a_i$ is the number of the handwriting sample attributed to the ith man$\}$,   ran $X = \{0, 1, \ldots, 10\}$

10. 0.0037

Section 8.2

1. $\{X = 7\} = \{(1, 6), (2, 5), (3, 4), (4, 3), (5, 2), (6, 1)\}$, $\{X = 3\} = \{(1, 2), (2, 1)\}$

3. $(0.7)^{10}$, $\binom{10}{7}(0.7)^7(0.3)^3$, $\binom{10}{6}(0.7)^6(0.3)^4 + \binom{10}{7}(0.7)^7(0.3)^3$

$$+ \binom{10}{8}(0.7)^8(0.3)^2$$

4. $\frac{1}{100}$, $1 - 10^{-200}$

5. $\sum_{k=0}^{10} \binom{1000}{k}\left(\frac{1}{100}\right)^k\left(\frac{99}{100}\right)^{1000-k}$

7. $g(p) = \sum_{k=4}^{100} \binom{100}{k} p^k (1 - p)^{100-k}$

8. (a) $p = \dfrac{v}{V}$ (b) $P(X_N = k) = \binom{N}{k} p^k q^{N-k}$, $k = 0, 1, 2, \ldots, N$

   (c) $\dfrac{Nq}{N - k}$ (d) no

   (e) $\hat{N}$ = greatest integer less than or equal to k/p.

Section 8.3

1. $S' = \{a\}$, $P'(\{a\}) = 1$

2. $S' = \{0, 1, \ldots, n\}$, $P'(\{k\}) = \dfrac{\binom{M}{k}\binom{N - M}{n - k}}{\binom{N}{n}}$, $k = 0, 1, \ldots, n$,

   where n, N, M are fixed positive integers with $n \le N$ and $N \ge M$.

3. $S' = \{0, 1, 2, \ldots, n\}$, $P'(\{k\}) = \dfrac{1}{k!}\left[1 - \dfrac{1}{1!} + \dfrac{1}{2!} - \dfrac{1}{3!} + \cdots + \dfrac{(-1)^{n-k}}{(n - k)!}\right]$,

   $k = 0, 1, 2, \ldots, n$.

4. $S' = \{0, 1, 2, \ldots, 10\}$,

   $$P'(\{k\}) = \frac{1}{k!}\left[1 - \frac{1}{1!} + \frac{1}{2!} - \frac{1}{3!} + \cdots + \frac{(-1)^{10-k}}{(10 - k)!}\right],\qquad k = 0, 1, 2, \ldots, 10.$$

5. $S' = \{2, 3, \ldots, 12\}$, $P'(\{2\}) = \frac{1}{36} = P'(\{12\})$, $P'(\{3\}) = \frac{2}{36} = P'(\{11\})$,
   $P'(\{4\}) = \frac{3}{36} = P'(\{10\})$, $P'(\{5\}) = \frac{4}{36} = P'(\{9\})$,
   $P'(\{6\}) = \frac{5}{36} = P'(\{8\})$, $P'(\{7\}) = \frac{6}{36}$

6. $S' = \{0, 1, 2\}$, $P'(\{0\}) = \frac{1}{4}$, $P'(\{1\}) = \frac{1}{2}$, $P'(\{2\}) = \frac{1}{4}$

7. (a) $S = \{4, 5, 6, (1, 1), (2, 1), (3, 1), \ldots, (1, 6), (2, 6), (3, 6)\}$
   (b) $S' = \{2, 3, 4, \ldots, 9\}$, $P'(\{2\}) = \frac{1}{36}$, $P'(\{3\}) = \frac{2}{36}$,
   $P'(\{4\}) = \frac{9}{36}$, $P'(\{5\}) = \frac{9}{36}$, $P'(\{6\}) = \frac{9}{36}$, $P'(\{7\}) = \frac{3}{36}$,
   $P'(\{8\}) = \frac{2}{36}$, $P'(\{9\}) = \frac{1}{36}$

Section 8.4

7. $f(k) = \binom{10}{k}\left(\frac{1}{3}\right)^k\left(\frac{2}{3}\right)^{10-k}$, $k = 0, 1, 2, \ldots, 10$

8. (a) $\frac{1}{8}$ (b) $\frac{7}{8}$ (c) $\frac{7}{8}$ (d) $\frac{1}{8}$ (e) $\frac{7}{8}$ (f) $\frac{1}{8}$

9. (a) $\frac{16}{81}$ (b) $\frac{65}{81}$ (c) $\frac{72}{81}$ (d) $\frac{32}{81}$ (e) $\frac{72}{81}$ (f) $\frac{17}{81}$

13. (a) $\{x \mid 3 \leq x < 4\}$ (b) $\{x \mid 3 \leq x\}$ (c) $\{x \mid x \leq 4\}$ (d) $M = \{x \mid 3 \leq x \leq 4\}$

14. (a) $\varnothing$ (b) $\{x \mid 1 \leq x\}$ (c) $\{x \mid x \leq 1\}$ (d) $\{1\}$

15. (a) $\varnothing$ (b) $\{x \mid 0 \leq x\}$ (c) $\{x \mid x \leq 0\}$ (d) $\{0\}$

16. (a) $\varnothing$ (b) $\{x \mid 2 \leq x\}$ (c) $\{x \mid x \leq 2\}$ (d) $\{2\}$

Section 8.5

1. $\frac{43}{10}, \frac{221}{10}, -\frac{109}{10}, \frac{614}{10}$ 2. $\frac{7}{4}$ 3. $\frac{91}{21}$

4. Not enough information is known to answer these questions.

5. 0.5, 40 or more   6. 15   7. \$2250   8. \$900   9. \$1360   12. 4

13. $\displaystyle\sum_{n=k}^{N-M+k} \frac{\dbinom{M}{k-1}\dbinom{N-M}{n-k}(n-1)!(M-k+1)}{(N)_n}$

Section 8.6

1. (a) 2   (b) 50   (c) 8   (d) $\frac{324}{25}$ (e) 0

2. 5, $\frac{5}{2}$, $n \geq 100$ 3. $\frac{21}{4}, \frac{35}{16}$ 5. 6   6. $(550)^2 \cdot \frac{19}{4}, (100)^2 \cdot 289$

9. Smaller; 19,825 are needed.

10. $P(\{X \leq (0.05)n\}) = \displaystyle\sum_{0 \leq k \leq (0.05)n} \dbinom{n}{k}(0.06)^k(0.94)^{n-k}.$ We do not know n.

12. (a) $\displaystyle\sum_{k=85}^{100} \dbinom{100}{k}(0.8)^k(0.2)^{100-k}$ (b) approximately 0.64, no

16. (b) var $(Y) = (n+1)(n-1)/12$

Section 8.7

1. (a) your total gain; $S = \{(H, T), (T, H)\}$
    (b) $\{2, 0, 1, -3\}$ (c) $\frac{1}{4}, \frac{1}{4}, 0, \frac{1}{4}, 0$
    (d) $\frac{1}{4}, \frac{1}{4}, \frac{1}{4}, \frac{1}{4}$ (e) 0

2. (a) $\frac{1}{2}$ (b) $\frac{7}{2}$ (c) 4   (d) $\{1, 2, 3, 4, 5, 6, 7\}$
    (e) $P(X + Y = 1) = \frac{1}{12}$; $P(X + Y = j) = \frac{1}{6}$, $2 \leq j \leq 6$;
    $P(X + Y = 7) = \frac{1}{12}$
    (f) 4   (g) 2   (h) $\frac{1}{2}$ (i) $\frac{35}{12}$ (j) $\frac{41}{12}$ (k) $\frac{105}{4}$ (l) $\frac{7}{4}$

4. 2250

5. (a) binomial   (b) The total time the two components last. yes
    (c) 12, 2.4   (d) $P(9 < X + Y < 15) \geq 0.36$
    (e) binomial with parameters $p = 0.8$ and $n = 15$

Section 8.8

1. (a) 2, $\frac{48}{5}$ (b) 2   2. (a) 0, $\frac{88}{5}$ (b) 0

3. $2\left[\displaystyle\sum_{k=0}^{12}(12 - k)\dbinom{20}{k}\left(\frac{3}{5}\right)^k\left(\frac{2}{5}\right)^{20-k} + \displaystyle\sum_{k=13}^{20}(k - 12)\dbinom{20}{k}\left(\frac{3}{5}\right)^k\left(\frac{2}{5}\right)^{20-k}\right]$

4. (a) $P(X = 0) = \left(\frac{1}{2}\right)^{10}$, $P(X = 1) = \binom{10}{1}\left(\frac{1}{2}\right)^{10}$, $P(X = 2) = \dfrac{1013}{1024}$

   (b) $P(X = j) = \binom{10}{j}\left(\frac{1}{2}\right)^{10}$, $j = 0, 1, 2, 3, 4$, $P(X = 2) = \dfrac{319}{512}$

   (c) $P(X = j) = \binom{10}{j}\left(\frac{1}{2}\right)^{10}$, $j = 0, 1, \ldots, 7$, $P(X = 8) = \dfrac{7}{128}$

   (d) $P(X = j) = \binom{10}{j}\left(\frac{1}{2}\right)^{10}$, $j = 0, 1, \ldots, 10$

5. $\frac{509}{256}$ (b) $\frac{2245}{512}$ (c) $\frac{2429}{512}$ (d) 5

6. $\max E[N] = 100\left[25\left(\dfrac{1 + \binom{20}{10}\left(\frac{1}{2}\right)^{20}}{2}\right) - 10\right] + 250 \sum_{k=0}^{9} k \binom{20}{k}\left(\frac{1}{2}\right)^{20}$

   Send 10 loaves to each outlet.

7. $100\left[30\left(\dfrac{1 + \binom{20}{10}\left(\frac{1}{2}\right)^{20}}{2}\right) - 10\right] + 300 \sum_{k=0}^{9} k \binom{20}{k}\left(\frac{1}{2}\right)^{20}$,

   $100\left[30\left(\dfrac{1 + \binom{20}{10}\left(\frac{1}{2}\right)^{20}}{2}\right) - 15\right] + 300 \sum_{k=0}^{9} k \binom{20}{k}\left(\frac{1}{2}\right)^{20}$

   Send 10 loaves to each outlet.

8. (a) 0, 10, 16, 8; $\max\{16E[X] - 5c\} = 16$

9. $\frac{38}{8}$. Lemma 6 does not apply.

10. 2, 40   11. 2, 40

12. $c_1 = 2$, $c_2 = 3$, $c_3 = 4$, $c_4 = 1$; 356.42

13. (a) $\frac{1}{2}$ (b) $\frac{2}{3}$ (c) $\frac{5}{7} + \frac{3}{14}(\frac{1}{6})^{99}$ (d) $\frac{3}{7} - \frac{1}{14}(\frac{1}{6})^{99}$

14. (a) $\frac{1}{2}, \frac{1}{2}$ (b) $\frac{2}{3}, \frac{1}{3}$ (c) $\frac{5}{7}, \frac{2}{7}$ (d) $\frac{3}{7}, \frac{4}{7}$

15. $\dfrac{p'}{1 - (p - p')}$ if $p - p' \neq 1$; no, if $p - p' \neq 1$

Index

A

Absolute value function, **65***
Acceptance number, **188**
Acceptance sampling, 187ff., 273
Additive set function, **160**
Aggregate, 1
Alleles, 262
    dominant, 262
    recessive, 262
Allelomorph, 265, 269
Alternating progression, 83
Amaurotic idiocy, 269
Analysis, combinatorial, 116
    of experiment, finer, **167**
Annuity, **85**
    equation, **90**
Antireflexive relation, **12**, 43
Antisymmetric relation, **12**, 43
Antitransitive relation, 13, 43
Application, 1: A Simple Inventory
        Problem, **316**
    2: The Bakery Chain Problem, **321**
    3: The Bakery Chain Problem, cont'd,
        329
    4: Estes' Learning Model, **334**
Applications to genetics, 262ff.
A priori, 167
Arithmetic mean, **78**
Arithmetic progression, **74**
    initial value of, **74**
    sum of, **77**
Arrangements, **117**, 120, 139, 166
    distinguishable, 149, **153**
    of n distinct elements taken r at a
        time, **120**
Associative law, 15
Authorship (Mosteller-Wallace Model),
        240–242, 248–249, 281
Axiom, **3**
    of extensionality, **3**

B

Bailey, N. T. J., 225
Bakery Chain Problem, The, **321,** 329
Balls in urn, 177ff.
    distinguishable, 178, 208–210

Bayes, Rev. Thomas, F. R. S., 234
Bayes' Theorem, 234ff., **237**
Belong to a set, 1–2
Bernoulli, J., 256
Bernoulli, random variable, **275,** 309
    trials, 256ff., 267, 272, 276, 309
Bias, 164, 168–169
Binary relation, **39**
Binomial coefficient, 115, 123, 131, 141,
        142, 178–180
Binomial probability, 187
    function, **287**
    space, **258**
Binomial random variable, **275,** 285,
        309, 315
Binomial Theorem, **141,** 203, 205–206
Birthday Problem, The, **185**
Blindness, color, 266
Brackets, use of, **4**
Branch of a tree, 118
Bureaucracy, 258, 294
Buyer's risk, **190**

C

Calculus, 156
Cardano, Girolamo, 156
Carrier (biological), 266
Cartesian, plane (cf. Euclidean), 35
    product, **35, 36**
Cell occupancy, 207ff., **212**
Census, zoological sample, 192ff.
Certain event, **157**
Chapman, D. G., 225
Chapman, D. W., 220, 225
Characteristic function, operating (OC),
        190
Chebyshev's inequality, **301,** 302, 313
Chromosomes, 262
    sex, 265
Circle, unit, **42**
Class, 1
Classification, k-part, 131, **143**
    function, 143
Coefficient, binomial, 115, 123, 131,
        141, **142,** 178–180
    multinomial, **144**

---

* A boldface number indicates that the principal reference is given on that page.

365

ABCDE698